Lipide
Chemistry

by **DONALD J. HANAHAN**_____

Department of Biochemistry
University of Washington
Seattle, Washington

.

with contributing chapters by

Frank R. N. Gurd

Bureau of Medical Research
Equitable Life Assurance Society
of the United States
and Department of Biochemistry
Cornell University Medical College, New York

.

Irving Zabin

Department of Physiological Chemistry
University of California
Los Angeles

Lipide
Chemistry

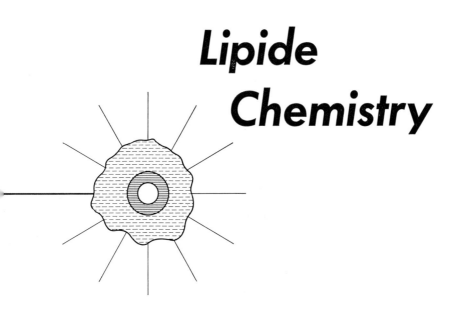

John Wiley & Sons, Inc., New York · London

Preface

The recent increased interest in lipides has been most encouraging and yet has assumed an air of great urgency. This is due in no small part to the great emphasis placed on the etiology and the possible cures for atherosclerosis and other related lipide diseases. As a consequence, many investigators have been content to use seriously outmoded or incompletely tested methods or concepts in their enthusiastic search for the solution to these perplexing problems. In part, this is understandable when one considers the complex mixtures encountered and the difficulties attendant on the effective separation and identification of all the usual constituents. Nonetheless, this does not support the use of the term "lipide soluble phosphorus" as a justifiable definition of a phospholipide—unless sufficient other criteria are employed to satisfactorily allow this usage. Many other similar examples could be cited, but suffice it to say that a primary difficulty appears to be associated with the incomplete or improper description or identification of lipides or lipide fractions.

While the above remarks have outlined a somewhat dour facet of the problem, a distinctly brighter outlook can be described. In the last ten years, a significant number of new and improved fractionation techniques, isolation procedures, and methods of assay, together with an increased amount of information on the chemical structure and characteristics of many of the naturally occurring fatty acid esters, have appeared in the literature. Through the use of this information, a more explicit chemical definition is possible in interpreting the metabolic behavior of the simple and complex lipides. Hence, in view of the rapidly expanding and dynamic nature of the field of lipide chemistry, it is one of the main purposes of this book to examine progress in this area and evaluate its present status.

During the last several years, a portion of the subject matter of this book was utilized as lecture material for a graduate course in lipide biochemistry. A previous preparation in organic chemistry and general biochemistry was required. The major emphasis in this course was directed towards an increased understanding of the simple and complex lipides as chemical compounds capable of isolation, purification, and structure proof. Concomitantly this approach was used as an orientation device for discussions on the reported biochemical behavior and role of these diverse substances. Other topics included in this graduate course offering, but not under discussion here, were: lipolytic enzymes, mode of action of enzyme and non-enzyme catalyzed oxidations of lipides and fatty acids, and the sterols and steroids. On this basis, it is intended that this book (and a subsequent volume on biochemistry, edited by K. Bloch) should serve as a text in an advanced course on lipides, wherein any particular area may be stressed in more or less detail depending on the lecturer's desires and time schedule. In addition, it is hoped that this book will function as an introduction to the subject of lipides for those persons either indirectly involved or newly embarked in this area of research and also as a concise résumé of a particular segment of the field for the confirmed lipide (bio)chemist.

DONALD J. HANAHAN

Seattle, Washington
October, 1959

Acknowledgments

I wish to express my sincere appreciation to Dr. Herbert E. Carter for his kind support of this project and his critical evaluation of the manuscript. In addition, I am very appreciative of the comments and suggestions of Drs. John C. Dittmer and Edward G. Barron. The capable assistance of Mrs. Judith Feminella in assembling and checking the manuscript is gratefully acknowledged.

The permission of the following sources to use certain tabular material is hereby acknowledged: *Analytical Chemistry, Biochemical Journal, Journal of the American Chemical Society,* and *Journal of Biological Chemistry.*

Contents

1

Introduction

The chemistry of naturally occurring lipides presents a challenging and complex field for scientific exploration. Substances ranging from the simple fatty acids and esters to the complex sphingolipides, from the sterols and steroids to certain pigments and vitamins, have been classified in the domain of the lipide (bio)chemist. Thus, at once, one is acutely aware of the chemical diversity of these substances and the fact that a chemical as well as a biochemical interrelation of these "lipides" is a very difficult and involved task. Most often these compounds are considered as related mainly on the basis of their mutual solubility properties and not on their chemical (or even biochemical) characteristics. In this book no attempt is made to blend all these areas into one harmonious and plausible story. Instead, a decided emphasis is placed on the chemistry of those compounds which essentially are derivatives of long-chain fatty acids and are found in mammals, plants, and microorganisms. However, in most instances the discussion is directed primarily towards those present in mammals, with some reference to unique constituents of plants and microorganisms. In certain instances where necessary, physiological observations are considered to a limited extent.

Well over a century and a half ago, two of the first investigators of animal lipides, Fourcroy [5, 6] and Vauquelin,[15, 16] sought to establish the distribution, relative abundance, and properties of lipides isolated from a number of species. In his revealing investigations, Fourcroy [5] studied the waxy products isolated from the abdomens of partly decomposed corpses unearthed from communal graves at the Innocens Cemetery of Paris. On the basis of this rather gruesome work and from his studies on the melting points of various lipides, Fourcroy can be regarded as the father of lipide chemistry. Later, Vauquelin,[16] confirming a proposal offered earlier by Fourcroy, demonstrated the presence of phosphorus containing products in animal lipides. Since this period of time, the field of lipide chemistry has expanded considerably in scope and detail, and a large group of scientists have been associated with various aspects of the progress in this area. Inasmuch as space does not permit an account of the contributions of these many different investigators, reference is made to the accurately detailed reports of this literature in the treatises of Wittcoff,[17] Deuel,[2] and Hilditch.[12]

In the past ten years, as witnessed by the volume of literature on this subject, a considerable and timely interest has been evidenced in the field of lipide chemistry and biochemistry. With all due respect to the past efforts in this area, there is little doubt that the information obtained within this more recent time period has changed significantly many of the older, completely accepted concepts of the structure, stability, reactivity, etc., of the naturally occurring lipides. As would be expected, these new and important data have helped immeasurably in orienting the field in a new direction and in emphasizing the possibility of handling the simple and complex lipides as distinct chemical compounds. Hence, it appears most reasonable to document the present knowledge on the chemical structure and properties of naturally occurring fatty acid esters (and derivatives) and to evaluate at this time the more recent advances.

While it is of obvious value to consider the chemical structure of the lipides isolated from a tissue or an organ, the application of this knowledge to their behavior in the intact or native system may be more difficult. As is well known, many of the properties of the lipides depend on their insolubility in an aqueous medium and their ability to assume certain configurations at an interface. Consequently, it may be difficult to define or detect by *in vitro* experiments chemical properties that may be apparent from *in vivo* experiments, and vice versa. This becomes evident when one considers that a major portion of the lipide of a tissue is found as a lipoprotein complex, and simple reorientation of the molecule or even combination by rather weak bonds may significantly alter its reactivity and general characteristics. Thus, an obviously important investigative area is that concerned with the mode of action and chemical nature of the lipide containing proteins.

Prior to the detailed consideration of the chemical characteristics of the lipides in subsequent chapters, it is worthwhile, for general background and orientation purposes, to present a brief summary of some of the types of compounds under consideration and their reported biological functions and metabolic behavior.

CHEMICAL NATURE OF LIPIDES

At best the term "lipide" (or "fat") is an ill-defined one and may cover a multitudinous array of compounds associated by a common solubility property. In this book, the term "lipide" or "fat" refers to esters of long-chain fatty acids and alcohols, or closely related derivatives.

As our knowledge of the chemistry of these compounds is still relatively limited, it appears most reasonable to maintain any strict classification at a minimum. Indeed, no internationally accepted system for nomenclature of these compounds is presently in use. Until such time as a suitable proposal may be adopted, the more commonly employed or obviously more definitive terms are utilized here. In part the nomenclature suggestions of Folch and Sperry [4] and Baer et al.[1] are followed.

Simple Lipides

These compounds are esters of fatty acids and an alcohol. The following are representative of the most predominant types of carboxylic acid esters found in mammals:

CH_2OCOR_1
$CHOCOR_2$
CH_2OCOR_3

Triglyceride
(α, β, α')

CH_2OCOR_1
$CHOCOR_2$
CH_2OH

Diglyceride
(α, β)

CH_2OH
$CHOCOR_2$
CH_2OH

Monoglyceride
(β)

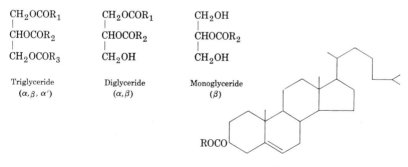

ROCO

Cholesterol ester

In the above structural formulae, the symbol "R" refers to the commonly encountered long-chain fatty acyl groups, ranging from C_{12} to C_{24} in chain length. While the exact chemical nature of these acyl groups may vary considerably from one type of compound to another and is dependent on the particular source, in general the majority of the fatty acids of mammalian lipides are straight-chain, even-numbered monocarboxylic acids. A further inspection of the acids found in the naturally occurring lipides reveals that an additional subdivision may be made with respect to the number of unsaturated (or double bond) linkages present, i.e., monoenoic (oleic acid), dienoic (linoleic acid), trienoic (linolenic acid), tetraenoic (arachidonic acid), etc. Both linoleic and arachidonic acids are regarded as typical essential fatty acids. A detailed treatment of the reactivity and characteristics of the long-chain fatty acids can be obtained by reference to books by Ralston,[14] Markley,[13] Deuel,[2] and Gunstone.[11] In recent review articles, Gensler [9] and Gunstone [10] have summarized in a very able manner the more recent developments in the area of chemical synthesis of fatty acids.

It is interesting to note that glycerol is by far the major polyhydroxy alcohol found esterified to the long-chain fatty acids and it may exist in part as a triglyceride, diglyceride, or monoglyceride in tissues. Whether these units are interrelated or not remains to be established. Similarly, in mammals, another important alcohol is cholesterol which occurs both in esterified and non-esterified form and appears to be the only sterol found associated with long-chain fatty acids. However, such is not the case in plants, where in wheat flour, for example, sitosterol palmitate is a major sterol ester.

While not found to any significant extent in land mammals, the waxes represent a relatively important group of lipides in aquatic animals, certain plants, and microorganisms. These substances can be represented as carboxylic acid esters of the type R_1C—OR_2, where R_1 is usually a long-chain fatty acid and R_2 is a long-chain fatty alcohol. A typical wax, myricyl palmitate, is found in high concentrations in beeswax.

Complex Lipides

These compounds are esters which may contain phosphorus, nitrogen bases (N base) and/or sugars, in addition to long-chain fatty acids and an alcohol. Typical representatives of this class of compounds are given below:

Glycerol-Containing Phospholipides

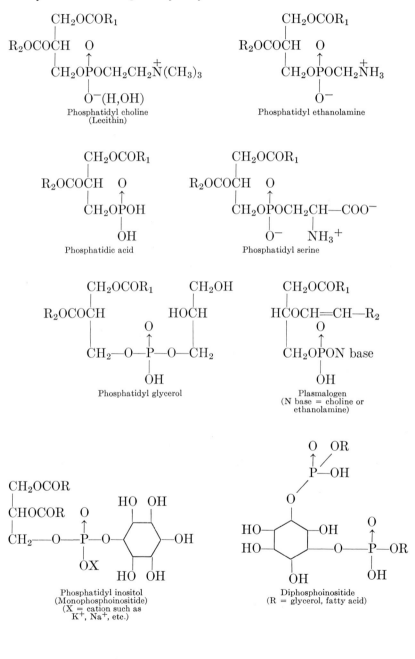

Phosphatidyl choline
(Lecithin)

Phosphatidyl ethanolamine

Phosphatidic acid

Phosphatidyl serine

Phosphatidyl glycerol

Plasmalogen
(N base = choline or
ethanolamine)

Phosphatidyl inositol
(Monophosphoinositide)
(X = cation such as
K⁺, Na⁺, etc.)

Diphosphoinositide
(R = glycerol, fatty acid)

Sphingosine-Containing Lipides

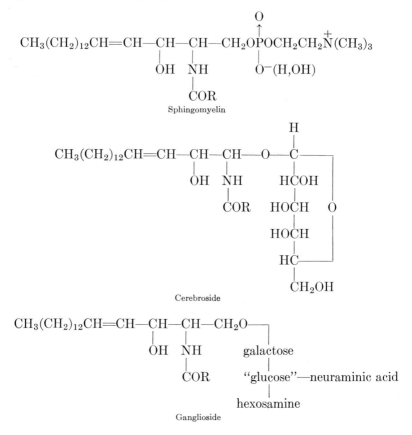

The system of employing the term "cephalin" for the definition of certain phospholipides, i.e., phosphatidyl ethanolamine, phosphatidyl serine, and sphingolipides, has led to a great deal of confusion, and its usage should be restricted. Particularly this criticism is directed towards use of the term "cephalin" to define a single component. This nomenclature was based primarily on the solubility characteristics of phospholipide mixtures, wherein the above compounds were largely insoluble in ethanol at room temperature. Fractions defined by their solubility can show differences in composition depending on the source of material and the intermediate steps in the procedure of isolation, since the solubility of any one phospholipide is greatly modified by the presence and concentration of the other lipides. Hence, a more reliable system is to identify the fractions as completely as possible by their chemical composition and characteristics, and, for the present, to employ the above-indicated nomenclature.

OBSERVATIONS ON METABOLIC FUNCTION OR BEHAVIOR

The study of lipide biochemistry today encompasses areas from the basic chemistry of the above lipides to the *in vitro* and *in vivo* aspects of their metabolism. Although the literature on the subject of lipide metabolism is large, the ultimate goal of the elucidation of the role (or function) of the various lipides has not been achieved. In part, this may be attributed to the difficult problem of the isolation and characterization of these compounds and also to the limited tools or techniques with which to follow their metabolic fate. Notwithstanding these impediments, a sizable number of observations have been made which have led to suggestions about the functions of the various lipides, and in particular the phospholipides. Owing to the ease of analyzing for phosphorus, the phospholipides have occupied a central part of the major number of investigations. Although it was possible to follow the metabolism of simple (neutral) lipides, these latter substances posed a more difficult identification problem. Now with the advent of suitable isolation procedures and additional information of the chemical characteristics of the many diverse types of lipides, it is possible to study them in a more effective manner. In the following résumé, certain observations on the metabolic pathway of the lipides are outlined, and should serve as a general introduction or reorientation to this segment of the field of lipide biochemistry.

Phospholipides

Phospholipides, and in particular the lecithins, have been the object of extensive chemical and biochemical research for many years. No doubt part of this impetus was due to the ease of detection of lecithin and its isolation in a fair state of purity by relatively simple means. The possible function of these various lipides has led to much speculation, but to date this remains an unsolved problem.

Nonetheless, it is of interest to outline briefly some of the general proposals reported for the metabolic function or role of the phospholipides. These lipides have been implicated in the blood clotting process, as storage forms for fatty acids and phosphate, and as a source of choline in nervous tissue; as a matrix for the structure of the living cell, integral components in biological oxidations, and as intermediates in the transport, absorption, and metabolism of fatty acids. Finally, within the past few years considerable interest has been stimulated in the possible involvement of the phospholipides, especially phosphatidyl serine, in the transport and utilization of sodium and potassium ions.

Simple Lipides

In mammals, the simple (neutral) lipides of most concern in fatty acid metabolism are the glycerides and the cholesterol esters. While the following functions have been cited for the glycerides: (a) an excellent source of potential chemical energy (especially the depot fats), (b) thermal insulators, and (c) a protective cushion for organs, an exact metabolic role of these compounds has not been clearly defined. At present the available evidence tends to favor the participation of the glycerides in the absorption of fatty acids in the intestinal tract. On the other hand, there is limited evidence available on the involvement of the glycerides in fatty acid metabolism in other tissues or organs, such as the liver. Similarly, although the cholesterol esters are generally thought to be concerned only with the metabolism or transport of polyunsaturated fatty acids, the exact metabolic proof for this hypothesis is still under active investigation.

On the basis of present knowledge, it would appear most improbable that the phospholipides would have any role in fatty acid metabolism; for that matter, their role in any metabolically important reaction would be of an equivocal nature. However, within the past few years, evidence has been accumulating that strongly suggests a reconsideration of the possible metabolic patterns of the phosphoglycerides. This information has shown that each of the ester (R) groups of a phosphoglyceride may not be of the same reactivity and hence may have different "turnover" characteristics. Furthermore, there may be a preferential metabolism of the fatty acids on a particular position of a lipide molecule. This argument leads ultimately to another phase of the problem, that of the existence of several species of phosphoglycerides which differ in fatty acid composition and are not necessarily metabolically interrelated. Thus, for example, one species may be concerned only with one type of reaction, another with a different type of reaction, etc. Consequently, it appears pertinent to isolate these various species and study their individual metabolic characteristics.

This same reasoning may well apply to the glycerides and cholesterol esters. At present no asymmetric arrangement of the fatty acids on the glycerides has been established, but this does not negate the fact that there are several different species of glycerides. Each of these glycerides, as well as the cholesterol esters, may participate in entirely different metabolic reactions or pathways and need not be interrelated except as to basic structure.

While the above comments have been related to the major and best recognized fatty acid derivatives found in tissues, another less well known fatty acid derivative, the non-esterified fatty acid-protein complex, should be mentioned here. In the past it was considered that any free fatty acid present in a tissue extract was the result of degradative action in the isolation procedures. However, recent reports have firmly established that these so-called "free fatty acids" are normal constituents of the tissue lipide pool and are associated in a reasonably firm bonding to tissue protein. On the basis of current observations, the non-esterified fatty acids are thought to play an important role in fatty acid transport and utilization. A concise outline of progress in this subject is presented in reports by Dole[3] and Fredrickson et al.,[8] and in an extensive review by Fredrickson and Gordon.[7]

In the ensuing chapters it is hoped to convey the thought that the simple and complex lipides, though most often not beautifully crystalline compounds, can be treated as definite chemical entities and thus subjected to the same critical examination as would be applied to any organic compounds. While in general not the usual practice, at present it is a necessity that as many criteria as possible be employed to define a particular lipide or lipide fraction. Through the application of certain technical advances, notably chromatographic techniques, the above consideration has become a distinct reality and has aided considerably in the rapid expansion of the field of lipide chemistry. As isolation and fractionation procedures are always of utmost concern in lipide research, this topic is considered first, and subsequent chapters describe the chemical nature of various simple and complex lipides. As a concluding topic, the subject of lipoproteins, a most important "crossover" item, is discussed and illustrates the ultimate phase for study of the metabolic behavior of lipides.

REFERENCES

1. Baer, E., J. Maurukas, and M. Russell, *J. Am. Chem. Soc.*, **74**, 152 (1952).
2. Deuel, H. J., Jr., *The Lipides*, Vol. I, *Chemistry*, Interscience (1951).

3. Dole, V. P., in *Chemistry of Lipides as Related to Atherosclerosis*, edited by Page, p. 205, Thomas (1958).

4. Folch, J., and W. M. Sperry, *Ann. Rev. Biochem.*, **17**, 147 (1948).

5. Fourcroy, A. F., *Ann. Chim.*, **5**, 154 (1789).

6. Fourcroy, A. F., *Ann. Chim.*, **7**, 146 (1790).

7. Fredrickson, D. S., and R. S. Gordon, *Physiol. Revs.*, **38**, 585 (1958).

8. Fredrickson, D. S., D. L. McCollester, R. J. Havel, and K. Ono, in *Chemistry of Lipides as Related to Atherosclerosis*, edited by Page, p. 205, Thomas (1958).

9. Gensler, W. J., *Chem. Revs.*, **57**, 191 (1957).

10. Gunstone, F. D., *Prog. in Org. Chem.*, **1** (1958).

11. Gunstone, F. D., *An Introduction to the Chemistry of Fats and Fatty Acids*, Wiley (1958).

12. Hilditch, T. P., *The Chemical Constitution of Natural Fats*, 3rd edition revised, Wiley (1956).

13. Markley, K. S., *Fatty Acids*, Interscience (1947).

14. Ralston, A. W., *Fatty Acids and Their Derivatives*, Wiley (1948).

15. Vauquelin, M., *Ann. Chim.*, **10**, 193 (1791).

16. Vauquelin, M., *J. Pharm. Sci. Access.*, **3**, 385 (1817).

17. Wittcoff, H., *The Phosphatides*, Reinhold (1951).

2

Isolation
and purification
of lipides

Perhaps one of the major difficulties associated with any study of the chemistry or biochemistry of the simple and complex lipides has been that of the isolation and separation into their individual components. Concomitantly there has been the question of the proper criteria for definition of the purity of the isolated lipide fractions. Often the "homogeneity" or uniformity of a lipide fraction is defined on the basis of the non-fatty acid skeleton, but there is no doubt that the fatty acid composition significantly affects the physical and chemical properties of the fraction. Hence, as used in many instances, the term "pure" lipide is a peculiar one. The closely related solubility properties, the interassociative effects (ability of compounds to solubilize others, etc.), the influence of contaminants have all contributed to the problem of the purification of the lipides. Although these factors have presented a formidable challenge, within the past few years new and improved procedures, especially in chromatography, have been forthcoming and have allowed a better fractionation and subsequent identification.

In this chapter the discussion is directed towards a description of some of the problems encountered in the isolation and purification of lipides and an exploration of the possible means by which one can accomplish a satisfactory fractionation. It is is not intended that this material be all-inclusive but only illustrative of this particular area of lipide chemistry. Additional information on individual compounds is presented in later chapters.

EXTRACTION PROCEDURE

Preliminary to the ensuing discussion, it is worthwhile to mention briefly the general schemes employed in extraction of lipides. In the main, a solvent system, such as ethanol-ether, or chloroform-methanol, may be used to separate the lipides from the proteins and many other components of a tissue. Subsequently the solvent is removed from this initial extract by vacuum evaporation, and the resultant aqueous mixture is subjected to extraction with solvents such as diethyl ether, petroleum ether, or chloroform. After suitable washing of this solution, the total lipide is obtained by removal of solvent. As such it may contain phospholipides and simple (neutral) lipides. Subsequently this preparation can be separated by solvent fractionation or chromatography into the two general classes of lipides or further into individual components. However, as noted below, many other substances may be extracted along with these lipides and it is necessary to define as carefully as possible the nature of the fraction in question.

Solvents

There are now sufficient data to establish the concept that in mammalian tissues the major portion of the lipides is present as lipoprotein. The nature of this bonding between the lipides and the protein is discussed in a later chapter, but for the present it is sufficient to indicate that bonding by water molecules plays an important part in this union. In order to obtain the lipide from a lipoprotein, it is necessary to employ such dehydrating agents as ethanol, acetone, methanol, etc., which essentially rupture the lipide-protein linkage. Hence, it is partly for this reason that one of the above solvents is ordinarily included in the initial solvent extraction of a tissue. As many of the commonly occurring lipides are not entirely soluble in solvents such as ethanol, acetone, methanol, it is always advisable to include a more non-polar solvent such as petroleum ether, chloroform, or diethyl ether. The various mixtures used in the extraction of the lipides of tissues are documented in a review by Entenman.[20] It is obvious from this article that variations in approaches exist among different investigators; however, for most purposes an initial trial of a chloroform-methanol (2:1, v/v) or an ethanol-diethyl ether (3:1, v/v) mixture is highly recommended. The optimum ratio and amount of solvent to tissue may vary considerably from tissue to tissue, but usually a ratio of 3 parts solvent to 1 part tissue suffices for an adequate extraction. A further check as regards temperature, concentrations, etc., is necessary in order to be assured of complete extraction. In most cases it is advisable to further subject the solvent extracted residue to acid or alkaline hydrolysis at reflux temperatures and check for the release of fatty acid (long-chain) or other lipide-like material. If no fatty acids are recovered, then it is reasonable to assume that the extracted material represents the "total lipide."

Of interest with respect to solvent extraction of tissues is the technique of MacFarlane.[41] In this procedure the tissue is frozen and then extracted with diethyl ether while allowing the mixture to warm to room temperature. This has worked successfully on plasma [41] and also on plant tissue.[28] Perhaps the major difficulty involved in this method is the difficulty inherent in obtaining a reproducible freezing procedure and ultimately in the optimal number of lipoprotein bonds broken, and the time required to bring the mixture to the desired temperature. However, in many instances this approach may be worthy of further investigation.

Perhaps the most reproducible and generally useful approach to the extraction of lipides from most mammalian tissues is the use of chloroform-methanol or ethanol-diethyl ether mixtures at room temperature. Although obviously no panacea, it does represent a reasonable first approximation to the extraction of lipides from any tissues. The use of room temperature extraction is advised because of the possible occurrence of solvent activated enzymatic degradations (see below). This, together with reduced exposure to atmosphere and avoidance of the influence of light (on the induction of peroxidative changes) on the lipides, will improve the quality of the final product.

Possible Alterations in Lipide Structure in Extraction Procedure

As indicated in the preceding section, optimum conditions for extraction of lipides will vary from tissue to tissue. The differences in the nature of the sample and in the procedures used can significantly influence the end result. As an example, the use of elevated temperatures can in many cases cause detrimental effects on some of the lipide components of a mixture. In the author's experience it is best to employ a room temperature extraction (25–28°) or at the most one at 30–35° for the most effective extraction. The use of temperatures below 20° is not usually advisable owing to the limited solubility of many of the lipides. As an example of the temperature effect, if the extraction of the lipides from yeast is performed in pure ethanol-diethyl ether (3:1, v/v) at 55–60°, the phospholipides, in particular, are obviously severely affected (even if a nitrogen atmosphere is used). They are obtained as very dark viscous oils, apparently lipide in nature with high N/P ratios, i.e., 6/1 to 8/1; however, if the extraction is performed at room temperature (25°) the isolated lipides are a very light yellow in color, not easily oxidized by the atmosphere, with the phospholipides having N/P ratios near 1.0. While the N/P ratios *per se* do not define the entire sample, they do indicate the possibility of any gross alteration.

Particularly pertinent to the effect of temperature on the extraction of lipides is that of the activation of certain lipolytic enzymes not only by an increased temperature (lipases, up to 45°) but also by solvents (phospholipase A, C, and D). Essentially, as is emphasized here, certain lipide hydrolyzing enzymes are activated by solvents most commonly used in extraction and this, coupled with an elevated temperature, can have a deleterious effect on the lipide components. The occurrence of enzymatic degradation was noted by Hanahan and Chaikoff [28] in the process of solvent extraction of lipides from carrots and cabbage. In this instance it was established that the action of a phospholipase C (lecithinase C) caused a production of phosphatidic acid-like compounds. Most probably this type of enzymatic degradation was responsible for the occurrence of high concentrations of phosphatidic acids found in cabbage leaves by Chibnall and Channon.[11] In a more detailed and refined report on the phospholipase C of plants, Kates [36] has shown conclusively that this enzyme is very strongly activated by diethyl ether and many other lipide solvents. In fact, it is interesting to note that phospholipase A and D are also similarly activated by such solvents.[27, 33] Thus, it is pointedly clear that commonly employed lipide solvents (plus an elevated temperature) can produce undesirable side effects by initiating the action of certain lipolytic enzymes. On the basis of observations by Desnuelle and Constantin,[16] lipase apparently is not lipide solvent activated, and hence in this sense this enzyme does not cause a serious isolation problem; however, at an increased temperature (up to 45°) its activity can be significantly increased.

It is amply clear that degradation influences of this type must be considered in any extraction procedure. Perhaps the most reasonable approach is the use of repeated short-term extractions (3 to 4 hours) at room temperature, with the first extraction containing the largest amount of water (a necessity for a hydrolytic reaction) worked up immediately and stored at $-25°$ to $-30°$. In practice this procedure has worked in a very excellent manner for lipides from such sources as beef liver, rat liver, yeast, and chicken eggs. As suggested by Kates,[36] another possible route is through the use of propanol as one of the solvents. A distinct diminution of any degradative effects of phospholipase C was observed when this solvent was introduced in the extraction mixture. One possible drawback is the high boiling point of propanol which makes its removal more difficult.

Contaminants

No doubt the least appreciated facet of lipide purification is the marked tendency for lipide preparations to "trap" non-lipide components. The phospholipides (more than the neutral lipides) have shown a remarkable ability to solubilize many non-lipide components. In general, the most commonly encountered substances are sugars, free amino acids, sterols and sterol esters, urea, and many inorganic substances. In certain instances, during the purification of phospholipides, sterols and sterol esters may be classed as contaminants.

A part of the contamination problem is attributable to the solubility of these substances in the lipide solvents but mostly it is due to the complexing ability of the various types of phospholipides. Indeed, the monophosphoinositide present in liver phospholipide may contain up to 8% free sugar [30] while the other lipide fractions may contain only trace amounts. The ease with which these compounds can be solubilized by the complex lipides is convincingly shown in Table 2.1.

The presence of sugar can be indicated by the Molisch or anthrone reaction and free sugar can usually be detected by paper chromatographic techniques. In the latter instance, the sugar can be identified by two-dimensional chromatography with added glucose standards, with the following solvents: (1) butanol-pyridine-water (45:25:40), and (2) ethyl acetate-pyridine-water (2:1:2), essentially as described by Block et al.[6] Free glucose can also be estimated by the method of Baar,[1] after paper chromatography in 80% n-propanol. The paper chromatographic technique described by Olley [48] may be utilized for micro scale work. Normally, glucose is the main con-

Table 2.1

Approximate Solubility of Certain Non-Lipide Components in 5% Solution of
L-α-(Dioleyl)-Lecithin *

(Values expressed in mg. per 100 ml. solution at 25°)

	Solvent		
Compound	Anhydrous Ether	Moist Diethyl Ether	Chloroform
Sodium chloride	0	25	0
L-Serine	0	15	0
Glucose	125	315	175
Saccharose	15	150	115

* Taken from Baer et al.[2]

taminating sugar present in the mammalian lipide preparations, with only traces of galactose usually detected (by two-dimensional chromatography as above). No report of any free inositol in phospholipide preparations has been made, but inositol phosphates are found in soybean and brain preparations. In plant tissues, many more esoteric forms of sugars may be encountered. While in the process of isolating the phospholipides of yeast, Hanahan and Rhodes [31] obtained a good yield of crystalline α,α'-trehalose, comparable to a large amount of the sugar present in the lipides. Similarly, raffinose and stachyose have been noted in commercial soybean phospholipides.

Usually the free amino acids may be best detected by the paper chromatographic technique of Lea and colleagues.[38] In this procedure, the sample in question, together with known amino acid and ethanolamine standards, is spotted on filter paper and subjected to ascending or descending chromatography in chloroform-methanol (4:1, v/v-water 0.5%). This procedure is complete within 3 to 4 hours; the paper is dried and sprayed with ninhydrin reagent. The free amino acids will remain at the origin, while the lipide sample usually moves rather near the solvent front. It is desirable to run a companion paper or use a section of the chromatogram for a test of phosphorus compounds. Westley et al.[64] have devised a paper chromatographic method useful for detecting as well as removing any free amino acids or peptides from phospholipide preparations. In this technique the samples are chromatographed in an ascending manner on filter paper with any of the following solvent systems: (1) *n*-butanol saturated with 0.05M phthalate buffer, pH 4.1; (2) *n*-propanol:0.25N aqueous NH_4OH:acetone (4:1:1, v/v/v); (3) diethyl ether:ethanol:concentrated NH_4OH (15:5:3); or (4) methanol:benzene:*n*-butanol:water (2:1:1:1). An adequate separation of any free amino acids and peptides can be achieved in these systems. However, in order to detect and also remove any cyclic peptides, paper electrophoresis of the lipide samples is necessary.

If desired, sterols and sterol esters (cholesterol-like) may be determined qualitatively and quantitatively by the Liebermann-Burchard test, and any urea (occasionally found in plasma lipide fractions) by the biuret test. While it is highly desirable to have a single procedure that will completely eliminate all these (and other) contaminants from a lipide mixture, none has been reported. However, there are means by which these non-lipide substances can be removed, but it should be emphasized that suitable tests must be employed to insure that a satisfactory purification has been achieved. A description of these techniques is outlined in the following sections.

Special Washing Technique. The most reproducible route to the removal of many of the impurities cited above is that of Folch et al.[23] In brief, this procedure involves solution of the lipide in chloroform-methanol (2:1, v/v) and slow passage into a large volume of water, in which the sample is then allowed to stand for several hours. Slow diffusion of the methanol allows some mechanical stirring and also aids in removal of certain of the impurities. It is often advisable to repeat this procedure two to three times for the most effective removal of many of the contaminants. However, one should always be cognizant of the possible loss of lipide phosphorus in the aqueous washes. Recently Folch et al.[24] have published a revised "wash" procedure in which the tissue is extracted with chloroform-methanol (2:1, v/v) and then mixed thoroughly with 0.2 volume of water or an adequate salt solution. In this manner, the interfacial fluff noted in the above procedure is avoided. Thus the upper phase contains all the non-lipide substances and the lower phase all the lipide components. These authors claim that the addition of mineral salts, containing Na, K, Ca, or Mg, aids in decreasing any loss of lipide (particularly the more acidic type) at the interface or in the water phase. Hence they reason that the cations would decrease the dissociation of the acidic lipide (presumably containing the same cations) by a mass action effect; also, that any displacement of one cation by another is minimal. However, this latter point was not supported by any experimental data and certainly must be considered as an important area of investigation. It would seem at first hand that addition of these salts might increase the contamination problem and also alter the cation relationship of the more acid types. No identification of the acidic lipides was given and also no indication of the amount of salt present in the lower phase was shown.

Despite the difficulties encountered, the Folch water wash technique is the most reliable procedure to date for removal of such contaminants as free sugars, free amino acids, urea, and salts.

Column Chromatography.

Cellulose. Through the use of cellulose columns, Lea et al.[38] were able to satisfactorily eliminate the free amino acids found in chicken egg mixed phospholipides. Experimentally this is accomplished by passing a solution of phospholipides in chloroform-methanol-water through a column of Whatman cellulose powder.* A continuation of washing of the column with the same solvent resulted in the removal of the phospholipides, but left the free amino acids adsorbed on the column. While quite useful in this particular case, it has been recognized that the inositides of cod muscle [47] and those of beef liver, rat liver, and yeast [29] may be retained on such a column. Whether this represents a useful fractionation procedure for the inositides remains to be proved.

Silicic acid. If a phospholipide preparation is contaminated with sterols or sterol esters (or sterol glycosides as in soybean phospholipides), these may be removed by passage of the lipide sample in pure chloroform or diethyl ether through a silicic acid column.[7,37] The non-phospholipide contaminants in this case are fast moving and are essentially eluted with the solvent front, while the phospholipides are slower moving and more firmly adsorbed. If the total phospholipide is required, it may be eluted with pure methanol, or it may be fractionated in the usual manner as described below with various chloroform-methanol mixtures.

It is of interest to note that on silicic acid chromatography of phospholipides from several different sources, free amino acids usually appeared in the more polar eluates (i.e., sphingomyelin fraction) while the free sugars tended to concentrate almost exclusively in the inositide fraction.[30] This behavior may not be general but establishes the

* Actually in an earlier publication on the purification of the lipides of rubber, Smith [*Biochem. J.*, **57**, 130 (1954)] had noted the removal of non-lipide impurities, including amino acids, glucose, and inositol, by a similar procedure.

point that all preparations should be subjected to a preliminary wash, such as suggested by Folch et al., or to a careful examination for such substances.

The occurrence of pigments or pigmented materials in lipide fractions is well recognized. These compounds are predominantly carotenoids together with trace amounts of hematin-like substances and some oxidized lipide components. A reasonable approach to the removal of this color can be achieved by silicic acid chromatography, where the pigmented substances in many cases will be eluted with the initial solvent front or the fastest moving component. While this helps immensely in the purification process, colored material may be found in later fractions, and this is not readily removed by activated charcoal or other decolorizing substances. More often than not the lipide component may be irreversibly bound to the charcoal. Some removal of this color can be achieved by rechromatography on silicic acid with different solvents.

Paper Chromatography. As indicated above, Westley et al.[64] have reported a paper chromatographic procedure for detection of free amino acids and peptides in phospholipide preparations. Using the solvent systems described, the phospholipides can be prepared in "bulk" amounts, free of these non-lipide contaminants, by chomatography on cellulose or heavy filter paper.

FRACTIONATION PROCEDURES

For a long time, the separation and purification of the lipides from naturally occurring sources have been major problems of the lipide chemist and biochemist. In addition to the possible oxidative changes and enzymatic alterations that can occur during the isolation procedure, one is confronted with the presence of a variety of possible contaminants, as outlined above, which complicate the fractionation scheme. Several possible routes of fractionation have been explored, i.e., complex formation, solvent fractionation, and chromatography, and these as well as other techniques are described below. While no one procedure can be labeled as all-encompassing, it appears reasonably certain that chromatographic techniques for lipide fractionation will play an important part in contributing to our knowledge and understanding of lipide structure and function.

It is of considerable interest to note that ion exchange resins appear to be unsuitable as agents for fractionation of the phospholipides.[38]

Most likely the necessity of a more aqueous solvent for exchange resins use tends to produce the myelin forms of phospholipides and hence renders less likely any definite exchange with the resin; moreover, any solvent in which the lipides are soluble may greatly alter the resin.

While there is the possibility of repression of the dissociation of the ionic type phospholipides by organic solvents, Wallach and Garvin [62] have presented evidence for the existence of charged species of phospholipides such as phosphatidyl ethanolamine and phosphatidyl serine in organic solvents (containing 3 to 5% water). On the other hand, Radin and co-workers [52,53] have utilized ion exchange resins in the final stages of purification of the cerebrosides of brain and spinal cord lipides, particularly with regard to the removal of ionic contaminants. Of interest in this report was the observation that the passage of the lipides in chloroform-methanol, 2:1 (v/v), through an activated magnesium silicate column resulted in the nearly complete adsorption of the phospholipides, whereas the cerebrosides, a sulfatide, and some acidic non-cerebroside carbohydrate lipides were not adsorbed. When this latter fraction was passed through a mixture of exchange resins, the non-ionic cerebrosides were not adsorbed and could be obtained in a high state of purity from the effluent.

General

Acetone Treatment. When the total lipide fraction has been obtained from a particular tissue, the question is raised as to the most expeditious approach to the subsequent fractionation of this material. There are many different possibilities; only three of the more useful ones will be discussed here. By and large a useful initial fractionation procedure involves the use of acetone, which can effectively separate the phospholipides (acetone insoluble) from the neutral lipides (acetone soluble). Thus, the phospholipides of beef and rat liver can be obtained in 95% yields by acetone treatment of the total lipide preparation at room temperature. While this procedure can be carried out at low temperatures (4° or lower), a significant amount of neutral lipides (cholesterol esters, glycerides) may be precipitated along with the phospholipides. Consequently, in any acetone precipitation procedure the best conditions must be established for optimum separation. In many instances, however, no suitable combination of temperature and acetone concentration can be found for maximum precipitation of the phospholipides. As an excellent example, the phospholipides of the erythrocyte are very difficult to precipitate with acetone, even at temperatures as low as -20 to $-25°$. At these latter temperatures as much as 20 to 25% of the phospholipides is still acetone soluble. A similar observation was made by Olley and Lovern [49] on the phospholipides of haddock flesh. On the other hand, acetone tends to give friable powders with certain phospholipides, cerebrosides, etc., which makes filtration and handling much easier.

It is apparent that acetone precipitation is adequate in the separation of certain fractions while rather less adequate with others. In order to circumvent this difficulty many investigators have added salts, such as $MgCl_2$, which aid considerably in precipitation of all the phospholipides. However, this only increases the contamination of the lipide fractions and may alter the cation composition of some of the more acidic phospholipides found in many tissues (i.e., phosphoinositides, phosphatidyl serine). In many instances trichloroacetic acid has been used as a phospholipide precipitant, but, as shown recently by Marinetti et al.,[45] this may cause some hydrolysis of labile compounds, such as the plasmalogens, even under gentle conditions.

Among other useful means for an initial fractionation, chromatography can be of considerable value. In particular, silicic acid appears to be of value and two routes are possible.

Chromatography.

General separation. In this procedure the sample, containing both the simple (neutral) lipides as well as the phospholipides, in chloroform or diethyl ether, is applied to a silicic acid column and washed with the same solvent until all the neutral lipide (as judged by weight assay, cholesterol, etc.) is removed. Subsequently, the more strongly absorbed phospholipides can be eluted with pure methanol, methanol-chloroform (9:1), or similar solvents. In this manner, the two major lipide fractions can be obtained and studied as desired. This type of approach can be valuable in establishing the initial distribution of radioactivity in lipide fractions, or can serve as the starting point for further fractionation by chromatography, solvent fractionation, etc. In repeated experiments with salmon lipides, LaRoche [37] was successful in applying this technique, with diethyl ether as the initial solvent, to lipide separation problems.

Specific separation. If necessary, the entire lipide sample may be fractionated by chromatography on silicic acid. In an extensive series of experiments, LaRoche [37] observed that a reasonable fractionation of the lipide of salmon liver could be effected first by the use of hexane and hexane-ether mixtures, as suggested by Barron and Hanahan,[4] and subsequently the phospholipides could be eluted fractionally by chloroform-methanol mixtures. One problem concerned with this type of approach is that a portion of the lipide remains on the column for a rather long period of time (depending on size of column) and hence some degradation can conceivably occur.

Specific Separations

Phospholipides. In early studies of the fractionation of phospholipides most attention was directed towards the isolation of lecithin (phosphatidyl choline). In part this was due to its greater concentration in most tissues, relative ease of isolation and assay, and lack of information as to other lipide forms in tissues. In the intervening years, our knowledge of other possible lipides present in tissues has expanded and concomitantly the techniques with which to fractionate the lipides have increased. The following section illustrates some of the methods used for the purification of phospholipides and an evaluation of efficacy of each approach is included.

Salt (complex) formation. As early as 1868, Strecker[58] observed that phospholipides could be precipitated from an alcoholic solution by cadmium chloride and other metallic salts. In the course of this investigation, the structure of lecithin was fairly well described. This method of purification was further improved by Bergell[5] in 1900 in an effort to remove as completely as possible the so-called cephalins, which were the chief contaminants in the crude preparations of lecithin. However, the results of Bergell's experiments were not completely satisfactory. In 1927, Levene and Rolf[39] reported on extensive studies on the fractionation of complex salts of phospholipides. Egg yolks and brain and liver tissues were used as a source of lecithin. In brief the procedure was as follows: The material was extracted with hot alcohol and the lecithin precipitated with a saturated solution of cadmium chloride. The cadmium chloride salt was washed eight to ten times with ether, which removed the cephalins. The washed salt was suspended in chloroform and a solution of ammonia in methanol added until complete precipitation was obtained. The insoluble material was extracted with chloroform, concentrated to dryness, and dissolved in ether. The ether was then removed by evaporation and the residue dissolved in ethanol. This part of the extraction was repeated three times and the product dissolved in alcohol. The above cadmium chloride precipitation was repeated and the lipide was reprecipitated from diethyl ether by acetone. Further purification was accomplished by washing the precipitate with acetic acid, then with acetone, and finally by emulsification with acetone. The yield of egg yolk lecithin was not quoted, but they did obtain N/P molar ratios of 1.1 to 1.2. However, no choline values were reported and these high N/P values indicated contamination most probably by free amino acids or sphingolipides.

Pangborn [50] attempted to modify the Levene and Rolf procedure by devising a method which offered advantages in convenience, purity, and high yield of the final product. This method was based on the fact that the cadmium salt of lecithin was not soluble in petroleum ether and only slightly soluble in 80% ethanol. However, it was readily soluble in 80% ethanol saturated with petroleum ether and separated from the solution when the ether was removed. This precipitation must be repeated some eight to ten times. Several ether washings were necessary to remove the sphingolipides and similar impurities. Yields are quite low and can be improved only by the time-consuming and involved procedure of concentration and re-extraction of all washes. The reported nitrogen and phosphorus values indicated that the product was improved by the modification. However, no analyses for choline were reported nor were any other constituents determined. Hence, as had been the case in many investigations, the N/P values were used as the sole indication of the purity of the lecithin obtained, but this can hardly be considered as a valid assumption. Later, Pangborn [51] reported on attempts to improve and simplify the cadmium chloride method, through use of a chloroform-methanol precipitation, but the procedure was much more involved and lower yields were obtained.

While useful as a convenient derivative form for the storage of lecithins (lysolecithins and glyceryl-phosphorylcholine), metallic salts (compared to the more effective and specific materials indicated below) *per se* are of limited value as an aid in the fractionation of the phospholipides.

"Solvent" fractionation. Inasmuch as there were many obvious difficulties involved in the salt fractionation method, interest was stimulated to find a more suitable approach. A temperature-dependent neutral solvent fractionation procedure reported by Sinclair [57] produced a product quite as pure as that obtained by the cadmium chloride method. This method consisted of cooling an alcohol solution of crude phospholipides to $-35°$ and separating the soluble fraction from the insoluble. The insoluble material was mostly non-choline containing phospholipide but also contained a significant amount of lecithin, while the soluble fraction was mainly lecithin. This fractionation was repeated several times, followed by washings with water and acetone, and the alcohol soluble fraction was then dialyzed against water for several days. The starting material was the mixed phospholipides from egg yolks and had an N/P ratio of 1.08 and a choline/P ratio of 0.77. The "lecithin" fraction with the highest degree of purity constituted approximately 5% of the starting material and had an N/P ratio of 1.00 and a choline/P ratio of 0.97. Other fractions were obtained which approached this degree of apparent purity.

In studies on the chemical nature of the brain "cephalin," Folch [22] made extensive use of neutral solvents for fractionation purposes. Basically this procedure took advantage of the fact that diphosphoinositide (one of the major components) was much less soluble in methanol than either phosphatidyl serine or phosphatidyl ethanolamine. Initially Folch prepared an "inositol phosphatide" fraction by chloroform-methanol (1:1.45, v/v) treatment, in which the inositol phospholipide was largely insoluble and the soluble portion was phosphatidyl serine and ethanolamine. Further purification of the inositol phospholipide could be achieved by use of chloroform-methanol (11:2, v/v) wherein several different phospholipide fractions containing mainly phosphatidyl serine and ethanolamine and also an impure diphosphoinositide, in approximately 20% yield, were obtained. Apparently a considerable amount of inorganic phosphate accompanied the inositide fraction and had to be removed. Out of the entire inositol phospholipide fraction, 74% of the phospholipide was recovered. This technique has been applied with varying success to other tissues and does represent a gentle fractionation procedure for the phospholipides. However, the yields do tend to be unsatisfactory and some questions arise as to the reliability with tissues (or preparations) having other than the ratio of phospholipides described in these preparations.

Countercurrent distribution. The principle of countercurrent distribution, essentially a multiple batch extraction procedure, has been applied to the fractionation of the phospholipides. In this type of fractionation, continuous portions of one solvent phase progressing in one direction are equilibrated with a second solvent phase progressing in the opposite direction. Thus, depending on partition coefficients and volume of solvent, components dissolved in one phase may distribute in one phase or the other in the immiscible solvent system. This type of fractionation offers some advantage over chromatographic procedures, where adsorbents may cause some irreversible changes in the lipides. However, in general, the countercurrent technique requires a comparatively large amount of material for proper identification of components and usually requires a large number of transfers for the separation of one or two components in a fair state of purity. Nonetheless, considerable information can be obtained on new types of lipides and possible solvent systems for fractionation of individual components. As shown by Olley,[46] variation in the distribution pattern can result from differences in solute concentrations. Only a rather brief résumé of results with this technique is described here, and for a more detailed discussion of this method reference is made to review articles by Dutton [19] and Olley.[47] Especially as regards lipides, it would appear that the countercurrent technique is more valuable with fractions first separated by other procedures.

An example of the usefulness of countercurrent distribution is the observation of Scholfield et al.[56] on the fractionation of the phospholipides of soybean. When a hexane-90% methanol solvent system was used, the presence of phosphoinositides, in addition to the usual phosphatidyl choline and phosphatidyl ethanolamine, was noted. In an examination of the phospholipides of ox brain, Lovern [40] obtained a reasonable separation of the phosphatidyl choline from the other phospholipides, with petroleum ether (40–60°)-95% ethanol solvent system. No separation of phosphatidyl ethanolamine from phosphatidyl serine was indicated. Cole et al.[12] investigated the countercurrent fractionation of human brain lipides with two different solvent systems. Their results indicated that a separation of many of the lipide components was possible and suggested a possibly more complete separation with different solvent systems. Quite recently, Carter and associates [10] found countercurrent distribution procedures of value in their studies on the chemistry of the plant phospholipides. Through use of a 400-stage transfer with a solvent system of n-heptane-n-butanol-methanol-water a satisfactory distribution of components (from 16 g. of starting material) resulted, and there was little or no emulsion problem. Most of the desired phytosphingolipides were concentrated in the intermediate partition range and showed a distinct separation from phosphatidyl inositol. However, further purification of the phytosphingosine lipides by other methods was necessary.

Column chromatography. In the past few years considerable interest has been aroused in the ultimate fractionation and identification of the lipides of a tissue. Today, there is no doubt that column chromatography can be of immeasurable value in the isolation and purification of the lipides and in the study of their metabolism. While these newer techniques and procedures represent sound improvements, it is important to stress again the necessity for as complete an identification of a fraction as possible. Mere observance of the elution point or a phosphorus value will not adequately define a complex lipide fraction.

Among the various adsorbents considered as feasible for the separation of the simple and/or complex lipides, silicic acid, and to a lesser extent, aluminum oxide now appear to be the most important and useful. No attempt is made here to outline all the possible techniques proposed for separations; only those of present value are discussed. Brief mention must be made of the use of magnesium oxide as a separation tool, since it still is used to some extent by investigators in this field. In essentially the pioneering experiments on the fractionation of phospholipides by adsorption techniques, Taurog et al.[59] reported the separation of the choline containing from the non-choline containing phospholipides of liver by use of "light" magnesium oxide. In this procedure the phospholipides were adsorbed from petroleum ether onto the adsorbent and then treated with methanol, which eluted only the choline containing phospholipides. The non-choline containing phospholipides could not be removed from the magnesium oxide in an intact form. Although this method was of general use, it suffered from the non-reproducibility of the commercially available material, especially as concerned size and density of the particles and their adsorptive capacity.

ALUMINUM OXIDE. This reagent has been particularly satisfactory in the preparation of lecithin fractions of high purity. In original observations with this adsorbent,[32] it was reported that the alcohol soluble fraction of the phospholipides of chicken egg could be selectively fractionated by passage through a column of aluminum oxide (previously prepared in the same solvent). The choline containing phospholipides could be eluted with the same solvent, while the non-choline containing phospholipides were firmly bound to the adsorbent. Later studies showed that the alcohol soluble fraction from liver and yeast could be fractionated in a similar manner. In these particular experiments, only traces of sphingomyelins were present. Recently, Rhodes and Lea[55] have presented evidence that sphingomyelins are also eluted with the choline containing fractions as well as lysolecithins. In these and all other studies reported to date the aluminum oxide has always been the basic type which tends to have a pH in these systems of near 7.5 to 8.0. Thus the success of this fractionation would appear to depend on the non-reactivity of the choline containing phospholipides (present as zwitterion at all pH values) with the aluminum oxide, whereas the more acidic fractions, such as phosphatidyl ethanolamine and monophosphoinositides, are adsorbed by reaction with the basic adsorbent.

Thus, a slightly acid or neutral aluminum oxide would probably not function successfully in this separation.

Of considerable interest is the fact that both the choline and non-choline containing phospholipides of chicken egg can be separated and recovered in good yield by chromatography on aluminum oxide, as shown by Rhodes and Lea.[55] Specifically, the mixed phospholipides were first placed on the column in chloroform-methanol (1:1, v/v) and washed with this same solvent. A very rapid elution of only the choline containing phospholipides then followed. Subsequent use of ethanol-chloroform-water (5:2:2, v/v) removed the non-choline containing fraction. The recoveries were 92 to 98%, based on the applied phosphorus. A typical elution pattern is depicted in Table 2.2.

Besides the type of fractionation realized by this procedure there is the added value that flow rates can be quite high and still allow a suitable resolution. For example, the first solvent can be passed through at a rate of 10 ml. per minute for the elution of the choline containing phospholipides, and the second solvent for removal of the non-choline containing lipides can be run at 2 to 3 ml. per minute. Thus this would tend to reduce the time each compound would be on the column and consequently reduce the possible degradative effects. However, on the basis of available data, no degradation of phospholipides has been reported on aluminum oxide. In general, the loading factor for this adsorbent is in the range from 1 to 2 mg. phospholipide phosphorus per gram of aluminum oxide.

Table 2.2

Fractionation of Mixed Phospholipides of Chicken Egg on Aluminum Oxide *

152.5 mg. phospholipide-P on 160 g. adsorbent

Eluting Solvent	Volume, in ml.	Recovery, % of Applied P
CHCl₃-methanol (1:1, v/v)	500	82
	10	0.02
Ethanol-CHCl₃-HOH (5:2:2, v/v)	500	14.4
	400	2.1
	400	1.2

* Taken from Rhodes and Lea.[55]

A particular value of this approach is that it may be used quite successfully with silicic acid chromatography (see below). As an example, in the silicic acid chromatography of large amounts of phospholipides, the time required for completion of the elution depends on the amount of lecithin and sphingomyelin, which are usually the last components eluted. Furthermore, the observed skewing of the lecithin elution can significantly prolong the time required for this type of chromatogram. Consequently, it might be more expedient to separate the lecithin and sphingomyelins together, e.g., by chromatography on aluminum oxide, and then further fractionate them more rapidly by suitable solvents on silicic acid. At the same time the non-choline containing components can usually be more easily fractionated directly on silicic acid and hence an over-all sharper separation may be obtained by this approach.

SILICIC ACID. Perhaps the most widely used and acclaimed adsorbent for lipide purification in recent years is silicic acid.* Its commercial availability in highly purified and reproducible form no doubt has aided in its widespread adoption. Not only has it been successfully applied to the fractionation of the phospholipides but to the neutral lipide components as well.

McKibbin, using silicic acid columns, found that the application of gradient elution with chloroform-methanol mixtures could effectively aid in the preparation of the polyglycerophosphatide from dog liver [43] and also an inositide from horse liver.[42] Through their studies on the phospholipides of egg yolk, Lea et al.[38] showed that silicic acid could be used for the fractionation of these lipides. In brief the procedure was as follows: Silicic acid, with or without added celite (to increase the flow rate), was washed thoroughly with the eluting solvent (chloroform-methanol 4:1, v/v) and packed into a column. The sample was

---

* In a recent article, J. Hirsch and E. H. Ahrens [*J. Biol. Chem.,* **233**, 311 (1958)] discuss the various aspects of the problems associated with the separation of artificial and naturally occurring mixtures on silicic acid. The adsorptive property of silicic acid for various known lipides (mostly of a more saturated type) in petroleum ether-ethyl ether mixtures was investigated, and on the basis of these results one may be able to select the proper solvent system for separation of a mixture of lipides. A separation of the lipides of human plasma proceeded in the expected manner. As is obvious, these data are of considerable value and use, but it should be emphasized that in naturally occurring mixtures, the presence of highly unsaturated derivatives and more complicated compounds than are found in the lipides of human plasma may pose a problem in the selection of proper solvents and the exact loading level. In this case, it is obvious that these facets of the problem can be solved only by the actual experimental approach.

placed on the column in the same solvent and the elution was initiated. While variations in solvent mixtures from 8 to 32% methanol in chloroform were tried, the most suitable one was 20% MeOH in CHCl₃ and this was used throughout the elution. Two major components, phosphatidyl ethanolamine and phosphatidyl choline, were separated. However, though the phosphatidyl ethanolamine fraction was eluted reasonably rapidly in this solvent, lecithin (phosphatidyl choline) was removed quite slowly. These investigators obtained evidence for the presence of a lysolecithin, which was eluted after the lecithin fraction.

The application of silicic acid to the separation of the more complicated phospholipide mixtures was outlined by Hanahan et al.[29] While the use of a strict gradient elution technique caused gross overlapping of nearly all the components, application of three different solvent mixtures was effective in separating the mixed phospholipides from rat liver, beef liver, and yeast into some five different fractions. These solvent mixtures were chloroform-methanol mixtures (4:1, 3:2, and 1:4, v/v) and were found to be quite reproducible in effecting these separations. An example of the separation of the mixed phospholipides of rat liver on silicic acid is shown in Fig. 2.1. In general, the more acidic type phospholipides (phosphatidyl ethanolamine) are eluted first, then the inosities and phosphatidyl choline types, and lastly the sphingomyelins. Lysolecithin tends to be found between the lecithin and the sphingomyelin fractions whereas any lysophosphatidyl serine or ethanolamine may be found in the inositide fractions.

Although the chromatography of the mixed phospholipides on silicic acid affords reasonable separation, in certain instances some overlap of components occurs. This is particularly true of the phosphoinositides which tend to contain some nitrogenous impurities as shown, for example, by N/P values of 0.20 to 0.30 in the rat liver fractionation. However, when rechromatographed on silicic acid with different mixtures of chloroform and methanol, the phosphoinositide, essentially devoid of nitrogen, could be obtained in good yield. A typical refractionation of impure phosphoinositide on silicic acid is shown in Fig. 2.2. While this procedure has worked well with both beef liver and rat liver phosphoinositide purification, the same separation could not be effected with yeast phosphoinositide fraction. In the latter case, rechromatography of this material on silicic acid gave only a partial separation, as shown in Fig. 2.3. In this case, the fast running component was the phosphoinositide and the slower component was a lysophosphatidyl serine-like compound. The nitrogenous impurity with the rat and beef liver preparations was a phosphatidyl ethanola-

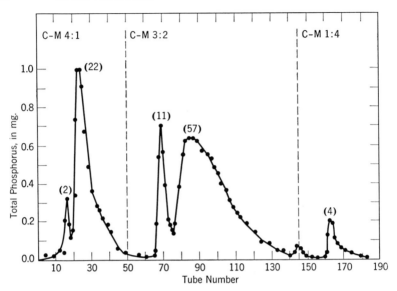

Fig. 2.1. Chromatography of rat liver mixed phospholipides on silicic acid. The eluting solvent was a mixture of chloroform (C) and methanol (M), v/v. The figures in parentheses refer to per cent of total phospholipide applied to column.

mine. A comparable situation may be expected with other fractions. Although not exactly a strict comparison, the observations of Weiss [63] on the heterogeneity of the sphingolipides of brain serve to illustrate this point. When the sphingolipides of monkey brain, previously isolated by ethanol fractionation, were chromatographed on silicic acid with gradient elution, at least seven different components were obtained. Among these were three different glycosphingosides and at least two phosphosphingosides.

While the above examples of fractionation show the presence of the more classical types of phospholipides, a more complicated pattern is exhibited with mixtures containing the plasmalogens. Marinetti et al.[45] have submitted the phospholipides of pig heart, unusually rich in the ethanolamine and choline type plasmalogens, to silicic acid chromatography. Through use of chloroform-methanol mixtures (4:1, 1:1) and pure methanol, these compounds were apparently separated from each other but were eluted with their diacyl counterparts. In such chromatograms some care must be exercised that the time of contact of the plasmalogens with silicic acid be reasonably short as some acid hydrolytic degradation could occur. However, recent evidence [34]

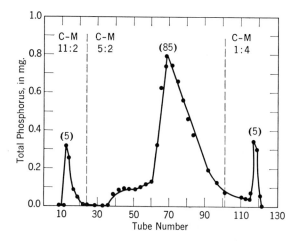

Fig. 2.2. Rechromatography of crude monophosphoinositide fraction from rat liver on silicic acid. A highly purified monophosphoinositide was found in the C-M 5:2 fraction.

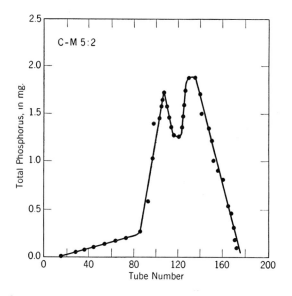

Fig. 2.3. Rechromatography of monophosphoinositide fraction from yeast on silicic acid. The fast-moving component contained a monophosphoinositide, and the slower-moving substance was apparently a lysophosphatidyl serine.

has been obtained that shows that the plasmalogens of beef heart mitochondrial phospholipides may not be altered by this procedure. Nevertheless, this is an important point which must be checked in all operations involving this type of compound. In their investigation on the plasmalogens of lymphosarcoma phospholipides, Rapport and Alonzo [54] isolated the choline containing plasmalogens (together with the lecithin) through its cadmium salt derivative, and the ethanolamine types (plus a small amount of diacyl derivative) by chromatography on silicic acid-celite columns. In this latter procedure, mixtures of ethanol in hexane and methanol in ethanol were found to be suitable eluting agents.

GENERAL COMMENTS. While dependent on the chemical nature of the phospholipide mixture in question, an adequate fractionation is obtained with a loading factor of 1 mg. or less of phospholipide phosphorus per gram of silicic acid. When larger amounts are used, there is a definite tendency to considerable overlapping and smearing of fractions. Subsequently, flow rates of 1.5 to 2.0 ml. per minute allow a satisfactory separation in most cases. As a general rule the use of fresh batches of silicic acid or material dried overnight at 110° is recommended, but the requirement for activation of this adsorbent is not as acute with the phospholipides as with the simple (neutral) lipides. It is important to note that the drying at a high temperature of any additives, such as celite, etc., may cause considerable overlapping and distortion in the elution pattern. Similarly, the use of cotton plugs for support of column material should be avoided as they are capable of adsorbing some of the phosphoinositides. Although admittedly an obvious fact, nevertheless it is strongly urged that the source of adsorbent be specified in any report on a fractionation procedure. For example, the silicic acid commercially available in England is quite different in adsorptive properties from that available in the United States. In the former case, only triglycerides are adsorbed while the phospholipides are not; in the latter type of silicic acid, both phospholipides and neutral lipides can be adsorbed and selectively eluted.

Paper chromatography. As in other fields of biochemical endeavor, the application of paper chromatography to the problem of identification of phospholipides has proved of considerable value. The need for a rapid and sensitive means of identifying lipides has been fulfilled in part by the paper chromatographic technique. As illustrated below, methods have been devised for the intact phospholipides as well as the hydrolytic products derived from these compounds. However, there is need to stress the point that an R_F value *per se* cannot adequately identify or prove the structure of a compound and certainly not those as complex as the phospholipides. Although this may prove to be an absolute rule in the future, at present additional evidence as furnished by physical and chemical methods is of great importance in confirming proof. Moreover, this approach has a valuable place as an aid in the isolation and purification processes and in following the progress of *in vitro* and *in vivo* reactions. When one is cognizant of the limitations of this technique, it can serve as a valuable adjunct to chemical and biochemical investigations. Inasmuch as an exhaustive survey of the reported paper chromatographic procedures is not intended here, the following section will illustrate some of the possible routes to identification and the problems involved.

Since early 1950 a considerable amount of attention has been devoted to the paper chromatographic separation of the phospholipides. Hack [26] described a micro method of lipide analysis with filter paper disk chromatograms. Huennekens et al.[35] outlined the possible solvent systems for separation of water soluble products derived from lecithin and to a limited extent water insoluble phospholipide mixtures.

An adequate separation of several different intact phospholipides on silicic acid impregnated paper has been described by Lea et al.[38] When a solvent mixture of 20% methanol in chloroform was employed, phosphatidyl ethanolamine, phosphatidyl choline (lecithin), and lysolecithin could be easily separated, as shown in Table 2.3. However, lysophosphatidyl ethanolamine and sphingomyelin tend to migrate to the same extent as do the plasmalogens and lecithin. Some difficulty was reported with saturated derivatives which tended to lag. While

Table 2.3

Chromatography of Phospholipides on Silicic Acid Impregnated Filter Paper *

Compound	R_F
Lysolecithin	0.27
Lysophosphatidyl ethanolamine	0.44
Sphingomyelin	0.45
Plasmalogen	0.62
Lecithin	0.63
Phosphatidyl ethanolamine	0.80

* Taken from Lea et al.[38]

phosphatidyl serine and phosphatidyl ethanolamine ran close together on a unidimensional chromatogram, these compounds could be separated on a two-dimensional chromatogram.

Recently it has been suggested that a better separation could be obtained if 2% water were present in the solvent.[45] In a study of the incorporation of P^{32}-phosphate into phospholipides of rat tissue, Marinetti et al.[45] investigated the chromatography of rat liver and heart phospholipides with two different solvents: A, diisobutyl ketone-acetic acid-water (40:30:7), and B, n-butyl ether-acetic acid-chloroform-water (40:35:6:5, v/v). In comparison with control runs with known compounds, the positive identification of these various components was claimed. However, no data on the composition of these individual fractions were supplied. Further, while the separations appear to be quite good, the overlapping of radioactivity, as indicated by a radioautogram of P^{32} labeled material, appeared to be rather great.

Dieckert and Reiser [17] reported that glass fiber filter paper impregnated with silicic acid could be used in the separation of phospholipides. The chromatograms could be run quite rapidly (in 2 hours) in methanol-ether solvents and the compounds located by spraying with 20% sulfuric acid. The sites of charring were then interpreted as representing phospholipides. Unless other means are used for identification, one cannot prove the absence of a sugar of any other type of organic compound. However, Brown et al.[9] later reported a modification of this system, using a different solvent system, namely phenol-ethyl ether-acetone-water. Furthermore, other means of identification were employed, namely ninhydrin, phosphomolybdate spray, etc., and the spots were described as well defined, slightly elliptical in shape. No evidence was presented on the separation of mixed phospholipides from naturally occurring sources. Typical R_F values for a variety of compounds are presented in Table 2.4.

In an investigation designed to study the incorporation of P^{32} into phospholipides, Dawson [14,15] devised a novel and simple procedure. The tissue lipides were subjected to short-term alkaline hydrolysis (37° for 15 minutes in $1M$ methanolic KOH) and the water soluble components isolated through extraction and exchange chromatography. Two-dimensional chromatography on paper in phenol-ammonia and in t-butanol-trichloracetic acid allowed a very adequate separation of compounds such as glycerylphosphorylcholine, glycerylphosphorylserine, glycerylphosphorylethanolamine, an inositol phosphate derivative, and two unknowns. While this technique has been widely and successfully used, it should be pointed out again that labeled phos-

Table 2.4

Chromatography of Phospholipides on Glass Fiber Silicic Acid
Impregnated Paper *

Substance	R_F
Lysolecithin	0.31
Sphingomyelin	0.50
Dimyristoyl lecithin	0.65
Egg lecithin	0.66
Phosphatidyl ethanolamine	0.85

* Taken from Brown et al.[9]

phorus may not be completely indicative of the metabolism of an intact phospholipide, and thus some limitation is posed by this technique.

In their studies on the identification of tissue lipides, Marinetti et al.[44] have described a quantitative paper chromatographic technique. They were able to separate phospholipides from pig heart ventricles into at least six different components by chromatography on silicic acid impregnated paper. The solvent system was diisobutyl ketone-acetic acid-water (40:25:5, v/v) and the temperature was maintained at 0–5° to minimize any hydrolysis of the plasmalogens. A control strip was run and the spots were located by staining with Rhodamine 6G dye. Then the unstained section was marked and the spots cut out and eluted by extracting three times for ½ hour each under reflux with 0.8 to 1.0N HCl in redistilled methanol. Lipide phosphorus values were then determined, and in most runs recoveries of near 100% were recorded. As pointed out by these authors, more than one component could possibly occur in a single spot. These observations were coupled with chromatography of the phospholipides on silicic acid. The major components appeared to be ethanolamine and choline type plasmalogens (plus some of the diacyl derivatives), and the remaining compounds were thought to be phosphoinositide, sphingomyelin, and lysolecithin.

Douste-Blazy et al.[18] have outlined a novel paper chromatographic procedure, which involves partitioning between two immiscible organic phases formed by a mixture of various solvents. Essentially in this technique, a paper strip is hung vertically from a trough in which one of the solvents is placed and the other end of the paper strip is immersed in the other solvent. The sample is placed near the top of the paper and the R_F values are calculated from the meeting point of the two phases; upwards (non-polar solvents), downwards (polar solvents). A typical solvent system used in this procedure was: acetic acid-methanol-water (10:10:1, v/v/v)–petroleum ether-chloroform (21:4, v/v). The lipide components were detected by various color reactions. However, no information, other than color reactions, was supplied on the identification of the lipide components claimed to have been separated from egg lecithin and a brain "cephalin" preparation.

Although in the past the use of filter paper electrophoresis for separation of lipides has met with limited success, recently Wallach and Garvin [62] have been able to obtain satisfactory and true electrophoresis of lipides in organic solvents containing 3 to 5% water. Various staining techniques were used for the location of the migrated compounds: ninhydrin reagent for amines, phosphotungstic acid for choline, Sudan Black for triglycerides, Rhodamine B for several lipide compounds (mainly phospholipides), Schiff reagent for plasmalogens, and phosphomolybdic acid for phosphorus. In order to obtain a suitable separation of lipides, attention must be paid to the control of pH, ionic strength, solvent composition, heat dissipation, etc. When this technique was applied to various lipides, it was observed that these substances can exist in organic solvents as charged species and can migrate in an electric field with a dependence on potential gradient, pH, and ionic strength. The separation of phosphatidyl serine from phosphatidyl ethanolamine and lecithin of artificial and natural mixtures was achieved, and the "migration values" for several other compounds were noted. In particular, it was noted that phosphatidyl ethanolamine and serine can exist in a dissociable form, but, as expected for a zwitterion such as lecithin, this latter compound had no net charge and hence no electrophoretic movement. This filter paper electrophoresis method should prove of considerable value in evaluating the general composition of a naturally occurring lipide mixture, as an aid in establishing the purity of a compound, and in the separation of otherwise difficultly separable mixtures.

Derivative formation. While of some question now, nevertheless the "derivative" formation technique of Collins and Wheeldon [13] deserves mention. These investigators subjected rat liver lipide to reaction with fluoro-2,4 dinitrobenzene for 2 hours at 40° in benzene. The conversion of free amino groups to the nitrophenyl derivative was then followed by esterification of the secondary phosphates and the carboxyl groups of serine with diazomethane. Subsequently, these lipides were chromatographed on Hyflo Super Cel and eluted with petroleum ether, benzene in chloroform, and 10% ethanol in chloroform. The eluants were examined spectrophotometrically, and it was reported that other components were present in addition to phosphatidyl ethanolamine, phosphatidyl serine, sphingomyelin, phosphatidyl choline, and inositides. However, Baer and Maurukas [3] found that diazometholysis can occur with certain of these compounds, i.e., the serine phospholipides, with the formation of dimethyl esters of phosphatidic acids. Hence, considerable reservation must be used in evaluating the advantages of the above procedures. Furthermore, for preparative purposes, the recovery of the original phospholipide would present a difficult problem.

Simple (Neutral) Lipides. One of the more difficult areas of lipide chemistry is concerned with the proper separation and identification of the neutral lipides. A number of routes to the partial identification of the types of naturally occurring glycerides on a large scale have been devised,[8] as have techniques for free sterol isolation by chromatography or digitonin precipitation, etc. However, until relatively recently no procedures were available for the separation of the entire neutral lipide fraction of a tissue on a small scale. While specific precipitating agents may work well for certain of the components, in general the most profitable approach has been that of column chromatography. Although this technique again is no panacea, it does allow a starting point for the further fractionation of groups of compounds, i.e., the glycerides by low temperature fractionation or rechromatography.

In his original observations on fractionation of lipides on adsorbents, Trappe [60,61] noted that glycerides were partially saponified on aluminum oxide columns, and this fact has been well recognized and hence negates the use of this adsorbent for glycerides. Later, Trappe performed some experiments on the separation of cholesterol esters, glycerides, and free fatty acids on two different types of silicic acid. Subsequently, Borgstrom [7] found that commercially available silicic acid was suitable for fractionation of the neutral lipides. Using model compounds, Borgstrom observed that cholesterol esters could be removed separately by use of petroleum ether-benzene (8:2, v/v), and the glycerides plus free fatty acids could be removed with chloroform. Then the free fatty acids could be removed by treatment with alkaline 50% ethanol or by passage through Amberlite IRA-400. The separation of naturally occurring mixtures was not reported.

In a widely adopted procedure Fillerup and Mead [21] reported that all the major neutral lipide fractions of plasma could be separated on silicic acid. Both artificial lipide mixtures and plasma lipides could be separated into the following fractions by the indicated solvents: 1% diethyl ether in petroleum ether, sterol esters; 3% diethyl ether in petroleum ether, triglycerides and free fatty acids; 10% diethyl ether in petroleum ether, free sterol; 25% methanol in diethyl ether, phospholipides. Perhaps one of the major difficulties is that concerned with maintaining the proper ether concentrations for best resolution, and preventing the bubbling of solvent on warm days. As is obvious, this could be remedied with a jacketed column, but even the administration of pressure on these columns can cause this effect.

Barron and Hanahan,[4] adapting the method of Fillerup and Mead, used hexane as the "basic" eluting solvent and benzene-hexane mixtures for the elution of the initial components. Thus, the following solvents would elute the indicated components: hexane, hydrocarbons; hexane-benzene (8.5:1.5, v/v), sterol esters; hexane-5% diethyl ether, triglycerides plus free fatty acids; hexane-15% diethyl ether, free sterol; hexane-30% diethyl ether, diglycerides; hexane-ethyl ether (1:10, v/v), monoglycerides (80% methanol in diethyl ether will remove any phospholipides present). A typical pattern of elution of the neutral lipide fraction (acetone soluble) from beef liver is depicted in Fig. 2.4. The neutral lipides of beef liver and yeast have been examined in a similar manner. Hence it is obvious that the various major components of this particular mixture can be fractionated to a reasonable degree on silicic acid. The free fatty acids in the triglyceride fraction may be removed by ethanolic-50% alkali, in the absence of diglycerides and monoglycerides. In such a medium, a β-monoglyceride in particular may undergo isomerization. The use of benzene aided considerably in allowing a sharp separation of the cholesterol esters from the triglycerides. In those runs where benzene was not included, 1% diethyl ether in hexane would elute the triglycerides and cholesterol esters. The best separations were achieved on columns of silicic acid previously dried at 110° for 12 hours and prewashed with appropriate solvents. The loading factor should be maintained between 15 to 20 mg. total lipides per gram of silicic acid and flow rates should be 1.5 to 2 ml. per minute for best resolution. The use of any celite or similar additives should be avoided as they tend to hamper the fractionation. A particular drawback to this procedure may be the use of benzene which may provide interference in any ultraviolet spectrophotometric examination of the fatty acids.

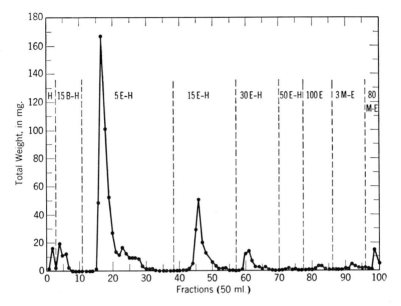

Fig. 2.4. Chromatography of neutral lipides of beef liver on silicic acid. The solvents were hexane (H), benzene (B), diethyl ether (E), and methanol (M).

Recently, Garton and Duncan [25] submitted the petroleum ether soluble lipides of the plasma of lactating cows to chromatography on silicic acid. The solvents were mixtures of 1% ether in petroleum ether, 3% ether in petroleum ether, 10% ether in petroleum ether. A separation into sterol esters, triglycerides plus fatty acids, sterols, and phospholipides was obtained.

General Summary

As is evident from the above comments, column chromatography, especially on silicic acid, can accomplish the fractionation of complex mixtures of phospholipides and neutral lipides. However, the very nature of the starting mixture may necessitate alterations in solvents, solvent composition, loading factor, etc. The results obtained by use of the foregoing adsorbents and solvent mixtures will indicate additional experimental approaches. In each experiment one should be cognizant of possible alterations to lipides, such as hydrolysis, isomerization (migration of acyl residues), oxidation by contact with adsorbents, etc.

While paper chromatography is in itself a useful technique for microscale investigations, it is highly advantageous to employ column chromatographic procedures (or specific solvent fractionation) for purposes of complete identification (and structure proof) of a particular component and isolation in large quantities. Finally, it should be emphasized again that as many criteria as possible should be used to satisfactorily and completely identify a naturally occurring lipide. Thus, with this type of information, a more logical approach to the behavior of these compounds in biological systems may be expected.

REFERENCES

1. Baar, S., *Biochem. J.,* **58,** 175 (1954).
2. Baer, E., D. Buchnea, and A. G. Newcombe, *J. Am. Chem. Soc.,* **78,** 232 (1956).
3. Baer, E., and J. Maurukas, *J. Biol. Chem.,* **212,** 39 (1955).
4. Barron, E. J., and D. J. Hanahan, *J. Biol. Chem.,* **231,** 493 (1958).
5. Bergell, P., *Ber.,* **33,** 2584 (1900).
6. Block, R. J., E. Durrum, and G. Zweig, *Paper Chromatography and Paper Electrophoresis,* 2nd edition, p. 128, Academic Press (1955).
7. Borgstrom, B., *Acta physiol. scand.,* **25,** 101, 111 (1952).
8. Brown, J. B., and D. K. Kolb, *Prog. in Chem. Fats Lipids,* **3,** 57 (1955).
9. Brown, M., D. A. Yeadon, L. A. Goldblatt, and J. W. Dieckert, *Anal. Chem.,* **29,** 30 (1957).
10. Carter, H. E., D. E. Galanos, R. H. Gigg, J. H. Law, T. Nakayama, D. B. Smith, and E. J. Weber, *Federation Proc.,* **16,** 817 (1957).
11. Chibnall, A. C., and H. J. Channon, *Biochem. J.,* **21,** 233 (1927).
12. Cole, P. G., G. H. Lathe, and C. R. Ruthuen, *Biochem. J.,* **55,** 17 (1953).
13. Collins, F. D., and L. W. Wheeldon, *Biochem. J.,* **66,** 441 (1957).
14. Dawson, R. M. C., *Biochim. et Biophys. Acta,* **14,** 374 (1954).
15. Dawson, R. M. C., *Biochem. J.,* **59,** 5 (1955).
16. Desnuelle, P., and M. J. Constantin, *Bull. soc. chim. biol.,* **35,** 382 (1953).
17. Dieckert, J. W., and R. Reiser, *J. Am. Oil Chem. Soc.,* **33,** 123 (1956).
18. Douste-Blazy, L., J. Polonovski, and P. Valdiguie, *Bull. soc. chim. biol.,* **37,** 19 (1956).
19. Dutton, H. J., *Prog. in Chem. Fats Lipids,* **2,** 292 (1954).
20. Entenman, C., *Methods in Enzymology,* Vol. 3, p. 299, Academic Press (1957).
21. Fillerup, D. L., and J. F. Mead, *Proc. Soc. Exptl. Biol. Med.,* **83,** 574 (1953).
22. Folch, J., *J. Biol. Chem.,* **146,** 35 (1942).
23. Folch, J., I. Ascoli, M. Lees, J. A. Meath, and F. N. LeBaron, *J. Biol. Chem.,* **191,** 833 (1951).
24. Folch, J., M. Lees, and G. H. Sloane-Stanley, *J. Biol. Chem.,* **226,** 497 (1957).
25. Garton, G. A., and W. R. Duncan, *Biochem. J.,* **67,** 340 (1957).
26. Hack, M. H., *Biochem. J.,* **54,** 602 (1953).
27. Hanahan, D. J., *J. Biol. Chem.,* **207,** 879 (1954).

28. Hanahan, D. J., and I. L. Chaikoff, *J. Biol. Chem.*, **168**, 233 (1947); **169**, 699 (1947).
29. Hanahan, D. J., J. C. Dittmer, and E. Warashina, *J. Biol. Chem.*, **228**, 685 (1957).
30. Hanahan, D. J., and J. N. Olley, *J. Biol. Chem.*, **231**, 813 (1958).
31. Hanahan, D. J., and D. N. Rhodes, *Federation Proc.*, **15**, 267 (1956).
32. Hanahan, D. J., M. B. Turner, and M. E. Jayko, *J. Biol. Chem.*, **192**, 623 (1951).
33. Hanahan, D. J., and R. Vercamer, *J. Am. Chem. Soc.*, **76**, 1804 (1954).
34. Hartree, E., and D. J. Hanahan, unpublished observations.
35. Huennekens, F. M., D. J. Hanahan, and M. Uziel, *J. Biol. Chem.*, **206**, 443 (1954).
36. Kates, M., *Can. J. Biochem. and Physiol.*, **35**, 127 (1957).
37. LaRoche, G., Thesis, University of Washington (1956).
38. Lea, C. H., D. N. Rhodes, and R. D. Stoll, *Biochem. J.*, **60**, 353 (1955).
39. Levene, P. A., and I. P. Rolf, *J. Biol. Chem.*, **72**, 587 (1927).
40. Lovern, J. A., *Biochem. J.*, **51**, 464 (1952).
41. MacFarlane, A. S., *Nature*, **149**, 439 (1942).
42. McKibbin, J. M., *J. Biol. Chem.*, **220**, 537 (1956).
43. McKibbin, J. M., and W. E. Taylor, *J. Biol. Chem.*, **196**, 427 (1952).
44. Marinetti, G. V., J. Erbland, and J. Kochen, *Federation Proc.*, **16**, 837 (1957).
45. Marinetti, G. V., R. F. Witter, and E. Stotz, *J. Biol. Chem.*, **226**, 475 (1958).
46. Olley, J., *Biochim. et Biophys. Acta*, **10**, 493 (1953).
47. Olley, J., *Chem. and Industry*, **1956**, 1120.
48. Olley, J., in *Biochemical Problems of Lipids,* edited by Popjak and LeBreton, p. 49, Interscience (1956).
49. Olley, J., and J. A. Lovern, *Biochem. J.*, **57**, 610 (1954).
50. Pangborn, M. C., *J. Biol. Chem.*, **137**, 545 (1941).
51. Pangborn, M. C., *J. Biol. Chem.*, **188**, 471 (1951).
52. Radin, N. S., J. R. Brown, and F. B. Lavin, *J. Biol. Chem.*, **219**, 977 (1957).
53. Radin, N. S., F. B. Martin, and J. R. Brown, *J. Biol. Chem.*, **217**, 789 (1955).
54. Rapport, M. M., and N. Alonzo, in *Biochemical Problems of Lipids,* edited by Popjak and LeBreton, p. 69, Interscience (1956).
55. Rhodes, D. N., and C. H. Lea, *Biochem. J.*, **65**, 526 (1957).
56. Scholfield, C. R., H. J. Dutton, F. W. Tanner, Jr., and J. C. Cowan, *J. Am. Oil Chem. Soc.*, **25**, 368 (1948).
57. Sinclair, R. G., *Can. J. Research, Sect. B*, **26**, 777 (1948).
58. Strecker, A., *Ann.*, **148**, 77 (1868).
59. Taurog, A., C. Entenman, B. A. Fries, and I. L. Chaikoff, *J. Biol. Chem.*, **155**, 19 (1944).
60. Trappe, W., *Biochem. Z.*, **306**, 316 (1940); **305**, 150 (1940).
61. Trappe, W., *Biochem. Z.*, **307**, 97 (1940).
62. Wallach, D. F. H., and J. E. Garvin, *J. Am. Chem. Soc.*, **80**, 2157 (1958).
63. Weiss, B., *J. Biol. Chem.*, **223**, 523 (1956).
64. Westley, J., J. J. Wren, and H. K. Mitchell, *J. Biol. Chem.*, **229**, 131 (1957).

3

Phosphoglycerides

Among the more abundant of the naturally occurring complex lipides are the phosphoglycerides, which in many instances comprise well over 70% of a particular tissue's phospholipides. As cited in Chapter 1, these compounds are usually found as diacyl esters of a nitrogenous base derivative of L-α-glycerophosphoric acid. While the plasmalogens are an exception, perhaps, to this general classification, their rather close physical properties warrant discussion at this time. Among the nitrogen bases commonly found in these lipides are choline, ethanolamine, and serine. On this basis attention is directed mainly to the chemistry of phosphatidyl choline (lecithin), phosphatidyl ethanolamine, phosphatidyl serine, and the plasmalogens.

Although the general structure of certain of the phosphoglycerides, as typified by phosphatidyl choline (lecithin), had been correctly deduced several years ago, there remained the questions of the establishment of the position of the phosphate ester grouping and the possible stereoisomeric forms. First, was the phosphate on the first (α) or second (β) carbon atom of the glycerol molecule (or did both forms exist)? Second, what was the nature of the stereochemical configuration about an asymmetric carbon atom (if the phosphate was on the α carbon)? Essentially, within the last ten years, both of these questions have been resolved and are discussed in the following sections.

GENERAL CONSIDERATIONS

Position of the Phosphate Ester (Question of α- and β-Isomers)

In early attempts to obtain detailed information on the structure of the phosphoglycerides, it was quite common to submit the compounds in question to hydrolytic degradation with subsequent isolation of the glycerophosphoric acid. Inasmuch as many of these experiments were conducted with lecithin, repeated observation and confirmation of the isolation of two forms of glycerophosphoric acid, α and β, led to the conclusion that there were two types of naturally occurring phosphoglycerides, namely: *

$$CH_2OCOR$$
$$|$$
$$CHOCOR$$
$$|$$
$$O$$
$$|\uparrow$$
$$CH_2OPOCH_2CH_2\overset{+}{N}(CH_3)_3$$
$$|$$
$$O^-(H,OH)$$

α-Lecithin

$$CH_2OCOR$$
$$|$$
$$O^-(H,OH)$$
$$|$$
$$CHOPOCH_2CH_2\overset{+}{N}(CH_3)_3$$
$$|\downarrow$$
$$O$$
$$|$$
$$CH_2OCOR$$

β-Lecithin

α-Lecithin possesses an asymmetric carbon atom and exists in the two diastereoisomeric D and L forms. On the contrary, β-lecithin possesses no asymmetric carbon atom and hence no enantiomeric forms are possible.

Over a period of years this concept of an α- and β-form gained considerable support. It is interesting to note that during this particular time evidence was accumulating in the literature that the migration of phosphate groups on glycerophosphoric acid and its derivative could occur under conditions comparable to those used in the studies on lecithin structure. However, this information was slow to be recognized. Nonetheless, strong and convincing counterarguments now have

* While the rather ambiguous terms, α, β, or α' are still widely used for designating the position of the phosphate ester on glycerol, it is strongly urged that this practice be abandoned and the numbering system commonly applied to "sugar phosphates" be adopted; i.e., glycerol-3-phosphoric acid instead of α-glycerophosphoric acid (see the footnote on page 53).

been presented which support the existence of only one type, the α form, of naturally occurring phosphoglycerides.

The phenomenon of phosphate migration was first recognized by Bailly and Gaume [7] in their experiments on the alkaline hydrolysis of alkyl esters of glycerophosphate. They observed that α-glycerophosphate (I), α-GPA, was stable to alkaline hydrolysis while a mono alkyl derivative (II), methyl glycerophosphate, underwent considerable alteration.*

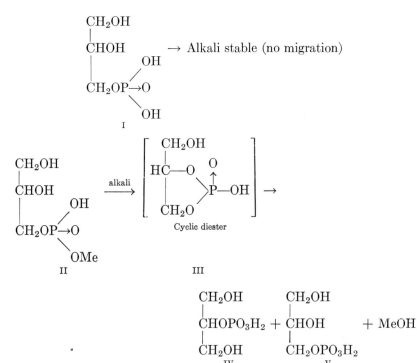

Bailly [6] also showed that β-glycerophosphoric acid (IV) can be quantitatively converted to α-glycerophosphoric acid (V) by treatment with boiling acid. Also, this was shown to be a reversible change, with the equilibrium depending on conditions of treatment (alkali promoted predominance of β form while acid produced higher amount of α form). These results were confirmed by Verkade et al.,[133] who

---

* In general, the mono esters, such as α(C-1) and β(C-2) glycerophosphoric acid, can be isomerized under acid, but not alkaline, conditions; on the other hand diesters, such as glycerylphosphorylcholine, can be isomerized both in acid and alkali.

proposed the formation of a cyclic intermediate. This migration has been shown to be intramolecular by Chargaff,[30] who found that α-GPA could be converted to β-GPA in an acid solution, in the presence of sodium P[32]-phosphate, without an exchange between the organic phosphoric acid ester and the inorganic phosphate. Thus, as will be pointed out below, it appears well established that this conversion operates through a cyclic diester intermediate (III), with release of an RO⁻ by attack of an adjacent hydroxyl group on the phosphorus. It is interesting to note that in the experiments of Bailly and Gaume cited above no methyl phosphate is formed; thus the phosphate is retained on the glycerol unit.

Folch[51] noted with concern that hydrolysis of naturally occurring phospholipides with acid or alkali yielded optically inactive mixtures of α- and β-glycerophosphoric acids, the amounts of which depended on conditions of hydrolysis. For example, three different preparations of phosphoglycerides, hydrolyzed for 30 minutes with 6N HCl, analyzed as 73% α form and 27% β form. Similarly, pure α- or β-glycerophosphoric acid, subjected to acid hydrolysis, yielded 73% α form and 27% β form. Thus, these observations strengthened the concept that hydrolytic procedures could not prove the nature of the glycerophosphoric acid residue in naturally occurring phospholipides.

It appears that the prerequisite to alkali lability in alkyl phosphates is the proximity of a hydroxyl function to the phosphoryl group. That the interaction between neighboring hydroxyl and phosphoryl groups can occur has been stressed by Kumler and Eiler,[83] who have shown that polyol and sugar phosphates are abnormally strong acids in comparison with mono alkyl phosphates. Fono[54] has pointed out the importance of neighboring hydroxyl groups in causing lability of diesters of phosphoric acid containing a glycerol or ethylene glycol residue and has postulated the existence of a cyclic triester intermediate in their hydrolysis. He also advanced the view that the alkali lability of ribonucleic acid in contrast to the alkali stability of deoxyribonucleic acid may be attributed to the extra hydroxyl at C-2 in the sugar residue of ribonucleic acid: thus, ribonucleic acids were analogous to glycerol alkyl phosphates in their hydrolytic behavior.

The most detailed and informative data on the reversible migration of phosphate esters were presented by Baer and Kates,[14, 15] who carried out experiments on the chemical hydrolysis of L-α-glycerylphosphorylcholine (GPC) in acid and in alkali at 37°. In the initial experiments, the liberation of choline, change in optical rotation, percentage of α-glyceryl esters, and isolation of glycerophosphoric acid (GPA) as the barium salt were followed. Thus, they found that 10 hours was required in $1N$ HCl for liberation of one-half of the choline. An examination of the loss in optical activity revealed a greater change than would be expected for only an α to β migration of the phosphoric acid. Thus, the progressively increasing change in optical activity was interpreted as a direct indication of the reversibility of this shift. Concomitantly the amount of α-glyceryl esters decreased fairly rapidly at first and then tended to maintain a constant level. The possible scheme of hydrolysis first considered was as follows:

(1) $$\text{L-}\alpha\text{-GPC} \xrightarrow{k_1} \text{L-}\alpha\text{-GPA} + \text{choline}$$

(2) $$\text{L-}\alpha\text{-GPA} \xrightarrow{k_2} \beta\text{-GPA}$$

(3) $$\beta\text{-GPA} \xrightarrow{k_3} \text{DL-}\alpha\text{-GPA}$$

The reaction constants k_2 and k_3 were obtained by following changes in optical activity (k_2) and the content of α-glyceryl ester $(k_2 + k_3)$ of L-α-GPA in $1N$ HCl at $37°$ for 90 hours. Then by use of k_1 from choline liberation and k_2 and k_3 values, they calculated changes which should occur if equations 1–3 described acid hydrolysis of L-α-GPC. However, the observed rates at which α-glycerol esters and optical activity decreased were far greater than those predicted by calculation, indicating equations 1–3 were inadequate. They argued that the greater change of observed values suggests that the major part of the migration must occur while the choline ester is intact, presumably via a cyclic ortho ester:

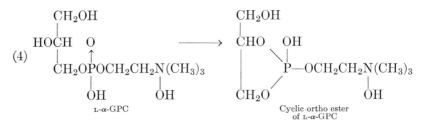

(4)

L-α-GPC   Cyclic ortho ester of L-α-GPC

Subsequently, this cyclic ortho ester could give rise to β-GPC, which could then form the cyclic ortho ester of D,L-GPC, and this latter compound could finally yield D,L-α-GPC. In addition, a complicating factor was that all of the above intermediates could lose choline at any stage, and the resulting glycerophosphoric acids could rearrange through cyclic diester intermediates. When L-α-GPC was subjected to treatment with $1N$ NaOH at $37°$, one-half of the choline was liberated in 0.9 hour. Hydrolysis was effected in one-tenth the time of acid hydrolysis. As in the acid reaction, migration of the phosphate group occurred. Thus Baer and Kates found that in acid and base, hydrolysis of L-α-GPC proceeded by a reversible $\alpha \rightleftharpoons \beta$ migration of phosphate group, resulting in the formation of L-α-, DL-α-, and β-GPA. The equilibrium values are functions of pH, with the α form predominating on acid hydrolysis and the β form predominating on alkaline hydrolysis. With pure enantiomeric lecithins, it was observed that hydrolysis of these compounds gave rise to identical equilibrium mixtures of α- and β-GPA. Of interest was the observation that all the lipides, with the exception of distearoyl-L-α-GPA (phosphatidic acid), underwent reversible migration in alkali. This result was comparable to the well-recognized stability of L-α-GPA to alkali. Thus, according to Baer and Kates, the most probable scheme for alkaline hydrolysis of α-lecithins can be depicted as follows:

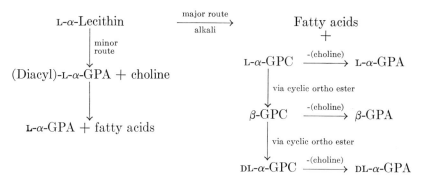

In a study of the structure of naturally occurring phosphoglycerides, Long and Maguire [89] extended the observations of Baer and Kates to include the naturally occurring compounds. They determined the proportions of β-, D-α-, and L-α-glycerophosphates formed after alkaline hydrolysis with those derived from synthetic substrates. Among the synthetic substrates were DL-α-lecithin, DL-α-phosphatidyl ethanolamine, and β-phosphatidyl ethanolamine. Of interest was the fact that these investigators employed a specific enzyme, L-α-glycerophosphate dehydrogenase, for the assay of the L-α-glycerophosphate formed. They felt that the polarimetric method of Baer and Kates was not suitable for their system. It is true that the optical rotation changes are of a very low order of magnitude (i.e., changes in angular degrees may be of the order of 0.1°) and require very exact measurements. The results of Long and Maguire indicated that the hydrolysis of the naturally occurring lecithins compared very favorably with that of the synthetic L-α-lecithins and not with the DL-α or β-type compounds. They reasoned that it was added proof that naturally occurring lecithins are of the L-α-configuration.

Long and Maguire argued that the Baer and Kates theory did not imply that an equilibrium mixture of the three glycerylphosphorylcholines is formed before any choline is split off. Hence, the removal of choline may proceed simultaneously with the isomerization reactions. They postulated that β-GPA and D-α-GPA can only arise through β-GPC; then the same ratio would be expected independently of whether the β-GPC originated from a β- or an L-α-phosphoglyceride. On the basis of their results they concluded that L-α-GPC was converted under alkaline conditions to the cyclic ortho ester. Then subsequent loss of choline was considered as the predominating reaction with the formation of the cyclic diester. Thus, with equal chance of cleavage at either bond, this compound would then be degraded to L-α-GPA and β-GPA in equal amounts. In Long and Maguire's estimation a minor pathway conversion of the cyclic triester to β-GPC to D-α-GPC would account for the small quantity of D-α-GPA found in alkaline hydrolyses of L-α-GPA. Thus their proposal may be represented as follows:

L-α-Phosphoglyceride →

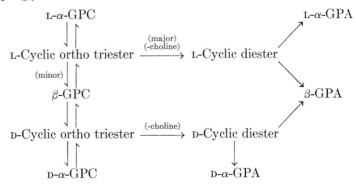

However, these above proposals (Baer and Kates; Long and Maguire) are not entirely correct according to the evidence secured by Brown et al.[22] In this study, alkyl esters of 2' and 3' mononucleotides (Ia) provided simple model systems for hydrolysis studies (see also ref. 25). An over-all process was considered in which the alkaline or acid conversion of the compounds, shown in skeleton form here, gave a mixture of 2′ and 3′ isomers of the free acids (IIIa, IVa). In both cases, an unstable cyclic ester intermediate (IIa) is formed and this

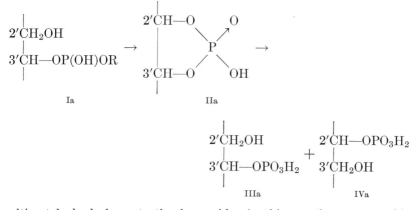

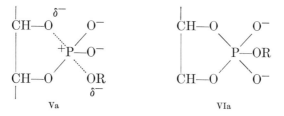

ultimately hydrolyzes to the free acid. As this reaction was considered essentially a transesterification, it seemed possible that a simultaneous migration of the intact alkyl phosphate, without loss of the R group, could also occur. However, when cytidine 3′-benzyl phosphate was partially hydrolyzed with 0.5N NaOH, the recovered ester contained none of the 2′ ester. Also, the 2′ methyl ester did not go to the 3′ methyl ester. Thus, under *alkaline* conditions, no migration of the alkyl phosphate occurred. On this basis they reasoned that this implied a conversion of the alkyl phosphate to a cyclic intermediate involving a transition state, which could be represented best by formula Va rather than a discrete molecule such as VIa. This latter

formulation (VIa) is analogous to that found in the alkaline hydrolysis of carboxylic esters.[20]

However, in *acid,* migration of the alkyl phosphate appears to occur to a significant extent, and apparently is an acid catalyzed reaction. Thus, these results are best accommodated if one assumes a protonate intermediate formed from derivatives such as VIIa or VIIIa. Thus P—O fission could lead to the original compound, a cyclic intermedi-

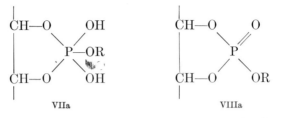

ate, or a rearranged ester. Brown et al.[22] concluded that in an alkaline hydrolysis no alkyl phosphate migration (in compounds such as glycerylphosphorylcholine) occurs, and hence the above proposals of Baer and Kates and of Long and Maguire in this respect may not be valid.

While a cyclic intermediate obviously is necessary to completion of phosphoryl migration, until recently neither the isolation nor the synthesis of this type of compound had been reported. However, Ukita et al.[130] prepared the barium salt of cyclic glycerophosphate from β-glycerophosphoric acid (GPA) by reaction with trifluoroacetic anhydride in a modification of the procedure of Brown et al.[23] This derivative was stable at pH 3.5 and 8.0, but rapidly decomposed (within 3 hours) at pH 1.5 and in 0.1N NaOH. Furthermore, they found that the main product of hydrolysis of lecithin in methanolic KOH, under conditions of Fleury,[47,48] was only the methyl ester of glycerophosphoric acid, and not the cyclic intermediate. Thus, they contended that the "glycerophosphatogen" of Fleury's prepared by incubation of lecithin in 0.5N KOH in methanol at 37° for 65 hours was not the cyclic diester intermediate, but rather the methyl ester of glycerophosphoric acid. The instability of synthetic cyclic glycerophosphate in alkaline solution made it appear most unlikely that the cyclic ester would persist in this hydrolytic procedure.

Thus it is evident from the above observations that the reported existence of β-lecithins was based on a misinterpretation of the results of the hydrolytic procedure used in structure proof. Consequently, the experimental evidence strongly supports the proposal that only the α form of phosphoglycerides occurs in nature. The topic of phosphate migration is discussed further in the next chapter.

Stereochemical Configuration

Concomitantly with the foregoing considerations, the question logically arose as to the possible stereochemical forms of these compounds present in the naturally occurring phospholipides. While it seemed likely that only one particular enantiomeric form would predominate, it was obviously necessary that this fact be proved in an absolute manner. Consequently, with the convincing evidence of the optical activity of the naturally occurring compounds, the most direct route of proof was through a synthetic procedure designed to show the relationship between the stereochemical reference compounds, D- and L-glyceraldehyde, and the naturally occurring phospholipides. This monumental and important task was completed by Baer and his colleagues at the University of Toronto over the past several years. While the specific synthetic pattern of several typical phosphoglycerides will be shown in a later section, the general format of these experiments and the conclusions are outlined here.

Perhaps the key observations and experiments were made by Baer and Fischer,[13] who were able to synthesize both the D- and L-acetone glycerols. Subsequently, these compounds have provided the necessary link to the preparation of optically active phosphoglycerides of known structure. In considering the assignment of a particular stereochemical configuration to a phosphoglyceride, e.g., lecithin, two choices are available as either the diglyceride or the glycerylphosphorylcholine portion of the molecule may be used. On the basis of the variability in the fatty acid portion of the phosphoglycerides and the constancy of the glycerylphosphorylcholine unit, Baer proposed that the latter compound be used as the reference unit. Thus, starting with D-acetone glycerol, D-α,β diglycerides could be prepared and then could be converted to lecithins, with the L-α configuration. In the latter case, if the D-α,β diglyceride is written according to convention with the free alcohol function at the top, and subsequently rotated through the plane of the paper and converted to lecithin, it assumes the L-α configuration by definition. The converse would hold, of course, if L-α-acetone glycerol were used as the starting material, with the resultant formation of D-α-lecithins.

In their series of studies, Baer and colleagues have prepared pure enantiomeric forms of all the more common phosphoglycerides, and comparison of the optical activity of these compounds with values reported for some of the naturally occurring ones are of considerable interest. It shows quite conclusively that the naturally occurring compounds must belong to the L-α series. Moreover, mild alkaline treatment of naturally occurring lecithins gives optically pure L-α-glycerylphosphorylcholine in good yields. Furthermore, enzymatic degradation of naturally occurring lecithins to glycerylphosphorylcholine yields only one optical form, namely the L-α derivative. Thus, it appears certain that all the naturally occurring phosphoglycerides isolated to date may be assigned the L-α configuration.

LECITHIN (PHOSPHATIDYL CHOLINE)

This particular compound is the most typical and most abundant of the naturally occurring phosphoglycerides. Its widespread presence in plants, animals, and microorganisms has led to considerable speculation as to its metabolic role. As has been suggested previously, the interest in the lecithins could be attributed, in part, to their comparative ease of isolation and, in part, to the idea that their relatively high concentration in tissues suggested an important role in lipide metabolism. It was not until the recent very able studies of Baer and his collaborators that the synthesis of lecithins, of known composition and stereochemical configuration, allowed a strict comparison with the naturally occurring compounds. Thus, a route became available for the assignment of stereo configuration to the natural lecithins. Examples of the routes to the synthesis of lecithins and the properties of both the synthetic and natural compounds will be illustrated.

Preparation of Lecithins

Direct Synthesis. Many different approaches to the synthesis of so-called lecithins have been reported in the literature, but in most cases unambiguous proof of the structure was lacking. Thus, the occurrence of salts, instead of esters, was not ruled out as well as the possibility of phosphoryl and acyl migration. The synthesis of enantiomeric forms of lecithins was first described by Baer and Kates [16] in 1950. Hence, it is only within the last few years that the stereochemical configuration of the naturally occurring lecithins has been established.

Fully saturated lecithins. In their classic study, Baer and Kates [16] reported the synthesis of enantiomeric and racemic forms of fully saturated lecithins. In this procedure, an α,β diglyceride was phenylphosphorylated with monophenylphosphoryl dichloride and the subsequent reaction products treated with choline chloride to yield a diacyl-α-glycerylphenylphosphoryl choline chloride which was then separated via a Reinecke salt. Subsequent removal of chloride ion and hydrogenolysis yielded the fully saturated α-lecithins. The yields were of the order of 30 to 35% (based on diglyceride used). However, the reineckate purification step proved somewhat cumbersome and an improved, simplified procedure of synthesis of dimyristoyl-, di-palmitoyl-, and distearoyl-L-α-lecithins was reported by Baer and Maurukas.[17] This is described in part by the following scheme: *

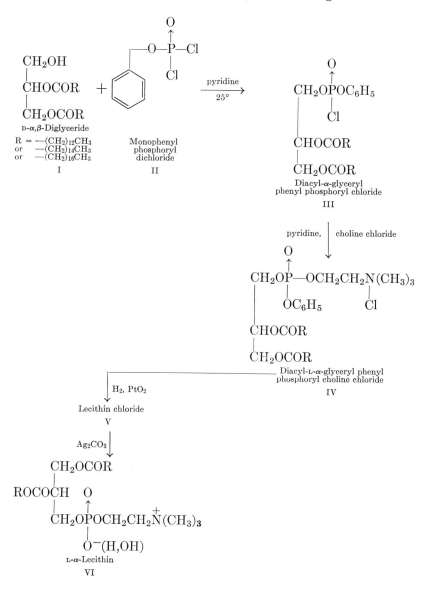

* The proper nomenclature of these compounds posed some problems. In particular, the designation α is an equivocal term. Hence, for example, com-

Table 3.1

Characteristics of Fully Saturated L-α-Lecithins *

| | Optical Activity | | Melting Point † | | |
| | | | Sintering | Meniscus | Meniscus |
Compound	[α]	Solvent	Point	Point (a)	Point (b)
L-α-(Dimyristoyl)- lecithin	+7.0°		90°	236–237°	226–227°
L-α-(Dipalmitoyl)- lecithin	+7.0°	Chloroform- methanol, 1:1 (v/v)	120°	235–236°	225–226°
L-α-(Distearoyl)- lecithin	+6.1°		120°	230–232°	222–223°

* From Baer and Maurukas.[17]

† The sintering point is the temperature at which the compound is converted to droplets which adhere to the sides of the capillary tube. The meniscus point is that temperature at which the droplets coalesce and form a meniscus.

In general, the sintering point is quite variable (perhaps dependent on any water present or a change in the position of certain of the components of the molecule). The meniscus point is by far the more characteristic and reproducible value. In the table the values (a) were obtained from a sample placed in a bath at approximately 60° and heated up to the meniscus point. In values (b), the sample was placed in a bath at a temperature within 10 to 20° of the meniscus point and heated rapidly until this point was reached. This latter procedure is the more reliable.

The over-all yield on these reactions for the three derivatives was 30 to 35% (based on diglyceride). The compounds were obtained as white, micro crystalline compounds, with the physical characteristics outlined in Table 3.1. Molecular weight determinations indicated only monomeric α-lecithins were formed. It is somewhat surprising that the optical activity values for the 14 carbon and 16 carbon fatty acid derivatives are the same, and it might be of value to examine

pound III could be a diacyl L-3-glyceryl—or a diacyl D-1-glyceryl—derivative but both are essentially α types. It would be most expedient to abandon the use of the term α with respect to these compounds and substitute numbers for the carbons of the glycerol moiety in all asymmetric situations. However, the convention of using the lowest number should be disregarded in favor of expressing the stereochemical relationship to D- or L-glyceraldehyde-3-phosphate.

the optical rotation of these substances at wave lengths other than the D line of sodium.

While these substances are in general quite stable compounds, some factors affecting their stability have been noted by Baer and Maurukas. For example, lecithins recrystallized from hot (60 to 80°) diisobutyl ketone were inclined to decompose more readily, with the liberation of trimethylamine, than either crude lecithins or lecithins precipitated from chloroform by acetone. Also, it is known in some instances that these compounds are slowly decomposed over a long period of exposure to light. Perhaps the best means for storage of these compounds is as the cadmium chloride salt in a desiccator in the dark at 4°.

Fully unsaturated lecithins. As is obvious from the above synthetic approach, the use of the hydrogenolysis step (for removal of the phenyl group) prohibited the use of any unsaturated fatty acids and subsequent formation of the unsaturated lecithins. However, this impediment was removed by Baer, Buchnea, and Newcombe,[12] who achieved the first synthesis of a fully unsaturated α-lecithin, L-α-(dioleyl)-lecithin. This fully unsaturated lecithin was an almost colorless, waxy material, which was soluble in methanol, ethanol, chloroform, diethyl ether, and 90% acetone. It had a specific rotation value of +6.2 and was quite resistant to atmospheric oxidation (no alteration on exposure of thin layer of sample for five days at room

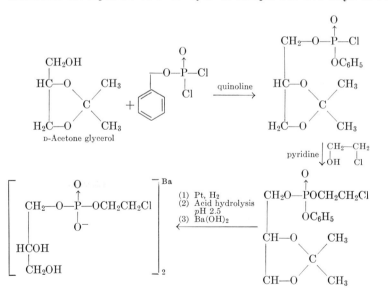

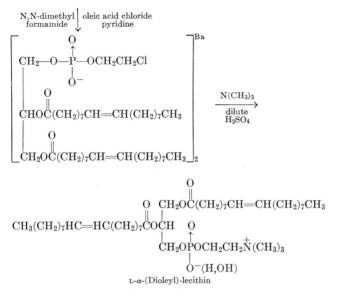

$$
\underset{\text{L-}\alpha\text{-(Dioleyl)-lecithin}}{}
$$

L-α-(Dioleyl)-lecithin

temperature). These properties were quite similar to those described for a fully unsaturated yeast lecithin,[63] which also was resistant to air oxidation and was soluble in 90% acetone. This latter property is of considerable interest as regards the isolation of lecithins from various sources. Thus, unless suitable precautions are taken, considerable losses can occur in the usual practice of "precipitating" the phosphoglycerides with acetone. The catalytic reduction of the L-α-(dioleyl)-lecithin gave in excellent yields optically pure L-α-(distearoyl)-lecithin. Thus, no racemization had occurred in the synthesis of the unsaturated lecithin.

The exact structure of crystalline lecithins has been the subject of some discussion. First, the existence of the zwitterion structure now seems well documented, especially from the recent work of Garvin and Karnovsky.[56] Second, the question of the nature of the "water" bond is still unsettled. Although the proposals by Howton [71] and Devor [37] for "water of crystallization" are provocative, the supportive evidence of this type of structure is lacking. Hence, as suggested by Baer,[10] it may be more advisable to formulate the structure as follows:

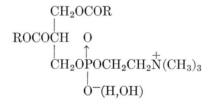

Indirect Synthesis. In their original publication on the preparation of lecithins, Baer and Kates [16] reported an inability to directly acylate L-α-glycerylphosphorylcholine with organic chlorides in a pyridine solvent. Also, lysolecithins cannot be acylated under somewhat similar conditions.[60] However, Tattrie and McArthur [127] reasoned that this might be due to the electrical state of the phosphorylcholine portion of the molecule, since the barium salt of L-α-glycerylphosphorylethylene chlorohydrin [12] and the cadmium chloride addition compound of glycerylphosphorylcholine [11] can be acylated. They were successful in acylating L-α-GPC with acyl chlorides when the reaction was carried out in amine free, dry solvents which would allow the hydrogen chloride (derived from acylation reaction) to combine with the phosphorylcholine group. Thus the apparent hydrogen bonding ability of the choline nitrogen with the free hydroxyl functions would be repressed. Their synthesis of L-α-(dipalmitoyl)-lecithin is outlined by the following equations:

$$
\begin{array}{l}
CH_2OH \\
| \\
HOCH \\
| \quad\quad O \\
| \quad\quad \uparrow \\
CH_2OPOCH_2CH_2\overset{+}{N}(CH_3)_3 \\
| \\
O^-(H,OH)
\end{array}
\xrightarrow[\substack{37°,\ 72\ hr.}]{\substack{RCOCl \\ CHCl_3}}
$$

$$
\begin{array}{l}
CH_2OCOR \\
| \\
ROCOCH \\
| \quad\quad O \\
| \quad\quad \uparrow \\
CH_2OPOCH_2CH_2\overset{+}{N}(CH_3)_3 \\
| \\
O^-(H,OH)
\end{array}
$$

The yield, calculated from glycerylphosphorylcholine, was 31%. The product analyzed correctly for a fully saturated lecithin but had an $[\alpha]_D^{26°}$ $+5.5°$, whereas that reported is $+6.6°$. No melting points were reported for this compound.

The L-α-glycerylphosphorylcholine used by Tattrie and McArthur in the above procedure was prepared by a method also devised by these same investigators [126] in which crude egg lecithin is hydrolyzed under reflux in the presence of mercuric ions. Subsequent work-ups of this reaction mixture gave L-α-GPC in yields of 60 to 70%. While certainly giving the desired product, this approach to L-α-GPC is not as convenient and simple as that outlined by Dawson.[33] In this latter method, the purified egg lecithin is subjected to alkaline hydrolysis at

37° for 10 minutes which essentially cleaves only the fatty acid ester groups. Pure L-α-GPC can be isolated in yields of 75 to 80% of theory.

A Possible Approach to Asymmetrically Substituted Lecithins

A question of considerable interest to the biochemist is the possible synthesis of lecithins with two known, but dissimilar, fatty acids on the molecule. For example, the preparation of a lecithin with one oleic acid molecule on one ester position and one stearic acid molecule on the other would be of considerable value. A conceivably facile means to this end could be afforded by the following suggested route of synthesis:

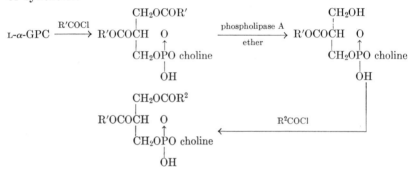

In such an approach an invaluable series of compounds of importance in studies on the metabolism of lecithins could be obtained. If desired, these compounds could then be subjected to the action of phospholipase D (lecithinase D), which could easily convert these compounds to D-α, β-diglycerides. Hence, an entire new series of diglycerides, not readily obtainable by direct synthesis, could be evolved. Consequently, one could easily see their use in the study of the biosynthesis of lecithins and triglycerides.

Isolation and Identification of Lecithins

In Chapter 2 the techniques available for the preparation of lecithins were outlined. In general, the chromatographic procedure, using either aluminum oxide or silicic acid, has allowed the most facile, high yield route to purified lecithins. On the basis of the usual noncrystallinity of these compounds, the purity of these substances can only be established by detailed analyses. Thus, by definition, a lecithin should contain 2 moles of fatty acid, 1 mole of choline, and 1 mole of

L-α-glycerophosphoric acid, and should exhibit optical activity comparable to synthetic compounds. In many respects the assay of these particular components presents some rather difficult problems and thus complicates the identification process. In the following sections, a description is made of certain of the available analytical techniques.

Fatty Acids. The heterogeneity of the fatty acids obtained from naturally occurring lecithins presents a respectable problem in proper assay and detection of each and every component. While great strides have recently been made, particularly via the perfection of the vapor phase chromatographic technique, no single method offers a panacea. However, there is little doubt that within the near future, advances in the assay of fatty acids should be such that regardless of chain length and unsaturation, unequivocal and immediate identification can be made by a single technique. As this is still a futuristic consideration, the techniques presently useful in fatty acid analysis are evaluated here. It should be emphasized that the procedures described below are applicable to any type of lipide, and not necessarily restricted to the lecithins.

Cleavage of ester bonds.

ACID OR ALKALINE HYDROLYSIS (COMPLETE). Prior to an actual discussion of the analytical procedures, it is advisable to consider the problem of the cleavage of the fatty acid ester bonds of the phosphoglycerides. Since most techniques below rely on the free acid or a simple ester derivative, the route to release of these acids in an unaltered form is of paramount importance. In general, the degradation of the ester bonds of these compounds presents no problem, both groups being readily attacked by acid or alkali, or specifically by enzymatic action. In most instances the complete release of the fatty acids of lecithins can be accomplished by refluxing of the compound in $2N$ aqueous HCl or $0.5N$ KOH for 4 to 6 hours. There are, of course, variations on this approach as regards time, strength or type of acid or alkali, solvent, etc., but usually the mixtures described above will allow a complete hydrolytic cleavage. At the end of the reflux period, the cooled mixture (acidified) is extracted with petroleum ether or diethyl ether and this extract, containing all the fatty acids, is washed thoroughly for the removal of any mineral acid. In all cases, it is advisable to protect these fatty acids from undue exposure to air and light. Prior to the more detailed analyses described below, these fatty acids may be submitted to total weight and neutral equivalent assays and unsaturation (number of double bonds per molecule) determination. If so desired, the phosphate recoverable in the non-petroleum soluble fraction can be used for calculation of molar ratios of fatty acid to phosphorus.

ENZYMATIC ACTION (PARTIAL). A more gentle and specific means for release of fatty acids from lecithin concerns the use of enzyme systems, in particular phospholipase A (lecithinase A). This enzyme will effect the specific release of the fatty acid from the α' (C-1) position of lecithin.[60] This enzyme, found in high concentration in snake venoms, can cause cleavage in a wet diethyl ether solution. The products of the reaction, free fatty acids (α' acyl) soluble in ether and lysolecithin (β' acyl) insoluble in ether, can be easily separated and identified. Thus, this type of reaction can be utilized to describe the distribution of fatty acids on the specific ester positions of the lecithin molecule.

Subsequently, the fatty acids may be submitted to a more detailed fractionation or analysis. In any of these procedures, it is very important that care be exercised to prevent any oxidative alteration of the polyunsaturated fatty acids.

Techniques for detection, isolation, and/or estimation of fatty acids.

LOW TEMPERATURE CRYSTALLIZATION. In effect this technique, described by Brown and Kolb,[26] utilizes the process of crystallization of fatty acids from a particular solvent by lowering of the temperature below 0°. When completely equilibrated at a particular temperature, the crystallized fatty acids are filtered and the filtrate then adjusted to the next lower desired temperature. This then allows the fractionation of fatty acids having the same chain length but different numbers of double bonds. Consequently, the separation is rather loosely correlated with the melting point of the fatty acids. In general, one may obtain three broad groups of fatty acids as the temperature is lowered, i.e., saturated, monounsaturated, and polyunsaturated types. The principles and practices involved in this method are described in greater detail by Brown and Kolb.[26] While this technique has not been readily adaptable to use on a milligram scale required in some isolation work, it is of interest to note that Mead and Howton [99] have used this procedure to remove the saturated fatty acids from their mixtures.

DISTILLATION. The use of distillation for separation of long-chain fatty acids is a time-honored procedure in lipide chemistry. However, though still of considerable value in many areas of investigation, this technique has not been adaptable to a really milligram scale. Perhaps the best-recognized work on a small scale was that of Hofmann et al.,[66] who fractionated the fatty acids from *Lactobacillus arabinosus* through use of a micro Piros-Glover spinning band type fractionating column. Charges of methyl esters as low as 0.5 ml. (roughly equivalent to 400 mg. fatty acids) can be satisfactorily separated by this procedure. Thus, mixtures can be separated into fractions equivalent to the length of the carbon chain and, in addition, separation of fatty acids with different degrees of unsaturation can be effected by this approach. However, the amounts of acids necessary for this assay and the advent of more expedient means of fractionation (i.e., chromatographic procedures) makes this technique less advantageous.

SPECTROPHOTOMETRIC ASSAY. The application of spectrophotometry to the identification and estimation of fatty acids has been reasonably successful. While perhaps not all-inclusive or quantitative in all instances, nevertheless the techniques described below are of considerable merit and will continue to be useful adjuncts in any study of fatty acids and their derivatives.

Hydroxamate Reaction. This test is based on the well-established ability of carboxylic acid esters to react with hydroxylamine in alkaline solutions to form hydroxamic acids:

$$\text{RCOOR}' + \text{NH}_2\text{OH} \xrightarrow{\text{alkali}} \text{RCONHOH} + \text{R}'\text{OH}$$

Subsequent reaction of the hydroxamic acids with ferric chloride produced a red to violet color, which can be used as a quantitative measure of the amount of ester present. As originally applied to the short-chain esters, this reaction was not successful with the longer chain fatty acid esters mainly because of the relative insolubility of the latter. However, this difficulty was overcome by Stern and Shapiro,[124] who found that the presence of aqueous alcohol allowed a reproducible evaluation of long-chain fatty acid esters. Using triolein as a standard, 0.5 to 3 milliequivalents of ester could be estimated in an over-all time of 30 minutes. The reaction works well with various chain length esters found in either simple or complex lipide compounds.

A particular use of this procedure is as a rapid check on the fatty acid to phosphorus ratios of a preparation, during fractionation procedures, enzymatic reactions, synthetic processes, etc.

Alkali Isomerization Technique. The use of this procedure is restricted exclusively to those fatty acids which show absorption in the ultraviolet region of the spectrum, namely, the conjugated polyenoic acids. In particular, this procedure is based on the well-known method of Herb and Riemenschneider,[64] wherein it was established that polyunsaturated fatty acids containing a 1:4 diene system and normally showing little spectral absorption in the ultraviolet region of the spectrum (220 mμ to 340 mμ), under the influence of alkali are isomerized to 1:3 diene or conjugated systems which show considerable absorption. This observation has been made the subject of a quantitative procedure for estimating polyunsaturated fatty acids, such as linoleic and arachidonic acid. The measurement of the absorption at specific wave lengths will allow a calculation of the amounts of the various unsaturated fatty acids. The method is quite sensitive and may be used on samples of 1 to 10 mg. total lipide. While the procedure is based on the isomerization rate of *cis* fatty acids, the presence of *trans* acids may cause difficulty in the interpretation of spectral data.

A comprehensive and well-organized discussion of the ultraviolet spectrophotometry of fatty acids is the subject of a recent review by Pitt and Morton.[107] In this review, especial attention is paid to the factors operative in the alkali isomerization technique for assay of unconjugated polyunsaturated fatty acids. Likewise, a similar consideration of this problem constitutes the subject of a review by Holman.[68]

Enzymatic Assay. MacGee and Mattson [93] have devised a rapid enzymatic method for the determination of linoleic, linolenic, and arachidonic acid. The potassium salts of the fatty acids are oxidized by atmospheric oxygen in the presence of the enzyme, lipoxidase, and the spectral absorption of the diene hydroperoxide formed by this reaction is measured at 234 mμ. However, no differentiation between the above acids is possible, as each gives only a single hydroperoxide. As little as 4 gamma of linoleic acid can be detected. This reaction appears to be specific for compounds bearing methylene interrupted diene structures in which the double bonds are in the *cis* configuration. The *trans* forms of these acids will apparently not serve as substrates for this enzyme. Thus, this technique differs from the above alkali isomerization method which affects all polyenoic acids.

Infrared Examination. Sufficient evidence has now accumulated to support the use of infrared spectrophotometry as an excellent method for identifying various lipide components. This subject has been discussed in a very competent manner by Wheeler.[138] With the long-chain fatty acids, the *trans* configuration can be detected with ease by virtue of its 10.3 μ band. However, the number of double bonds in a molecule or the presence of *cis* isomers cannot be easily determined in the normally studied regions of the infrared spectra (2 to 15 μ). Recently Holman and Edmondson [69] studied the spectral absorption characteristics of various fatty acids in the near infrared (overtone) region (0.9 to 3.0 μ). In particular, *cis* unsaturation may be readily identified as well as peroxide groups which can be of considerable aid in ascertaining whether the fatty acids have been air-oxidized in work-up.

In an interesting study, Meiklejohn et al.[100] have shown by infrared examination of long-chain fatty acids (and their soaps) a close relationship between band progression and chain lengths. When the soaps of long-chain saturated fatty acids were examined by the KBr disk technique in the 7.43 to 8.47 μ region, these investigators noted that the number of bands (uniformly spaced) were approximately equal to one-half of the number of carbons in the chain. Mixtures of two fatty acids could be identified by visual unscrambling of the two sets of uniformly spaced bands. No information was supplied as to the behavior of long-chain unsaturated fatty acids in this region of the spectra. Also, it would seem most likely that complex mixtures of fatty acids normally encountered might present a more difficult proposition.

Freeman and co-workers[55] have applied infrared spectroscopy, together with chromatographic fractionation, for analysis of serum lipides. Free fatty acids were estimated by measurement of absorbance at 5.85 μ, using oleic acid as a calibration standard. According to these authors, this method is reliable to $\pm 10\%$ for any component present to the extent of 0.5 mg. and which comprises more than 10% of the total lipide. This procedure would appear to offer the most advantage in the examination of free fatty acids in a mixture of lipides and not solely for free fatty acids alone. However, it should be emphasized that infrared examination of a fatty acid can yield valuable information regarding the structure of the acid.

COUNTERCURRENT DISTRIBUTION. The use of countercurrent distribution in the fractionation of the complex lipides was discussed in part in Chapter 2. Its most refined use as an analytical tool has been shown by Ahrens and Craig[1] in the fractionation of the long-chain fatty acids. Through the use of a solvent mixture of heptane-formamide-methanol-water and acetic acid (3:1:1:1, v/v), an essentially complete separation of saturated fatty acids from C_{12} to C_{18} could be effected after 400 transfers. Perhaps the most useful application has been to the separation of the C_{18} unsaturated acids, linoleic, linolenic, and oleic. The partition coefficients were such that an almost complete separation was obtained after 650 transfers in the same solvent systems as described above. In this same study, this procedure was applied to the analysis of the fatty acids of pig mesenteric fat and the results were comparable to those obtained by more classical procedures. The assay by countercurrent distribution is usually conducted by weight analysis of each fraction and a typical run may require an original mixture of at least 500 mg. fatty acids. While perhaps not as useful on a small scale as techniques outlined below, nevertheless this method represents a powerful and useful tool for relatively large amounts of material and for a check on the purity of a particular component.

CHROMATOGRAPHY. As in nearly every field of research endeavor today, chromatographic analysis has been most ably applied to the fatty acid problem. Especially as regards the detection of fatty acids on a small scale, these techniques have been of immeasurable value.

Paper Chromatography. Through the use of filter paper impregnated with high boiling petroleum hydrocarbon, as the stationary phase, Kaufman and Nitsch,[78] in particular, have been quite successful in obtaining fairly sharp separation of fatty acids from C_2 to C_{24} with mobile phase solvents, such as aqueous acetic acid. By employing radial chromatography, Mangold et al.[96] obtained a good separation of unsaturated and saturated long-chain fatty acids on filter paper impregnated with silicone and a solvent system of 70% acetic acid. A similar separation can be effected by use of descending paper chromatography with the same system. The fatty acids can be located by exposure of the paper to iodine vapors (for unsaturation), treatment with lead acetate followed by hydrogen sulfide (for general location), as well as through the use of indicators and complex colored salt formation (i.e., with copper-ferricyanide mixtures).

A technique that appears to offer considerable improvement over the above procedures is that devised by Inouye and his associates.[72, 73] In this technique, the fatty acids are refluxed with *p*-bromophenacyl bromide to yield the corresponding phenacyl esters. These esters are converted to 2,4 dinitrophenylhydrazones, or the "bromozones." One portion of the mixed bromozones is treated with mercuric acetate in methanol, which forms an acetoxymercuri methoxy derivative with the unsaturated fatty acids. Another portion is not treated further. These fractions are chromatographed on tetralin (b.p. 185–215°) impregnated paper in a solvent composed of 90% methanol-acetic acid-tetralin (10:2:1, v/v/v). This procedure allowed a separation of acids from C_4 to C_{20}. Both the saturated and unsaturated acids were located visually by color reaction with diphenylcarbazone and the individual spots then cut out, eluted, and the amount of acid estimated quantitatively by spectrophotometric examination.

A summary of other paper chromatographic techniques is given by Shorland [120] and by Lederer and Lederer.[86]

Column Chromatography. A number of different procedures have been proposed for the separation of fatty acids by column partition chromatography. In essence, two general procedures, reverse phase chromatography and gas-liquid (vapor phase) chromatography, appear to be the most satisfactory available today. For the details of other proposed techniques, the reader is referred to Lederer and Lederer [86] and Savary and Desnuelle.[117]

In these techniques, suitable precautions must be taken against oxidation of polyunsaturated fatty acids. For example, in the isolation of the esters of polyethenoid fatty acids on silicic acid-celite columns, Herb et al.[65] passed CO_2 or N_2 for 3 hours through a packed column heated at 70 to 75°. Similarly, Hammond and Lundberg [58] passed N_2 through their columns for 24 hours at room temperature before use and still found some auto-oxidation. The subject of auto-oxidation of polyunsaturated fatty acids is adequately covered in a review by Holman.[67]

Reversed phase chromatography. Perhaps the most widely used system is that described by Howard and Martin [70] and modified by Silk and Hahn.[122] In their original procedure, Howard and Martin made Hyflo Super Cel (Johns Mansville) hydrophobic by exposure to vapors of dimethyldichlorosilane. Through the use of this material the fractionation of saturated acids from C_{12} to C_{18} could be obtained. Silk and Hahn extended this procedure to include mixtures of saturated fatty acids from C_{16} to C_{24}. They used paraffin oil on the hydrophobic (silane treated) Hyflo Super Cel as the stationary phase and acetone-water mixtures (containing paraffin oil) as the developing solvent. Subsequently, the eluted acids were estimated by titration with alkali.

However, the separation of the fatty acids by these columns is limited. The complete separation of the even-numbered saturated fatty acids is possible. On the other hand, the more common unsaturated fatty acids have been shown to partition as follows: palmitoleic, linoleic, and arachidonic with myristic; oleic with palmitic.[31, 108, 117] Linolenic acid is eluted from the column before myristic as shown by Mead,[98] but he was unable to detect any of these polyunsaturated acids in rats even when they were maintained on a linolenate supplemented diet.

Popjak and Tietz [108] recognized the possibility of effecting a further separation for quantitative determination of the various fatty acids by hydrogenation of the fractions and rechromatography. This technique was applied to the determination of palmitic and oleic acid in a fatty acid fraction obtained in studies with cell-free mammary gland suspensions. Thus, oleic acid, after complete hydrogenation to stearic acid, could be separated from the palmitic acid. Mead [98] extended this technique to the assay of palmitoleic, linoleic, and arachidonic acids in rat lipides. In the former case, oleic acid, after hydrogenation, is separated from palmitic acid as stearic acid and in the latter case, palmitoleic, linoleic, and arachidonic acids are separated as palmitic, stearic, and arachidic acids respectively. As has been pointed out by Mead, this approach does not allow for the detection of positional isomers of the unsaturated fatty acids.

In a detailed study of the metabolism of long-chain fatty acids, Dittmer [39] employed reversed phase chromatography for separation of the acids in various lipide derivatives. In the main, the principal interest was in the fate of ingested C^{14} labeled palmitic, stearic, oleic, and linoleic acids. As a check on the separation of the acids on these columns, specific labeled acids were added to the fatty acids isolated from the phospholipides isolated from rat liver. The results of this study are illustrated in Figs. 3.1 through 3.4 and show that the columns do allow an effective separation of palmitic, stearic, and linoleic acid, but that oleic acid is eluted together with palmitic acid fraction. As

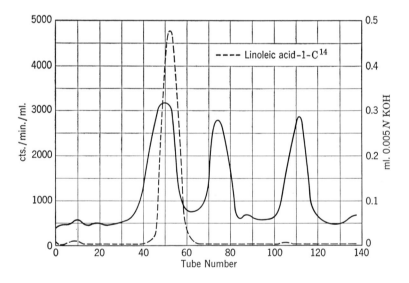

Fig. 3.1. Reversed phase chromatography of fatty acids of rat liver phospholipides with added linoleic acid-1-C^{14}.

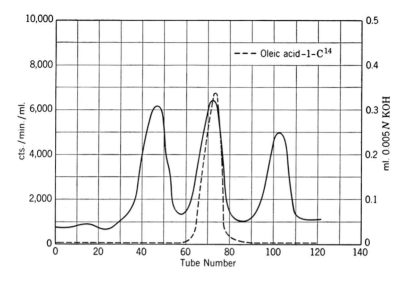

Fig. 3.2. Reversed phase chromatography of fatty acids of rat liver phospholipides with added oleic acid-1-C^{14}.

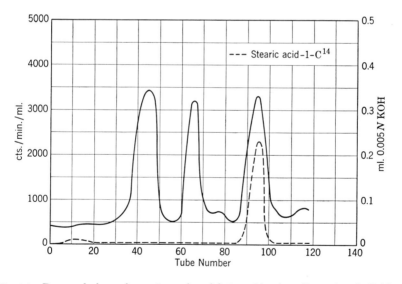

Fig. 3.3. Reversed phase chromatography of fatty acids of rat liver phospholipides with added stearic acid-1-C^{14}.

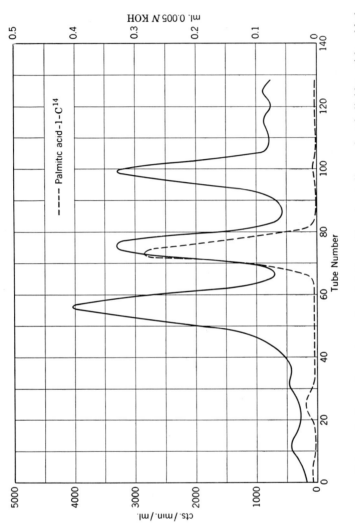

Fig. 3.4. Reversed phase chromatography of fatty acids of rat liver phospholipides with added palmitic acid-1-C¹⁴.

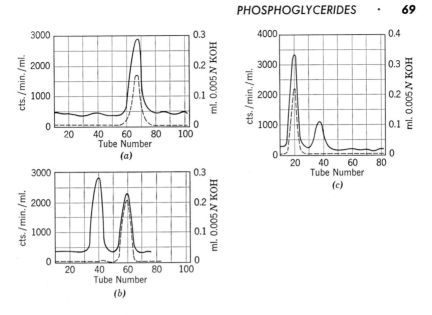

Fig. 3.5. Reversed phase chromatography of fatty acids of rat liver phospholipides: (*a*) Hydrogenated stearic acid fraction with added stearic acid-1-C^{14}; (*b*) Hydrogenated palmitic-oleic acid fraction with added oleic acid-1-C^{14}; (*c*) Hydrogenated palmitic-oleic acid fraction with added palmitic acid-1-C^{14}.

indicated above, hydrogenation will allow a satisfactory separation (Fig. 3.5). In general, the concentration of fatty acids is 1.5 mg. or less per gram adsorbent, with 20 to 25 mg. total acids representing a suitable amount for an adequate fractionation.

Gas-liquid (vapor phase) chromatography. This technique appears to be a most promising route to a rapid quantitative evaluation of the composition of a mixture of fatty acids on a milligram basis. This type of partition chromatography involves the use of columns containing a stationary liquid phase and a mobile gas phase, such as nitrogen or helium. The liquid stationary phase, i.e., silicone grease, is usually supported on materials such as celite (Johns Mansville), and the separation of the methyl esters (not the free acids) is obtained by passing the sample in the vapor state (at temperatures of 200–225°) through the column at the same temperature, in a stream of nitrogen at reduced pressure. The effluent esters are measured by a thermal conductivity unit or gas density balance.

Originally, the technique was first introduced by James and Martin [74] for the separation of fatty acids (in the free form up to C_{11} in chain length, on a column of stearic acid on silicone oil). The effluent acids were measured by a titrimetric procedure. Subsequently, Cropper and Heywood [32] reported a good separation of the methyl esters of fatty acids from C_{12} to C_{22} at 230° on a column composed of celite and a high vacuum silicone grease. The emerging esters were measured by a differential catharometer device. Later, Ray [113] suggested usage of the thermal conductivity unit for measurements of the effluent gases. This method of detection has been widely applied, but has not always been as completely reliable as desired (hysteresis effects, decomposition of acids on the thermistor beads at high temperatures, etc.). More recently, James and Martin [75] proposed a new technique which utilized a gas density balance for detection purposes. It is an extremely sensitive device, permitting detection of amounts as low as 0.06 μg. per ml. nitrogen.* While undoubtedly vapor phase chromatography will replace most existing methods for analysis of fatty acids, the entire field is experiencing some "preliminary" difficulties. In part, this is due to the inadequacies of certain available stationary phases in separations, variability in response, and reliability of detection devices and the fact that only partial separations have been effected.

However, Orr and Callen [106] reported a reasonably complete separation of methyl esters of commonly known fatty acids including polyunsaturated compounds through use of a plasticizer (30% Reoplex 400) on celite at 240°. The time required for analysis was considerably less than in previous procedures (where the first band usually emerged in 2 hours) with methyl stearate emerging in 27 minutes. The retention times, as a measure of time required for a given fatty acid ester to emerge from a column, were of the order of 2 to 3 hours for C_{18} acids. It was interesting to note that the fatty acid esters in each carbon number class emerged from the column in times which increased with the number of double bonds on the compound. This was the reverse of the order of emergence obtained with Apiezon M or L. Actually Orr and Callen were the first investigators to report that

* Recently, J. E. Lovelock [*J. Chromat.*, **1**, 1 (1958)] has described an ionization detector for measurement of concentration of effluent gases from a gas phase chromatograph. Its high sensitivity to concentration changes (approximately 100 times that of conventional thermal detectors) and its relative insensitivity to temperature and flow rate changes make it an ideal detector unit. Certain commercially available gas phase chromatographic units now utilize this measurement principle.

through use of a more polar adsorbent than the Apiezons the unsaturated and saturated fatty acids of the same chain length could be separated. This represented an important advance.

According to Lipsky and Landowne,[88] the difficulties associated with the separation of stearic and oleic acids on gas-liquid columns can be overcome by use of an adipate polyester of diethylene glycol cross-linked with pentaerythritol (M.W. 30,000), on celite 545. It was possible to completely resolve the following mixture of methyl esters in 35 minutes at 190° in the order listed: caprylic, capric, lauric, myristic, palmitic, palmitoleic, stearic, oleic, linoleic, linolenic, arachidic, and behenic acids. In contrast with the procedure of Orr and Callen, this allowed a complete separation of stearic and oleic acid in a reasonable period of time. Under similar conditions, arachidonic acid has a retention time of 34 minutes, while a saturated C_{26} acid is eluted in 110 minutes. In a previous publication on this subject, Lipsky and Landowne had demonstrated the separation of the individual saturated and unsaturated long-chain fatty acid esters (C_{12} to C_{22}) within 85 minutes by use of an adipate polyester of diethylene glycol (M.W. 10,000) as the stationary phase. On the basis of these reports it appears probable that the rapid separation of long-chain fatty acids on a quantitative basis (and without degradation) is a possibility. Subsequently, the individual fatty acid can be subjected to specific degradation procedures for proof of structure, further study by infrared examination, etc.

Comments on types of fatty acids found in lecithins.

GENERAL. Inasmuch as it is only within the past few years that highly purified lecithins have been prepared, it is natural that a rather limited amount of data is available on the nature of the fatty acids present. There is little doubt that variations in composition will occur from one source to another and, while variability is to be expected, it is interesting to note that in certain instances rather striking differences have been noted. Thus, both fully saturated [129] as well as fully unsaturated lecithins [63] have been found in natural sources. On the other hand, in the liver of a variety of animals and in chicken egg, the lecithins appeared to have their fatty acids rather specifically distributed. Thus, these lecithins tend to contain predominantly unsaturated fatty acids in the α(C-1) ester group and saturated fatty acids in the β(C-2) position.[59] This is illustrated by the following formula:

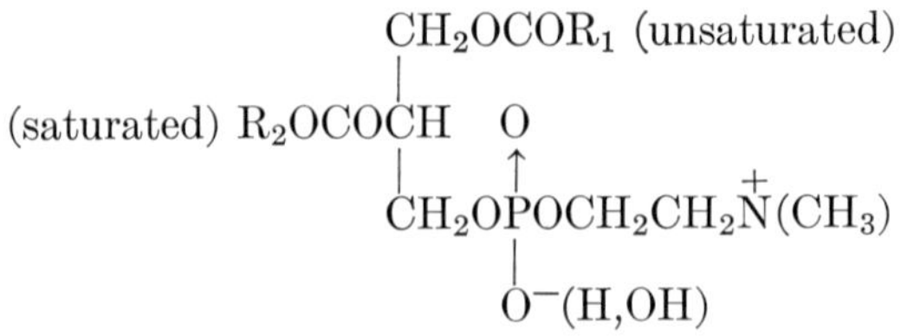

$$CH_2OCOR_1 \text{ (unsaturated)}$$

(saturated) $R_2OCOCH \quad O$

$$CH_2OPOCH_2CH_2\overset{+}{N}(CH_3)$$

$$O^-(H,OH)$$

Through the use of reversed phase chromatography of the fatty acids from the lecithins of rat liver, Dittmer [39] was able to obtain the distribution pattern in this fraction. These results are recorded in Table 3.2 and again illustrate that approximately 50% are saturated and approximately 50% are unsaturated fatty acids. This is as expected for an "asymmetric" arrangement to the fatty acids of the lecithins in liver.[59]

It is interesting to note that on silicic acid chromatography of mixed phospholipides of chicken egg,[115] rat and beef liver and yeast,[62] considerable skewing of the lecithin curve was noted. In both cases the more unsaturated components were eluted at the front of the band and a more saturated type at the tail of the curve. Data on the distribu-

Table 3.2

Nature of Fatty Acids of Phosphatidyl Choline of Rat Liver *

Fraction	Mole %
α' fatty acid	
"Linoleic" †	71.1
Oleic	19.2
Palmitic	6.0
Stearic	3.2
β fatty acid	
"Linoleic" †	3.0
Oleic	4.3
Palmitic	54.3
Stearic	38.3

* Taken from Dittmer.[39]

† This fraction may contain linoleic, arachidonic, palmitoleic, and myristic acids.

Table 3.3

Distribution of Unsaturation in Phosphatidyl Choline (Lecithin) Fraction of
Chicken Egg on Silicic Acid Chromatograms *

Unsaturation, Double Bonds/Atom P	% Lipide P Recovered
Above 5 (fast moving)	1.1
4–5	5.8
3–4	14.8
2–3	21.8
Below 2 (slow moving)	56.5

* Taken from Rhodes.[114]

tion of unsaturation in the fractions obtained from chicken egg are
given in Table 3.3.

ASYMMETRIC ARRANGEMENT OF THE FATTY ACIDS OF PHOSPHOGLYC-
ERIDES AND POSSIBLE INFLUENCE IN METABOLIC RATE. When confronted with the information cited in Chapter 1, it would appear most
improbable that phospholipides would have any role in fatty acid
metabolism, or for that matter their role in any metabolically important reaction would be of an equivocal nature. However, within
the past few years, evidence has been accumulating that strongly suggests a reconsideration of the metabolic patterns of the phosphoglycerides. In regard to the phospholipides, this newer information has
emphasized the fact that all the ester groups of a phosphoglyceride
may not be of the same reactivity and hence may have different "turnover" characteristics. Furthermore, there may be a preferential
handling of the fatty acids on a particular position of the molecule,
especially as regards the nature of the unsaturation in the fatty acid
molecule.

In an investigation of the mode of action of lecithinase A (phospholipase A) on lecithin, Hanahan [59] noted that there was a decided
difference in the unsaturation of the fatty acids on this compound.
Thus, as indicated in the formula below, the lecithins of the liver of
a variety of species of animals were found to contain unsaturated fatty
acids on the α' ester (C-1) position and saturated fatty acids on the
β ester (C-2) position:

$$CH_2OCOR \text{ (unsaturated), } (\alpha',C\text{-}1)$$

$$OCOR \text{ (saturated), } (\beta,C\text{-}2) \; CH$$

$$CH_2O\overset{O}{\overset{\uparrow}{P}}OCH_2CH_2\overset{+}{N}(CH_3)_3$$

$$\overset{|}{O^-}(H,OH)$$

A similar structure has been found for the lecithins of chicken egg.[59] Recently, Borgstrom [21] has identified the lecithin of rat bile as (α'-oleyl-β-palmityl)-glycerylphosphorylcholine.

In an effort to ascertain the significance of the asymmetry of the lecithins, Hanahan and Blomstrand [61] fed palmitic acid-1-C^{14} and oleic acid-1-C^{14} to rats and followed the incorporation of label into the lecithins of the intestinal mucosa and the liver. When radioactive palmitic acid was administered, over 90% of the label in the lecithins of the liver was localized in the β position. In the lecithins of the intestinal mucosa 72 to 82% of the label was detected in the β position. In each case any label found in the α' ester position was present as an unsaturated fatty acid. However, when oleic acid was given to rats, the amount of label found in the lecithins was very small (some tenfold less than with labeled palmitic acid). In both the intestine and the liver, the label was evenly distributed between the two positions of the lecithin.

In subsequent experiments Dittmer [39] has corroborated and extended these observations. In these experiments linoleic acid-1-C^{14}-, oleic acid-1-C^{14}, palmitic acid-1-C^{14}, and stearic acid-1-C^{14} were administered in either corn or olive oil to rats and at suitable time intervals the livers were removed and the total neutral lipides and phospholipides isolated and subjected to chromatography on silicic acid. The major fractions associated with any uptake of labeled acid were lecithin, phosphatidyl ethanolamine, triglycerides, and cholesterol esters. When the lecithins were subjected to degradation with lecithinase A, the distribution of isotope in the two ester positions proved most interesting. As indicated by some of the results obtained in Table 3.4, both stearic acid and palmitic acid appear almost specifically to be located in the β(C-2) position while linoleic acid appears to be mainly incorporated in the α' (C-1) position. Oleic acid again is divided to an almost equal extent between the two positions. This has led to the proposal that the two ester groups of lecithin represent metabolically different groups and may be represented by the following formulation:

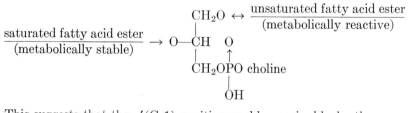

This suggests that the α'(C-1) position could conceivably be the more metabolically active ester position and the C-2 ester position could be the more stable position. Furthermore, a definitive difference in the nature of the fatty acids found in these two positions and the results on the uptake of labeled fatty acids would also certainly indicate a preferential treatment of saturated and unsaturated fatty acids.

In a recent investigation, Rhodes [114] reported on experiments designed to study the alteration in the nature of the fatty acids of the lecithins of chicken egg. Chickens were maintained on diets containing varying degrees of unsaturation (cod liver oil was the oil used for high unsaturation studies) and the lecithins of the egg were isolated in the usual manner and assayed for unsaturation. They were then subjected to the action of lecithinase A and the resulting lysolecithin [representing β(C-2) ester] and the free fatty acid [representing α'(C-1) ester] assayed for unsaturation. The predominating feature of the results was that even though the diet was increased to a very high intake of unsaturated fatty acids, only the C-1 ester group re-

Table 3.4 *

Distribution of Labeled Fatty Acids in α' Position of Liver Lecithin †

	% Specific Activity of Total Fatty Acid	
	Corn Oil	Olive Oil
Palmitic	12.4	5.5
Stearic	3.7	4.0
Oleic	28.9	34.2
Linoleic	86.5	80.0

* Taken from Dittmer.[39]
† Remainder of activity in β position.

flected this change. This can be shown by a typical set of data obtained in these experiments (Table 3.5).

Also, Rhodes observed that phosphatidyl ethanolamine had a similar positional asymmetry to its fatty acids and reflected a comparable alteration in fatty acid composition, only not so pronounced, as in the lecithins. Hence, again this shows a distinctly different type of handling with regard to the nature of the fatty acids, on the two ester positions of lecithin, and certainly confirms the distinctly different nature of the acids. It supports the concept that the α'(C-1) position is concerned mainly with the unsaturated acids and the β(C-2) position is concerned mainly with the saturated acids. This same reasoning could apply to an explanation of the results of Weinman et al.,[136] where they concluded from studies with biosynthesized phospholipides, labeled with palmitic acid-1-C^{14} and P^{32}, that similar turnover rates of these labeled constituents indicated that the entire phospholipide molecule was removed as a unit from the blood stream. Hence this in part formed a basis of the proposition that phospholipides could not be involved in fatty acid transport, etc. However, on the basis of the above arguments, these investigators were possibly studying the turnover of the metabolically more stable C-2 ester group. Thus, it seems reasonable to suggest strongly that a re-evaluation of the role of lecithin in fat transport and metabolism is feasible and timely.

In a study of the effect of dietary oleic acid and palmitic acid feeding on the composition of liver phospholipides, Campbell et al.[28] re-

Table 3.5

Influence of Cod Liver Oil on Composition of
Chicken Egg * Phosphatidyl Choline

Unsaturation, Double Bonds/Atom P	% Lipide P Recovered	
	Normal Feed	Highest Liver Oil Supplement
Above 5	1.1	14.4
4–5	5.8	20.6
3–4	14.8	19.5
2–3	21.8	25.8
Below 2	56.5	19.7

* Taken from Rhodes.[114]

ported a significant difference in the handling of these long-chain acids by rats maintained on a low protein, high fat diet. While ingestion of large amounts of dietary palmitic acid is accompanied by a simultaneous release of depot fats, they noted that oleic acid did not impose a similar demand on depot fats. A pronounced difference was observed in the per cent of fat in the liver between litters of rats fed oleic acid and those fed palmitic acid; in animals from litters in which liver fat accumulated, significantly higher values of fat were obtained for palmitic acid fed than oleic acid fed animals. Moreover, palmitic acid feeding reduced liver phospholipides, while oleic acid did not affect it. Although no fractionation of the individual phospholipides was made, it is evident from these observations that there is decided difference in the handling of two typical long-chain fatty acids, one a saturated and the other an unsaturated type.

NOTES ON SPECIES OF PHOSPHOGLYCERIDES. In a continuation of the argument regarding the metabolic asymmetry or reactivity of the esters on the lecithin molecule, another provocative phase of this problem should be considered. This centers about the well-known fact that there are several different lecithins in the liver (or any tissue) and that each one of these may not necessarily be interrelated. Hence, in discussing phosphoglyceride metabolism, it may be necessary to consider the possible species of lecithins involved in a particular reaction. For purposes of illustration the following lecithins containing a saturated fatty acid, R_s, and three different unsaturated fatty acids (R_1, R_2, and R_3) are shown:

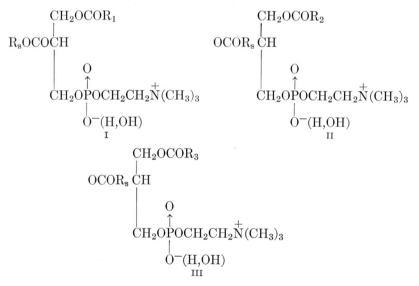

It is obviously not necessary that the three substances be related metabolically simply because mutual solubility properties resulted in their isolation in the same fraction. Consequently, lecithin I may be exclusively concerned only with fatty acid transport, lecithin II with fatty acid oxidation, and lecithin III as an intermediate in oxidative reactions. As is obvious, it is necessary for a more explicit understanding of lipide metabolism that these individual species be isolated and identified as such. That this is in the realm of possibility is indicated by recent findings on the fractionation of lipides by chromatographic procedures. Rhodes and Lea [115] have noted that in silicic acid chromatography of egg phospholipide there is a definite skewing to the lecithin elution curve, which on assay of various portions of this curve shows a decided difference in the degree of unsaturation. The initially eluted portion of the lecithin fraction shows the largest amount of unsaturation, approximately 5 to 6 double bonds per phosphorus while the latter portions show the smallest amount, 1 to 2 double bonds per phosphorus. In an analogous experiment with the liver phospholipides, Hanahan et al.[62] noted that the fast running lecithin fraction had a higher degree of unsaturation, 1.4 double bonds per fatty acid, while the slower moving material had a lower unsaturation, 0.4 double bonds per fatty acid. Pursuant to the point of different species of lecithin, Inouye and Noda [72] reported the paper chromatographic separation, through use of mercurated derivatives, of at least four different lecithins from chicken egg. Thus, it is feasible that different species of lecithins and also all other phospholipides can be isolated in part by this technique. Thereafter, the intriguing possibility of investigating the metabolic pathway of these different types is available.

Choline. This very strongly alkaline compound (pK 13.9) is a hygroscopic compound, which is usually isolated as a water insoluble reineckate, phosphotungstate, or phosphomolybdate salt.* Its quantitative estimation is accomplished by a colorimetric procedure.

* Wheeldon and Collins [*Biochem. J.*, **70**, 43 (1948)] have described a new apparently satisfactory approach to the micro determination of choline. Briefly, in this technique the choline was precipitated from a lipide hydrolysate by phosphomolybdic acid, reduced with $SnCl_2$, and the blue color subsequently assayed by colorimetric examination. The procedure agreed well with the reineckate method and was useful in the range of 0.3 to 3.0 μmoles. In relatively high concentrations serine and ethanolamine (20 μmoles) interfered; in addition, any potassium (>20 μequiv.), barium, or calcium ions formed insoluble salts with phosphomolybdic acid, but could be distinguished from the choline derivative on the basis of their insolubility in acetone.

Briefly, in this assay the choline can be most effectively released from the lecithin by hydrolysis with saturated barium hydroxide for 4 to 6 hours and the resultant freed choline is precipitated as the Reinecke salt. The insoluble salt is dissolved in acetone and the amount determined by spectroscopic examination. This technique can be used to estimate amounts of choline from 0.5 to 3.0 mg. Choline may also be analyzed by the periodide method [5] and by the paper chromatographic procedure of Levine and Chargaff.[87] The advantages and disadvantages of methods proposed for assay of choline are very ably outlined by Engel et al.[42]

Glycerophosphoric Acid. As established by Baer and his colleagues, the L-α-configuration of glycerophosphoric acid is the only form found in naturally occurring phosphoglycerides. In the usual manner of isolation of glycerophosphoric acid from acid or alkaline hydrolyses of lecithin, a reversible migration of the phosphate group occurs. Thus, the resultant mixture contains L-α, D,L-α, and β forms of this compound. The presence of this acid can be checked by: (a) paper chromatography,[104] with due respect for the influence of cations on the R_F values;[132] (b) insolubility of sodium and potassium glycerophosphates in absolute ethanol;[49, 103] (c) solubility of barium glycerophosphate in water, insolubility in ethanol;[105] and (d) hydrolysis at pH 4.0 at 15 lb. pressure in an autoclave for 7 hours,[50] with the liberation of 1 mole of glycerol and 1 mole of inorganic phosphate.

In a study of the enzymatic incorporation of glycerophosphate into phospholipides, Kennedy[79] isolated this component by the following procedure: The reaction mixture free of protein was passed through the acid form of Amberlite IR-120 resin for removal of cations. The glycerophosphate (and other anions) were then adsorbed on Amberlite IR-4B resin and eluted with $1N$ NH$_4$OH. The ammonium salts were then subjected to paper chromatography in a solvent system of absolute ethanol-$1M$ NaOH (3:1, v/v) and the glycerophosphate detected by phosphate spray reagent.

In most of the above procedures no differentiation between forms of glycerophosphoric acid is possible. This could be obviated by the following procedure, shown at the top of the next page, which would utilize a combined enzymatic and non-enzymatic attack. Essentially the procedure of choice for this enzyme degradation would be that of Kates,[77] who found that the action of phospholipase C (lecithinase C) from carrots, cabbage, or spinach is strongly activated by diethyl ether in its hydrolytic attack on lecithin. The resulting

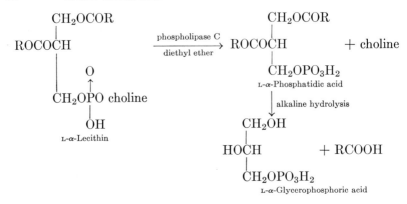

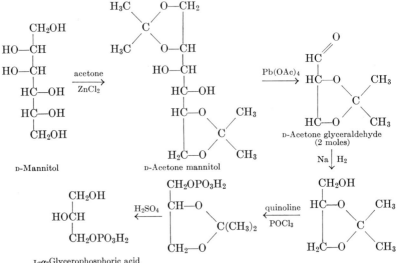

phosphatidic acid could then be hydrolyzed with alkali, wherein no phosphate migration occurs, and the L-α-glycerophosphoric acid could be isolated in good yields.

If the synthetic product is desired for comparative or other purposes, it may be synthesized by the procedure of Baer.[8] This synthesis is illustrated in the following reaction scheme:

Criteria of Purity. The criteria submitted for purity determination of a naturally occurring phosphoglyceride are many. Coupled with the information obtained by the above procedures, the use of infrared, optical rotation values, melting point (where feasible), hydrogen or iodine uptake, solubility, and ash content all constitute extremely useful and valuable criteria for establishing the properties and purity of this or any other type of lipide.

PHOSPHATIDYL ETHANOLAMINE

This phosphoglyceride is found widely distributed in nature and next to lecithin is the most abundant naturally occurring phosphoglyceride. Unfortunately, for many years this compound has been referred to as "cephalin," which is an ill-defined term now and certainly is misleading. Without recourse to all the historical implications of this term, it seems most advisable to employ a more definitive term, such as phosphatidyl ethanolamine.

The isolation of a highly purified phosphatidyl ethanolamine from natural sources has not proved an easy task. Perhaps one of the chief difficulties encountered is the great sensitivity of these compounds to atmospheric oxidation and light. This may be attributable in some instances to the presence of traces of pigments in the preparations, which catalytically stimulate oxidation of the unsaturated fatty acids. However, this phosphoglyceride does tend to contain a much higher amount of unsaturated fatty acids than lecithin or any of the other more commonly encountered phospholipides. Lea [84] has described the high susceptibility of films of phosphatidyl ethanolamine from eggs to atmospheric oxidation.

While the isolation of reasonably "high" purity phosphatidyl ethanolamines has only been recently accomplished, there has accumulated sufficient evidence to support an L-α-configuration for this compound. The synthesis of fully saturated L-α-phosphatidyl ethanolamine has allowed a strict comparison. Consequently, by definition, phosphatidyl ethanolamine should contain 2 moles of fatty acid, 1 mole of ethanolamine, and 1 mole of L-α-glycerophosphoric acid and can be classified as an L-α-(diacyl)-glycerophosphoryl ethanolamine.

Preparation and Properties

Direct Synthesis. Utilizing the general scheme outlined for the enantiomeric lecithin synthesis, Baer and Maurukas [17] have reported the preparation of dimyristoyl-, dipalmityl-, and distearoyl-L-α-glycerylphosphoryl ethanolamine. This can be illustrated in the following reaction scheme:

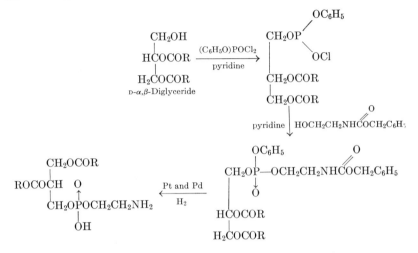

Thus, again the monophenylphosphoryl dichloride procedure was successfully employed in this case. N-Carbobenzoxyethanolamine was used to prevent the formation of amides. Malkin and Bevan [95] and Baer and Maurukas [17] made note of the possible formation of salts during synthetic procedures designed to produce esters. Thus, a comparison of the specific rotation, melting points, and solubilities of synthetic, fully saturated diacyl glycerylphosphorylethanolamines and ethanolamine salts of the corresponding α-phosphatidic acids emphasized the difficulty in distinguishing these two classes of compounds solely by these criteria. This is clearly illustrated in Table 3.6. Unfortunately, most of the earlier work on the synthesis of phosphatidyl ethanolamine did not obviate the formation of salts of α- and β-phosphatidic acids. A more detailed description of the synthesis of various types of phospholipides is given by Malkin and Bevan [95] and by Baer.[11] If chloroform solutions of the synthetic ester compounds were treated with cold dilute sulfuric acid, only a few per cent of the nitrogen was lost; however, with the salts a similar treatment released all their ethanolamine into the aqueous solution. An additional means for differentiating salt and ester formation would be by inspection of their infrared spectra.

Natural Sources. Until the report of Folch,[52] little success had been achieved in the isolation of phosphatidyl ethanolamine from natural sources. In his preparation of this compound from brain tissues, Folch employed a neutral solvent (chloroform-ethanol) fractionation scheme. The isolated "low carboxyl" nitrogen phospholipide contained 3.5% P,

Table 3.6

Comparison of Physical Properties of Salts and Esters of Diacyl-L-α-Glycerophosphoric Acid *

Compound	M.p., °C. (Meniscus Formation)	$[\alpha]_D^{26°}$	Solubility at 22–23° in Ethanol, mg./100 ml.
(1) Distearoyl-L-α-glycerophosphoric acid			
(a) Ethanolamine ester	172–173.5	+6.0°	8
(b) Ethanolamine salt	172–173	+6.8°	20
(2) Dipalmityl-L-α-glycerophosphoric acid			
(a) Ethanolamine ester	172–175	+6.4	36
(b) Ethanolamine salt	173–175	+7.7	40

* Taken from Baer and Maurukas.[17]

1.4% N (N/P, molar ratio, 0.86), 1.4% amino N, and 0.15% carboxyl N. After hydrolysis of this material in boiling $4N$ HCl for 2 hours, ethanolamine was isolated as the picrolonate and the hydrochloride. No further evidence on the structure of this compound was supplied but it corresponded, in elementary analyses at least, to a diacyl glycerylphosphorylethanolamine.

Scholfield and Dutton [119] outlined a solvent-salt scheme for the isolation of phosphatidyl ethanolamine from unbleached commercial soybean lecithin. In this technique, the alcohol insoluble phospholipides were treated with lead acetate. The insoluble lead salts, containing inositides, etc., were removed by filtration and the soluble fraction was treated with CO_2 to remove excess lead ion as the carbonate and filtered. A waxy, almost white, solid, free of inositol and choline, was obtained from the filtrate. It contained 62.3% fatty acid (neutral equivalent, 280.7; fatty acid/P, molar ratio, 1.91) and all of its nitrogen as ethanolamine. On the basis of the nitrogen and phosphorus values (3.82% P, 1.80% N, 1.65% ethanolamine, N/P, molar ratio, 0.96; glycerol/P, molar ratio, 1.03), these investigators calculated the phosphatidyl ethanolamine to be approximately 85% or more in purity. The major impurities appeared to be sterol glycosides. No data were supplied as to the nature of the fatty acids or the optical activity of the intact compound.

Recently, Debuch [34] in a careful study of the ethanolamine containing phospholipides of brain isolated phosphatidyl ethanolamine in a high state of purity. The "crude" ethanolamine phospholipides, containing both diacyl and "plasmalogen" type derivatives, were isolated by chloroform-methanol fractionation. Subsequent treatment of this fraction with acetic acid under mild conditions selectively decomposed the plasmalogens and the phosphatidyl ethanolamines were isolated by countercurrent distribution. This phospholipide fraction contained all its nitrogen as ethanolamine and approximately equal amounts of saturated and unsaturated fatty acids. This latter observation is consonant with the proposal of a positional asymmetry to the arrangement of the fatty acids on phosphoglycerides (see below).

Perhaps one of the more profitable approaches to the preparation of a highly purified phosphatidyl ethanolamine is afforded by chromatographic procedures. In a study of the composition of egg phospholipides, Lea et al.[85] selectively fractionated the phospholipides by chromatography on silicic acid with chloroform-methanol (4:1, v/v). The major non-choline containing fraction was phosphatidyl ethanolamine (containing small amounts of phosphatidyl serine), but no detailed analyses of this fraction were supplied. Later, Rhodes and Lea [116] showed that through chromatography on aluminum oxide the choline containing phospholipides could be obtained by elution with chloroform-methanol (1:1, v/v) and the non-choline containing phospholipides by elution with ethanol-chloroform-water (5:2:2, by volume). The latter fraction assayed as follows: N/P, 1.00; amino N/P, 1.00; ester/P, 1.99; inositol/P, 0.02; amino acid, as serine, a maximum of 1.2%. Thus, they considered this to be nearly pure phosphatidyl ethanolamine. In a later study, Rhodes [114] demonstrated that the phosphatidyl ethanolamine fraction contained a greater amount of unsaturation (average, 3.64 double bonds per atom of P) than the lecithin component (average, 2 double bonds per atom of P).

In an investigation of the chemical nature of the phospholipides of rat and beef liver and yeast, Hanahan et al.[62] were able to separate by silicic acid chromatography a highly purified phosphatidyl ethanolamine fraction. The data on the composition of these preparations are recorded in Table 3.7.

It is interesting to note that these preparations exhibited optical activity in the expected range and support an L-α-configuration for the phosphatidyl ethanolamines. While the major portion of the total

Table 3.7

Chemical Composition of Phosphatidyl Ethanolamine Fraction from Rat and Beef Liver and Yeast *

	Rat Liver †	Beef Liver †	Yeast †
P, %	4.01	3.71	3.80
N, %	1.79	1.63	1.63
N/P, molar ratio	0.98	0.98	0.95
Ethanolamine, % of total N	92.0 ‡	92.0 ‡	91.0‡
Serine, % of total N	2.1 ‡	3.2 ‡	2.3‡
Fatty acids, total %	70.4	74.1	66.7
Neutral equivalent	281	322	280
Fatty acid/P, molar ratio	1.97	1.91	1.95
$[\alpha]_D^{25}$	+6.1	+6.3	+6.1

* Taken from Dittmer et al.[40]

† These fractions contained no choline, inositol, sphingosine, sugar, or free amino acids.

‡ Remainder of nitrogen was released as ammonia in hydrolytic procedure.

phospholipide is represented by the ethanolamine derivative, 5% is evidently phosphatidyl serine. In an original communication on the characterization of these compounds,[62] a preliminary assay was reported which indicated a higher amount of the serine type. However, this has now been shown to be in error and attributable to unsuspected cation effects on the IRC-50 resin used in the assay system. This difficulty has been circumvented by use of Dowex 50 in a procedure described in more detail below. While these fractions contain small amounts of phosphatidyl serine, it has not been possible to completely separate these components by any chromatographic procedure. Dils and Hawthorne [38] have reported a similar inability to fractionate these compounds by silicic acid chromatography. However, Wallach and Garvin [135] have shown that phosphatidyl serine may be separated from phosphatidyl ethanolamine and lecithin by low aqueous filter paper electrophoresis. While the only criterion for this separation was a spot test, further analytical data on the composition of these components would be worthwhile.

Nature of the Fatty Acids on Phosphatidyl Ethanolamine. Although detailed data on the chemical nature of the fatty acids of these phosphoglycerides are not available as yet, the information to date does present a most interesting distribution pattern.

In studies on the phosphatidyl ethanolamine of brain, Debuch [34] noted that the fatty acids were composed of 48.8% saturated types and 51.2% unsaturated types (approximately 68% "weakly" unsaturated). In an investigation of the liver phospholipides, Dittmer [39] observed a comparable distribution of the fatty acids of the phosphatidyl ethanolamine fraction. These data obtained by reverse phase chromatography of the fatty acids are given in Table 3.8. As can be seen from these data, the phosphatidyl ethanolamine of rat liver contained 53.5% unsaturated fatty acids and 45.5% saturated fatty acids.

In a manner similar to that used for degradation of lecithin, Long and Penney [90] proved that phospholipase A (lecithinase A) will attack phosphatidyl ethanolamine with the liberation of free fatty acid and a monoacyl glycerylphosphorylethanolamine (lysophosphatidyl ethanolamine). The technique was successfully applied by Rhodes [114] to elucidation of the distribution of fatty acids in phosphatidyl ethanolamine isolated from chicken eggs. However, though most likely at the α' ester position, no proof was offered as to the exact position of attack of this enzyme on this particular phosphoglyceride.

When the phosphatidyl ethanolamines of chicken egg were subjected to the action of phospholipase A (lecithinase A), Rhodes [114] reported that over 90% of the unsaturation was located in the "α' fatty acid" ester group. Thus, these widely different observations tend to support a positional asymmetry to the fatty acids of phosphatidyl ethanolamine from brain, liver, and egg, much the same as that found

Table 3.8

Nature of Fatty Acids of Phosphatidyl Ethanolamine of Rat Liver *

Fraction	Mole %
"Linoleic" †	43.5
Oleic	10.0
Palmitic	23.0
Stearic	22.5

* Taken from Dittmer.[39]

† This fraction may contain linoleic, arachidonic, palmitoleic, and myristic acids.

for the lecithins from similar sources. As with the phosphatidyl cholines, the α'(C-1) position appears to be concerned metabolically only with unsaturated fatty acids. Furthermore, there is the distinct possibility of separation of phosphatidyl ethanolamines, containing varying degrees of unsaturation, by silicic acid chromatography.[115]

Quantitative Determination of Ethanolamine (and Serine)

Among the more common constituents of naturally occurring phospholipides are phosphatidyl ethanolamine and phosphatidyl serine. In the past, the analyses for these components have been based on the determination of ethanolamine and serine in a hydrolyzate of the lipide. Except for the method of Burmaster,[27] in which ethanolamine is determined as the difference in ammonia freed by periodate oxidation and carbon dioxide freed by ninhydrin oxidation, assays for serine and ethanolamine have consisted of three general steps: (1) hydrolysis of the lipide, (2) separation of serine and ethanolamine or their DNP derivatives, and (3) quantitative estimation of the serine and ethanolamine or their derivatives.

In a consideration of the hydrolytic release of these amino compounds from the intact lipide, basic hydrolysis, except as outlined by Axelrod et al.[5] and more recently Nojima and Utsugi,[102] has not been in general use due to the well-known instability of serine and ethanolamine under these conditions. Moreover, the difficulty of removing the base or, after neutralization, its salt, from the hydrolyzate has posed a problem. Although these two compounds are not completely stable to acid hydrolysis, this approach, especially with ease of removal of an acid such as HCl, has been the method of choice.

Paper chromatography,[87,125] fractionation on permutit [4,94] or Zeo-Karb,[91] and solvent fractionation of the DNP derivatives [3,102] have been used for the separation of the serine and ethanolamine in hydrolysates. Subsequently, quantitative estimation has been performed through colorimetric assay [87,94] and by photometry after paper chromatography,[125] by titrimetric assay of ammonia released by periodate oxidation of the bases after separation on ion exchangers,[3] and by spectrophotometric assay of the DNP derivatives.[5,102] Other methods of analysis have employed fractional distillation of ethanolamine [41] and determination of amino acid nitrogen as a measure of serine.[52]

In the course of an investigation of the fractionation of phospholipides, it became apparent that many of the available methods for serine and ethanolamine were unsatisfactory. Consequently,* the stability of serine and ethanolamine under varying conditions of hydrolysis, and the hydrolysis products from a phosphatidyl ethanolamine-phosphatidyl serine fraction, were studied. An improved method was devised by Dittmer et al.[40] for the separation of serine and estimation of serine and ethanolamine, based in part on Artom's use of periodate oxidation [3] and, in addition, ion exchangers.

In essence the separation of serine and ethanolamine was effected by a simplification of the elegant method of Moore and Stein.[101] The lipide was hydrolyzed in $6N$ HCl for 3 hours and then extracted with diethyl ether. The water soluble fraction was then evaporated to remove any acid, dissolved in $0.2N$ sodium acetate buffer (pH 5.0) and passed through a 100 to 200 mesh Dowex-50 ($\times$8) cation exchange resin in a similar buffer. Upon continued washing with the buffer, the serine (and any similar compound) was eluted. Subsequent elution with 10% sodium acetate, pH 8, removed the ethanolamine fraction (and any free ammonia). The eluants were analyzed for total nitrogen, free ammonia, and ammonia released from periodate oxidation. Excellent recoveries of standard sample of serine and ethanolamine alone and added to lipide hydrolyzates were obtained. Additional identification of the nitrogen components was afforded by paper electrophoresis and derivative formation. O-phosphoethanolamine was identified as one of the fragments of the hydrolysis of the "phosphatidyl ethanolamine" fraction from beef liver, rat liver, and yeast. However, in these fractions it was considered that phosphatidyl ethanolamine constituted over 95% of the total lipide present. In a previous preliminary report,[02] a high amount of serine phosphoglyceride was reported with IRC-50 as the exchange resin, but it was found that this was not a reproducible value and that this resin was very cation sensitive.

* In a recent article, Collins and Wheeldon [*Biochem. J.*, **70**, 46 (1958)] reported a differential color technique for the assay of ethanolamine and serine in lipides. Essentially this was based on the reaction of the lipides with fluorodinitrobenzene, hydrolysis, and spectrophotometric differentiation and assay of the dinitrophenylethanolamine (DNP-E) and dinitrophenyl serine (DNP-S). The latter is made possible through the use of tetramethyl ammonium hydroxide (TMAH), which has a significant influence on the ionization and hence molecular extinction coefficient at 500 mμ. At the concentration of TMAH employed, DNP-E is completely ionized while DNP-S is only 10% ionized. Thus maximum differentiation is realized at 500 mμ and total concentration can be obtained at 300 mμ where the two compounds have the same molecular extinction coefficient.

Qualitative Identification of Serine and Ethanolamine

The absolute identification of ethanolamine and serine (and other similar nitrogenous compounds) can be most adequately obtained by a combination of the following procedures: separation on resins as described above, paper electrophoresis, and derivative formation. In the paper electrophoresis technique, chromatographic separation can be effected on Whatman No. 3 paper in a pyridine-acetic acid buffer, pH 6.5. A clean, sharp separation can be obtained in 30 minutes under an applied potential of 1000 volts. Under these conditions ethanolamine migrates towards the cathode, while serine remains very near the origin. O-phosphoethanolamine, which is found as a product of the hydrolytic cleavage of phosphatidyl ethanolamine, will migrate towards the anode. These spots can be eluted and further identified by the procedures described below. As outlined in the above section on the quantitative assay, serine and ethanolamine can be separated in large amounts by exchange resin chromatography and subjected to further purification by paper electrophoresis and derivative preparation.

Ethanolamine can be most conveniently identified as its dinitrophenyl derivative, which can be prepared by reaction with dinitrofluorobenzene in alkaline solution; DNP-ethanolamine melts sharply at 90° and its purity may be checked by elemental analyses, R_F value, and infrared spectra. Other suitable derivatives are the picrolonate, flavianate, and the hydrochloride.

Serine can be separated as its p-hydroxyazobenzenesulfonate which can then be decomposed with barium or lead ions. The L-serine can be recovered by crystallization. It melts at 227–228° and gives an optical rotation value $[\alpha]_D^{25}$ of 14.2° (in $1N$ HCl).[123] Another suitable derivative is the DNP-serine preparation, prepared in a manner analogous to that for ethanolamine. It can be isolated in the crystalline state and melts at 199°.

PHOSPHATIDYL SERINE

Within recent years suggestive evidence has appeared for the occurrence of other amino acids in phospholipides. However, serine, present as phosphatidyl serine, is still the only well-authenticated example of such a combination. Recently Westley et al.[137] have presented evidence for the existence of amino acids other than ethanolamine in phospholipides from several different sources. While this report was of a provocative nature, further corroborative evidence for the occurrence of these compounds in well-defined phospholipide fractions is necessary.

It is interesting to note that a serine phosphoglyceride was first isolated from a natural source in 1948.[53] Within the following ten-year period, the synthesis of known enantiomeric forms of phosphatidyl serine was achieved and a comparison with the naturally occurring material was possible. Consequently, as with the previously discussed phosphoglycerides, this compound should yield 2 moles of fatty acids, 1 mole of L-α-glycerophosphoric acid, and 1 mole of L-serine. Thus, it can be classified as an L-α-(diacyl)-glycerylphosphoryl-L-serine.

Preparation and Properties

Direct Synthesis. The only reported synthesis of a serine containing phosphoglyceride is that of Baer and Maurukas,[18] who prepared L-α-(distearoyl)-glycerylphosphoryl-L-serine. This procedure can be illustrated as follows:

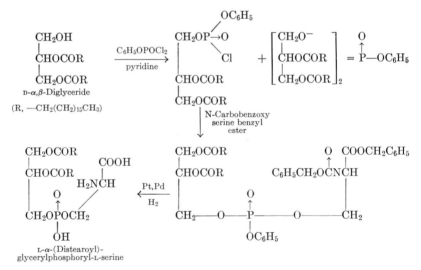

The final product was obtained in yields of 22.9%, based on starting diglyceride. It had an $[\alpha]_D^{40}$ −5.2°; ($[\alpha]_D^{20}$ −16.2°) and melted, with decomposition, at 159–161°.

Natural Sources. In studies on the phospholipides of brain, Folch [53] by means of solvent fractionation was able to isolate phosphatidyl serine of approximately 92% purity. On the basis of the non-reactivity of the compound with periodate and the presence of a free amino group (by ninhydrin and nitrous acid reaction), Folch concluded that the serine was linked through its —OH group. Upon hydrolysis glycerophosphoric acid, L-serine, and fatty acids (mainly stearic and oleic) were obtained in ratios of 1:1:2. Thus these data supported a diacyl glycerylphosphorylserine structure. As isolated, the phosphatidyl serine was obtained as a salt (one equivalent of base per atom of P), mainly potassium and sodium. Potassium represented at least 75% of the total salt present. It is interesting to note that phosphatidyl serine is always found as a salt, either the Na, K, Ca, or Mg, in natural sources. It is provocative to consider, as is proposed for red blood cells, that this compound is involved in cation metabolism. However, considerable more proof must be obtained before this is accepted.

While no optical rotation data were supplied by Folch, later Baer and Maurukas [18] hydrogenated phosphatidyl serine (prepared from brain) and compared it with their synthetic product. The optical rotation values for both compounds were similar and established the L-α-configuration of the natural compound.* No evidence has been forthcoming as to the possible asymmetric arrangement of the fatty acids on this phosphoglyceride. The small amounts of this material normally found in tissues have retarded efforts to study it in more detail.

The quantitative assay systems for serine are described in the previous section (on phosphatidyl ethanolamine) and, in addition, the usual derivatives for this amino acid.

Notes on Stability of Phosphatidyl Serine

In an attempt to prepare the methyl ester of L-α-(distearoyl)-glycerylphosphoryl serine, by the action of diazomethane, Baer and Maurukas [18] observed that this reagent caused the cleavage of the serine to phosphate ester bond and led to the formation in good yields of

---

*It is now indicated [G. V. Marinetti, J. Erbland, and E. Stotz, *Biochim. Biophy. Acta.*, **30**, 41 (1958)] that the phosphatidyl serine of brain may exist as two ionic species, one of which is the free acid and the other of which is a sodium salt. A separation of these two components was effected by silicic acid chromatography.

the dimethyl ester of L-α-(distearoyl)-glycerophosphoric acid (phosphatidic acid). It is interesting to note that this reaction, termed diazometholysis by these authors, proceeded without any structural or configurational changes in the phosphatidic acid portion of the molecule. This reaction also occurred with phosphatidyl ethanolamine and presented a unique and absolute route to the elucidation of the structure and configuration of naturally occurring phosphatidyl ethanolamines and serines. No action was noted with the phosphatidyl cholines (lecithins). When this reaction was carried out on the phosphatidyl serine of ox brain, the L-configuration and α-structure were confirmed and agreed with the previous proof obtained through comparison of the optical rotation values of the hydrogenated (natural) and synthetic products.

According to Brown and Osborne,[24] the above diazometholysis reaction is the result of the formation of an intermediate phosphotriester. (This can form due to the probable repressed formation of zwitterions in a non-polar solvent such as chloroform-ether.) Subsequently, by attack of the vicinal amino group on carbon (not phosphorus) with a resultant alkyl-oxygen fission, this triester decomposes with the formation of a monomethyl ester. Finally, this derivative is further methylated to yield the diester. This is illustrated in part by the following equations:

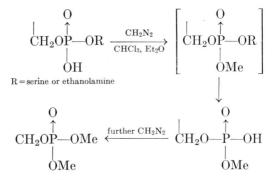

Under similar conditions, phosphatidyl choline, which contains a quarternary nitrogen, would not be expected to undergo such a reaction.

PLASMALOGENS

It is well established now that the plasmalogens may be considered as phosphoglycerides, which contain a fatty acid residue, an aldehydogenic unit (a vinyl ether), and glycerylphosphorylethanolamine or choline. These compounds are found widely distributed in animal tissues, with particularly high concentrations in the myelin of brain and nerve,[2, 139] in heart and skeletal muscle,[139] in semen,[92] and they also have been found in green peas.[134]

Only within the recent past the classical concept of the "acetal" phosphoglyceride (formula A below; see also reference 19) as the naturally occurring plasmalogen has been challenged. Rapport and Franzl [110] have presented conclusive evidence that the "acetal" phosphoglyceride was in reality a mono vinyl ether derivative, which is best represented by formula B. Furthermore, this latter compound is formed during the course of certain isolation procedures, which involve alkaline treatment of a tissue, and hence must be considered as a derivative of the native plasmalogens.

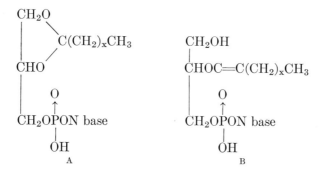

Chemical Structure

Phase I (Classical "Acetal" Structure). Historically the presence of plasmalogens in tissues was first noted by Feulgen and Rossenbeck [45] in 1924. These investigators subjected various tissues to mild acid hydrolysis and observed that fuchsin-sulfurous acid (Schiff reagent) stained both the nuclear (designated nucleal) and the cytoplasmic (designated plasmal) portions of the cells. The former reaction was believed due to sugar aldehydes and the latter reaction to the presence of other aldehydes. Further study of the plasmal constituent showed it to be soluble in "lipide" solvents and to be sensitive to acid and mercuric salts.[46] Subsequently, Feulgen et al.[44] isolated a mixture of thiosemicarbazones from the muscle "acetal" phospholipides and interpreted it as proof for the presence of long-chain aldehydes. However, no analytical or other data were offered in support of this proposal.

After a vigorous alkaline hydrolysis of muscle phospholipides, Feulgen and Bersin [43] isolated a crystalline compound containing fatty aldehyde, glycerol, phosphorus, and ethanolamine. Later Klenk et al.[82] were able to isolate long-chain (C_{16} and C_{18}) aldehydes from brain phospholipides in the (derivative) form of dimethyl acetals. At the same time they presented evidence for the similarity of these compounds to the diacyl phosphoglycerides. In studies on the "aldehyde" containing lipides of brain, Thannhauser et al.[128] were able to isolate, after saponification of the lipide mixture for five days at 37° (primarily intended for removal of acyl groups), a crystalline "acetal" phospholipide ($[\alpha]_D^{25} + 6.25°$). Upon analysis, this preparation agreed in theory with formula A above. When the crystalline preparation was subjected to hydrolysis with $HgCl_2$ or acetic acid, the phosphorus could be isolated as L-α-glycerylphosphorylethanolamine ($[\alpha]_D^{25}$ $-3.2°$). Apparently, no rearrangement of the phosphate had occurred. In addition, they found that the only aldehydes were C_{16} and C_{18} saturated types, with no unsaturated components present.

In a later study, it was recognized by Schmidt et al.[118] that the alkali treatment used in the isolation of these above compounds seriously altered the structure of this type of compound. Essentially they found that the isolated material did not correspond to native plasmalogen in the crude extracts. The former material upon treatment with mercuric salts had all of its phosphorus converted to a trichloracetic acid soluble form, whereas in the latter fractions the formation of acid soluble phosphorus required a pretreatment with alkali. On the basis of these results they suggested that native plasmalogens contained an alkali labile residue.*

Phase II (Present Concept). In the recent studies on these most interesting compounds, there is general agreement that fatty acids are present and that the over-all composition of the plasmalogens corresponds to glycerylphosphoryl derivatives of ethanolamine or choline which contain, in addition, a long-chain fatty acyl group and an aldehydogenic residue (a long-chain vinyl ether). However, the nature

---

* However, while the acetal type compound is indicated as not existing in mammalian tissues, W. Bergmann and R. A. Landowne [*J. Org. Chem.*, **23**, 1241 (1959)] have reported the isolation of an acetal phospholipide (containing no fatty acid) from the sea anemone, *Anthropleura elegantissima*. This lipide component was isolated through use of neutral solvents at room temperature. Interestingly, the only other lipide present was a sphingomyelin which was found in an amount twenty times that of the acetal compound.

of this latter group and its position of attachment to the glyceryl residue has only recently been clarified. While some argument has reigned in this area, it is interesting to note that in all cases no pure specimen of naturally occurring plasmalogens has been obtained, i.e., none free of the diacyl phosphoglyceride type compounds. Although it is most unlikely that these latter substances will alter very seriously the picture already developed on structure, it is worthwhile to consider that in certain instances these contaminants might cause some "unusual" observations. The developments in this field of endeavor are outlined below.

Presence of acyl radicals. A sufficient amount of evidence has now been assembled in support of the occurrence of fatty acids in the plasmalogens. When a plasmalogen-rich fraction from human brain was hydrogenated, and then submitted to acid hydrolysis, Klenk and Debuch [80] found that over 60% of the phosphorus was insoluble and on isolation this material appeared to be a mixture of chimyl and batyl alcohol phosphates. Accordingly, these investigators suggested this as a possible indication of a compound with a fatty aldehyde in the α' position and a fatty acid in the β position. Evidence was presented for the occurrence of choline and ethanolamine in the native plasmalogens. At nearly the same time, Rapport and associates reported a silicic acid chromatographic procedure which could be used in the preparation of plasmalogen-rich fractions from bovine muscle. Thus, alkaline hydrolysis was avoided. In addition, they also found two major types of plasmalogens, one an ethanolamine and the other a choline derivative. Further analysis showed that a long-chain fatty acid ester and a fatty "aldehyde" were present.

Later, Rapport and Franzl [111] studied the rates of hydrolysis of phosphatidyl cholines and plasmalogen-rich fractions with snake venom phospholipase A (lecithinase A). A similar rate of hydrolysis was obtained for each compound and a 90 to 96% complete reaction was indicated. In this study the aldehydogenic group appeared in the insoluble "lysol" fraction. Within 7 hours only 15% of the original aldehyde was ether soluble, and 89% was ether insoluble. Thus the conclusion was reached that the fatty acid ester was on the α' position and the aldehydogenic group was on the β position. A high degree of unsaturation was found in the enzymatically liberated fatty acids. An average of two double bonds per mole was noted and on this basis it was felt that a positional asymmetry of fatty acids on the plasmalogens occurred comparable to that found in the lecithins of liver.[59] In this approach these authors assumed that the venom enzyme attacked the plasmalogen at the same α' ester position as found for the lecithins.[60] However, this reasoning *per se* does not necessarily follow when one considers the heterogeneity of the snake venom preparations and the possible presence of a specific plasmalogen attacking enzyme. Moreover, this latter enzyme might not attack the plasmalogens at the same bond as the corresponding enzyme for the lecithins. Nonetheless, other observations (see below) tend to support their findings.

Debuch [34] also has presented evidence for the presence of fatty acid and aldehydogenic groups in the plasmalogens of brain. She obtained analytically pure lysophosphatidyl ethanolamine from brain phospholipides by treatment with 95% acetic acid at 37°, followed by a countercurrent distribution. This preparation contained 70% of the phosphorus of the fraction and contained only mixed, unsaturated fatty acids. According to Rapport and Franzl, Debuch's results would support their conclusion that the fatty acids are located on the α' ester position and that a positional asymmetry of the fatty acid exists with these compounds. Recently Gray [58] also presented evidence that ox heart plasmalogens contained fatty acid residues and that these acyl groups were present only on the α' ester position (see below).

Chemical nature and position of attachment of the aldehydogenic group. It is well agreed among all workers in this field that catalytic hydrogenation of the native plasmalogens leads to the complete disappearance of any "aldehyde" reaction and concomitant formation of a glyceryl ether. Klenk and Debuch [80] originally proposed the following three possible structures for plasmalogens:

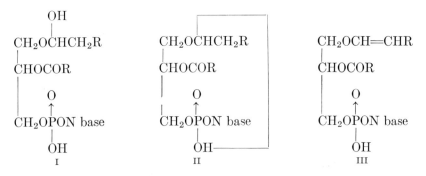

As is evident, formula I is essentially a hemiacetal, with formula II being its "anhydride" form, and formula III is an α,β unsaturated ether (arising, according to these authors, by reaction of the enol form of an aldehyde with the glycerol hydroxyl). Subsequent investigation in several laboratories has indicated the following two structures as most likely:

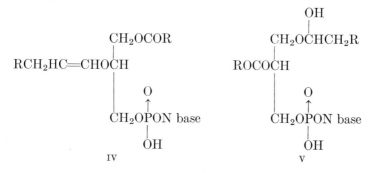

Thus, as is obvious, formulas IV and V differ as to the positioning of the acyl and aldehydogenic groups and also in the exact nature of the aldehydogenic unit.

The evidence for support of a vinyl ether structure (IV) has largely stemmed from the experiments of Rapport et al.[112] According to these investigators, the aldehydogenic group must be located in the secondary hydroxyl group for two reasons: (a) liberation of fatty acid by snake venom action (presumably phospholipase A) would indicate an α' position for the ester group; (b) isolation of L-α-glycerylphosphorylethanolamine from lyso plasmalogen by alkaline and acid hydrolysis. If the latter treatment, designed to release fatty acid groups, were to liberate the secondary hydroxyl function, reversible α to β phosphate migration would surely occur, but it did not. In support of Rapport's proposal, Gray [57] investigated the structure of the lysolecithin derived from intact plasmalogen of ox heart by action of 90% acetic acid at 37° for 17 hours.* After purification of this compound via silicic acid chomatography, the lysolecithin (a monoacyl derivative) was hydrogenated and oxidized with $KMnO_4$ as follows:

* A more detailed treatment of these structure proof studies on the ethanolamine and choline plasmalogens of ox heart is given in a recent article [G. M. Gray, *Biochem. J.*, **70**, 425 (1958)]. Again, it was observed that all the fatty acids present in the plasmalogens (in the C-1 or α' position; vinyl ether considered in the C-2 or β position) were unsaturated. In an accompanying paper [G. M. Gray, and M. G. MacFarlane, *Biochem. J.*, **70**, 409 (1958)], some aspects of the chromatographic separation of the plasmalogens and other phospholipides of ox heart are considered.

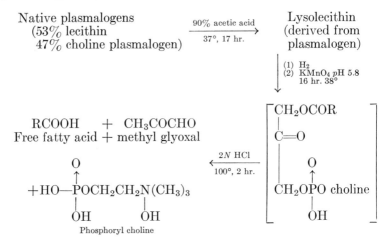

Thus, the oxidation and hydrolysis yielded free fatty acids, methyl glyoxal, and phosphorylcholine. Whereas β monoglycerides are known to be isomerized by passage through silicic acid,[21] Gray noted no similar reaction with the lysolecithin derived from plasmalogen. In a study of the enzyme and non-enzyme catalyzed migration of the β-acyl group to the α' position of lysolecithin, Uziel and Hanahan [131] observed that a procedure similar to that described here yielded fatty acids, methyl glyoxal, free phosphate, and free choline, but no phosphorylcholine. This discrepancy has not been resolved.

Recently, Debuch [35, 36] discussed the possibility that the plasmalogen "aldehyde" unit could be visualized as the enol form of an aldehyde, thus producing an enol ether (vinyl ether) type structure. Consequently, the double bond between the α and β carbons of the chain would be susceptible to attack by ozone. After ozonolysis, hydrolysis and further oxidation of the enol ether of a hexadecanal, for example, would yield n-pentadecanoic acid and that of octadecanal would yield n-heptadecanoic acid. The ester linkage would not be affected by this treatment. Inasmuch as all the double bonds of the unsaturated ether and any unsaturated acids would be oxidized, mono and dicarboxylic acids would be formed. In the latter case, only acids of carbon 9 or less would be formed, while with the long-chain saturated "aldehyde" derivatives only long-chain fatty acids with an odd number of carbon atoms would result. Through solvent separation procedures, the long-chain fatty acids were isolated and subjected to column and paper chromatography. Two main fractions, corresponding to C_{15} and

C_{17} acids, were obtained. Thus, Debuch presented strong chemical evidence that the "aldehyde" of plasmalogens is present in an enol form, in effect giving an enol (or vinyl) ether. The exact location of this grouping on the molecule was not indicated.

While there remains the possibility of existence of two forms of plasmalogens (see below), the accumulated evidence tends to support a structure best represented by formula IV (see above).

Occurrence of two forms of plasmalogens. Throughout the course of the more recent investigations on the structure of the plasmalogens, there has been indications of the possible occurrence of vinyl ether derivatives at the α and β positions. In all cases where the plasmalogens have been hydrogenated and the glyceryl ethers isolated and identified, both the α and β forms (though not in equal proportions) have been found.

When the plasmalogens were hydrogenated and subjected to acid hydrolysis for 48 hours, Rapport [109] was able to isolate a glyceryl ether. The use of lead tetra acetate and periodate oxidation showed 70% β form and 30% α form and presented the possibility of two types of plasmalogens. However, this does not rule out the possibility that under these conditions migration of some of the β form to the α form could have occurred. Evidence supporting the presence of both forms in nature has been outlined by Marinetti et al.[97] Using the general technique of reduction of the plasmalogens by hydrogenation and subsequent isolation of the glyceryl ethers (after extensive acid hydrolysis) by silicic acid chomatography, both the α and β types of glycerol ethers were obtained. However, the ratio of these types was dependent on the source of material, with pig heart phospholipides containing 75% α and 25% β form and beef heart phospholipides containing 87% β and 13% α forms. Whether these latter data reflect a species difference remains to be clarified.

Assay for long-chain aldehydes and vinyl ethers. Until recently, the most effective means for the quantitative assay of long-chain fatty aldehydes in plasmalogens was by the Schiff fuchsin-sulfurous acid reagent [2,92] and dimethylacetal formation.[81] In part, this assay could be made on the free "aldehydes" as such, or more exactly after isolation as the dimethylacetals. However, the Schiff reagent reacts with a variety of compounds other than aldehydes and the presence of excess lipide in the sample interferes with the color development. A discussion of certain aspects of this problem is considered by Lovern et al.[92] and Wittenberg et al.[139]

Perhaps one of the more reliable methods for the examination of aldehydes is that described by Wittenberg et al.[139] This involves the reaction of *p*-nitrophenylhydrazine with tissue lipides to form the corresponding hydrazones. Through the use of non-polar extractants, only higher fatty aldehydes, C_{14} or higher, can be measured; apparently it is specific for these long-chain aldehydes. The range of the procedure is 0.1 to 7 μmoles and is reproducible to $\pm 5\%$. A distinct advantage of this method is the possibility of subsequent isolation of the hydrazones by aluminum oxide chromatography. Thus such a procedure can be of considerable aid in metabolic studies, especially where these might involve the use of radioactive materials.

In an extension of the observations of Siggia and Edsberg [121] on the determination of vinyl alkyl ethers by methanolic iodine, Rapport and Franzl [110] noted that this reagent was specific and quantitative for α,β unsaturated ethers in the presence of ordinary olefinic unsaturation. The evidence presented on the reactivity of the choline and ethanolamine plasmalogens with methanolic iodine strongly supports the vinyl ether structure (formula IV). No evidence of methanolic iodine attack on glyceryl acetals of higher fatty aldehydes or with the more rapidly hydrolyzable dimethyl acetals was obtained.

Summation of views on structure and properties of plasmalogens. On the basis of information to date, it is amply clear that a vinyl ether (or an enol ether) type linkage best represents the kind of unit present as the "aldehydogenic" group of ethanolamine and choline plasmalogens of mammalian tissues. Further study of model compounds would aid in resolving certain of the problems of a final decision on the most adequate formulation. Depending on the source of these lipides, this grouping may be found on the α' or β position and the acyl group on the other position. Finally, concomitant with the question of the position of the acyl and aldehydogenic residues is that of the stereochemical configuration of this compound. Primarily on the basis of the optical activity of the intact material and its derivatives, an L-α-configuration is favored. No synthetic route to these compounds has been reported.

A related compound: a saturated glycerol ether phospholipide. Recently, in a very interesting study, Carter and co-workers [29] isolated a new ethanolamine containing phospholipide from egg yolk. Subsequent examination revealed it to be the O-phosphorylethanolamine derivative of batyl alcohol:

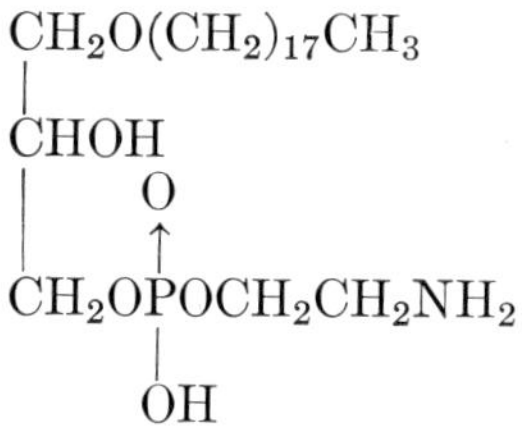

$$CH_2O(CH_2)_{17}CH_3$$
$$|$$
$$CHOH$$
$$| \quad O$$
$$| \quad \uparrow$$
$$CH_2OPOCH_2CH_2NH_2$$
$$|$$
$$OH$$

In the isolation procedure employed, alkaline hydrolysis ($1N$ KOH at 37° for 1 hour) of the phospholipides of chicken egg yielded an "alkali stable," ninhydrin positive fraction. Usually this has indicated the presence of a sphingosine derivative and hence was suggestive of a sphingoethanolamine type compound. However, through solvent fraction and column separation, a phospholipide devoid of long-chain base (sphingosine) was obtained. Through examination of the infrared spectra of this compound, an ether type linkage was indicated. When the phospholipide was subjected to acetolysis by reflux with acetic anhydride and acetic acid, ethanolamine (plus O-phosphoethanolamine), free phosphorus, and a waxy alcohol were obtained. When the proton magnetic resonance spectrum of this waxy alcohol was compared with certain known compounds, there was little doubt that the compound was α-octadecyl glycerol ether (batyl alcohol). Additional proof of structure was offered by the results of periodate oxidation of this substance.

As pointed out by Carter et al., the hydrolytic procedure used for isolation of the ether may well have caused removal of an ester group. Hence, this may be analogous to the observations on the hydrolytic cleavage of the ester group of plasmalogens by an alkaline treatment. It will prove of considerable interest to learn the stereochemical configuration of this ether and the possible presence of an ester group in the "native" compound. Karnovsky[76] has suggested that a phospholipide analogous in structure to the glyceryl ethers exists in the lipides of marine animals.

REFERENCES

1. Ahrens, E. H., Jr., and L. C. Craig, *J. Biol. Chem.*, **195**, 299 (1952).
2. Anchel, M., and H. Waelsch, *J. Biol. Chem.*, **152**, 501 (1944).
3. Appleton, H. D., B. N. LaDu, B. B. Levy, J. M. Steele, and B. Brodie, *J. Biol. Chem.*, **205**, 603 (1953).

4. Artom, C., *J. Biol. Chem.*, **157**, 585 (1945).
5. Axelrod, J., J. Reichenthal, and B. R. Brodie, *J. Biol. Chem.*, **204**, 103 (1953).
6. Bailly, O., *Compt. rend.*, **206**, 1902 (1938); **208**, 443, 1820 (1939).
7. Bailly, O., and J. Gaume, *Bull. soc. chim.*, **2**, 254 (1935); **3**, 1396 (1936).
8. Baer, E., *J. Biol. Chem.*, **189**, 235 (1951).
9. Baer, E., *Can. J. Biochem. and Physiol.*, **34**, 304 (1952).
10. Baer, E., *Ann. Rev. Biochem.*, **24**, 135 (1955).
11. Baer, E., *Can. J. Biochem. and Physiol.*, **34**, 288 (1956).
12. Baer, E., D. Buchnea, and A. G. Newcombe, *J. Am. Chem. Soc.*, **78**, 232 (1956).
13. Baer, E., and H. O. L. Fischer, *J. Biol. Chem.*, **128**, 463, 491 (1939).
14. Baer, E., and M. Kates, *J. Biol. Chem.*, **175**, 79 (1948).
15. Baer, E., and M. Kates, *J. Biol. Chem.*, **185**, 615 (1950).
16. Baer, E., and M. Kates, *J. Am. Chem. Soc.*, **72**, 942 (1950).
17. Baer, E., and J. Maurukas, *J. Am. Chem. Soc.*, **74**, 158 (1952).
18. Baer, E., and J. Maurukas, *J. Biol. Chem.*, **212**, 25, 39 (1955).
19. Baer, E., and H. C. Stancer, *J. Am. Chem. Soc.*, **75**, 4510 (1953).
20. Bender, M., *J. Am. Chem. Soc.*, **73**, 1626 (1951).
21. Borgstrom, B., *Acta Chem. Scand.*, **11**, 749 (1957).
22. Brown, D. M., D. I. Magrath, A. H. Neilson, and A. R. Todd, *Nature*, **177**, 1124 (1956).
23. Brown, D. M., D. I. Magrath, and A. R. Todd, *J. Chem. Soc.*, **1952**, 2708.
24. Brown, D. M., and G. O. Osborne, *J. Chem. Soc.*, **1957**, 2590.
25. Brown, D. M., and A. R. Todd, *J. Chem. Soc.*, **1952**, 52.
26. Brown, J. B., and D. K. Kolb, *Prog. in Chem. Fats Lipids*, **3**, 57 (1955).
27. Burmaster, C. F., *J. Biol. Chem.*, **165**, 577 (1946).
28. Campbell, I. G., J. N. Olley, and M. Blewett, *Biochem. J.*, **45**, 105 (1949).
29. Carter, H. E., D. B. Smith, and D. N. Jones, *J. Biol. Chem.*, **232**, 681 (1958).
30. Chargaff, E., *J. Biol. Chem.*, **144**, 455 (1942).
31. Crombie, W. M., R. Comber, and S. G. Boatman, *Biochem. J.*, **59**, 309 (1955).
32. Cropper, F. R., and A. Heywood, *Nature*, **174**, 1063 (1954).
33. Dawson, R. M. C., *Biochem. J.*, **62**, 689 (1956).
34. Debuch, H., *Z. physiol. Chem.*, **304**, 109 (1956).
35. Debuch, H., *Biochem. J.*, **67**, 27P (1957).
36. Debuch, H., *J. Neurochem.*, **2**, 243 (1958).
37. Devor, A. W., *Science*, **120**, 434 (1954).
38. Dils, R. M., and J. N. Hawthorne, *Biochem. J.*, **64**, 49P (1956).
39. Dittmer, J. C., Thesis, University of Washington (1958).
40. Dittmer, J. C., J. L. Feminella, and D. J. Hanahan, *J. Biol. Chem.*, **233**, 862 (1958).
41. Edman, P. V., and S. E. G. Aquist, *Acta Physiol. Scand.*, **10**, 144 (1945).
42. Engel, R. W., W. D. Salmon, and C. J. Ackerman, *Methods of Biochem. Anal.*, **1**, 265 (1954).
43. Feulgen, R., and T. Bersin, *Z. physiol. Chem.*, **260**, 217 (1939).
44. Feulgen, R., K. Imhauser, and M. Behrens, *Z. physiol. Chem.*, **180**, 161 (1929).
45. Feulgen, R., and H. Rossenbeck, *Z. physiol. Chem.*, **135**, 230 (1924).
46. Feulgen, R., and K. Voit, *Arch. ges. Physiol.*, **206**, 389 (1924).
47. Fleury, P., *Bull. soc. chim. biol.*, **30**, 519 (1948).
48. Fleury, P., *Bull. soc. chim. biol.*, **30**, 52 (1948).
49. Fleury, P., and L. LeDizet, *Bull. soc. chim. biol.*, **32**, 495 (1950).

50. Fleury, P., and L. LeDizet, *Bull. soc. chim. biol.*, **36**, 971 (1954); **35**, 883 (1953).
51. Folch, J., *J. Biol. Chem.*, **146**, 31 (1942).
52. Folch, J., *J. Biol. Chem.*, **146**, 35 (1942).
53. Folch, J., *J. Biol. Chem.*, **174**, 439 (1948).
54. Fono, C., *Arkiv Kemi, Minerali. Geol.*, **24A**, No. 33, 14 (1947).
55. Freeman, N. K., F. T. Lindgren, Y. C. Ng, and A. V. Nichols, *J. Biol. Chem.*, **227**, 449 (1957).
56. Garvin, J. E., and M. L. Karnovsky, *J. Biol. Chem.*, **221**, 211 (1956).
57. Gray, G., *Biochem. J.*, **67**, 26P (1957).
58. Hammond, E. G., and W. O. Lundberg, *J. Am. Oil Chem. Soc.*, **30**, 438 (1953).
59. Hanahan, D. J., *J. Biol. Chem.*, **211**, 313 (1954).
60. Hanahan, D. J., *J. Biol. Chem.*, **207**, 879 (1954).
61. Hanahan, D. J., and R. Blomstrand, *J. Biol. Chem.*, **222**, 677 (1956).
62. Hanahan, D. J., J. C. Dittmer, and E. Warashina, *J. Biol. Chem.*, **228**, 685 (1957).
63. Hanahan, D. J., and M. E. Jayko, *J. Am. Chem. Soc.*, **74**, 5070 (1952).
64. Herb, S. F., and R. W. Riemenschneider, *J. Am. Oil Chem. Soc.*, **29**, 456 (1952).
65. Herb, S. F., L. P. Witnauer, and R. W. Riemenschneider, *J. Am. Oil Chem. Soc.*, **28**, 505 (1951).
66. Hofmann, K., R. A. Lucas, and S. M. Sax, *J. Biol. Chem.*, **195**, 473 (1952).
67. Holman, R. T., *Prog. in Chem. Fats Lipids*, **2**, 51 (1954).
68. Holman, R. T., *Methods of Biochem. Anal.*, **4**, 99 (1957).
69. Holman, R. T., and P. R. Edmondson, *Anal. Chem.*, **28**, 1533 (1956).
70. Howard, G. A., and A. J. P. Martin, *Biochem. J.*, **46**, 532 (1950).
71. Howton, D. R., *Science*, **119**, 420 (1954).
72. Inouye, Y., and M. Noda, *Arch. Biochem. Biophys.*, **76**, 245 (1958).
73. Inouye, Y., M. Noda, and C. Hirayama, *J. Am. Oil Chem. Soc.*, **32**, 132 (1955).
74. James, A. T., and A. J. P. Martin, *Brit. Med. Bull.*, **10**, 170 (1954).
75. James, A. T., and A. J. P. Martin, *Biochem. J.*, **63**, 144 (1956).
76. Karnovsky, M., *Biol. Bull.*, **101**, 23B (1951).
77. Kates, M., *Can. J. Biochem. and Physiol.*, **35**, 127 (1957).
78. Kaufman, H. P., and W. H. Nitsch, *Fette Seifen Anstrichmittel*, **57**, 473 (1955).
79. Kennedy, E. P., *J. Biol. Chem.*, **201**, 399 (1953).
80. Klenk, E., and H. Debuch, *Z. physiol. Chem.*, **299**, 661 (1955).
81. Klenk, E., and E. Friedrich, *Z. physiol. Chem.*, **290**, 169 (1952).
82. Klenk, E., W. Stoffel, and H. J. Eggers, *Z. physiol. Chem.*, **290**, 246 (1952).
83. Kumler, W. D., and J. J. Eiler, *J. Am. Chem. Soc.*, **65**, 2355 (1943).
84. Lea, C. H., in *Biochemical Problems of Lipids*, edited by Popjak and Le-Breton, p. 81, Interscience (1956).
85. Lea, C. H., D. N. Rhodes, and R. D. Stoll, *Biochem. J.*, **60**, 353 (1955).
86. Lederer, E., and M. Lederer, *Chromatography*, Elsevier (1957).
87. Levine, C., and E. Chargaff, *J. Biol. Chem.*, **192**, 465 (1951).
88. Lipsky, S. R., and R. A. Landowne, *Biochim. et Biophys. Acta*, **27**, 666 (1958).
89. Long, C., and M. F. Maguire, *Biochem. J.*, **54**, 612 (1953).
90. Long, C., and I. F. Penney, *Biochem. J.*, **65**, 382 (1957).
91. Lovern, J. A., *Biochem. J.*, **51**, 464 (1952).
92. Lovern, J. A., J. N. Olley, E. F. Hartree, and T. Mann, *Biochem. J.*, **67**, 630 (1957).

93. MacGee, J., and F. H. Mattson, *Federation Proc.*, **16**, 391 (1957).
94. McKibbin, J. M., *Federation Proc.*, **16**, 835 (1957).
95. Malkin, T., and T. H. Bevan, *Prog. in Chem. Fats Lipids,* **4**, 97 (1957).
96. Mangold, H. K., B. G. Lamp, and H. Schlenk, *J. Am. Chem. Soc.,* **77**, 6070 (1955).
97. Marinetti, G. V., J. Erbland, and E. Stotz, *J. Am. Chem. Soc.,* **80**, 1624 (1958).
98. Mead, J. F., *J. Biol. Chem.,* **227**, 1025 (1957).
99. Mead, J. F., and D. R. Howton, *J. Biol. Chem.,* **229**, 575 (1957).
100. Meiklejohn, R. A., R. J. Meyer, S. M. Aronovic, H. A. Schuette, and V. W. Meloch, *Anal. Chem.,* **29**, 329 (1957).
101. Moore, S., and W. H. Stein, *J. Biol. Chem.,* **192**, 663 (1951).
102. Nojima, S., and N. Utsugi, *J. Biochem. (Japan),* **44**, 565 (1957).
103. Olley, J. N., in *Biochemical Problems of Lipids,* edited by Popjak and Le-Breton, p. 49, Interscience (1956).
104. Olley, J. N., *Biochem. J.,* **62**, 107 (1956).
105. Olley, J. N., and M. Blewett, *Biochem. J.,* **47**, 564 (1950).
106. Orr, C. H., and J. E. Callen, *J. Am. Chem. Soc.,* **80**, 249 (1958).
107. Pitt, G. A. J., and R. A. Morton, *Prog. in Chem. Fats Lipids,* **4**, 227 (1957).
108. Popjak, G., and A. Tietz, *Biochem. J.,* **56**, 46 (1954).
109. Rapport, M. M., in *Biochemical Problems of Lipids,* edited by Popjak and LeBreton, p. 102, Interscience (1956).
110. Rapport, M. M., and R. E. Franzl, *J. Neurochem.,* **1**, 303 (1957).
111. Rapport, M. M., and R. E. Franzl, *J. Biol. Chem.,* **225**, 851 (1957).
112. Rapport, M. M., B. Lerner, N. Alonzo, and R. E. Franzl, *J. Biol. Chem.,* **225**, 859 (1957).
113. Ray, N. H., *J. Appl. Chem.,* **4**, 21 (1954).
114. Rhodes, D. N., *Biochem. J.,* **68**, 380 (1958).
115. Rhodes, D. N., and C. H. Lea, in *Biochemical Problems of Lipids,* edited by Popjak and LeBreton, p. 73, Interscience (1956).
116. Rhodes, D. N., and C. H. Lea, *Biochem. J.,* **65**, 526 (1957).
117. Savary, P., and P. Desnuelle, *Bull. soc. chim.,* **20**, 939 (1953).
118. Schmidt, G., B. Ottenstein, and M. J. Bessman, *Federation Proc.,* **12**, 265 (1953).
119. Scholfield, C. R., and H. J. Dutton, *Biochem. Preparations,* **5**, 5 (1957).
120. Shorland, F. B., *Ann. Rev. Biochem.,* **25**, 101 (1956).
121. Siggia, S., and R. L. Edsberg, *Anal. Chem.,* **20**, 762 (1948).
122. Silk, M. H., and H. H. Hahn, *Biochem. J.,* **56**, 406 (1954).
123. Stein, W. H., and S. Moore, *Biochem. Preparations,* **1**, 9 (1949).
124. Stern, I., and B. Shapiro, *J. Clin. Path.,* **6**, 158 (1953).
125. Sulser, H., *Mitt. Geb. Lebensmittel. Hyg.,* **45**, 518 (1954).
126. Tattrie, N. H., and C. S. McArthur, *Can. J. Biochem. and Physiol.,* **33**, 761 (1955).
127. Tattrie, N. H., and C. S. McArthur, *Can. J. Biochem. and Physiol.,* **35**, 1165 (1957).
128. Thannhauser, S. J., J. Benotti, and N. F. Boncoddo, *J. Biol. Chem.,* **166**, 669 (1946).
129. Thannhauser, S. J., N. F. Boncoddo, and G. Schmidt, *J. Biol. Chem.,* **188**, 417, 423, 427 (1951).
130. Ukita, T., N. A. Bates, and H. E. Carter, *J. Biol. Chem.,* **216**, 867 (1955).

131. Uziel, M., and D. J. Hanahan, *J. Biol. Chem.,* **226,** 789 (1957).
132. VanHeyningen, R., and A. Pirie, *Biochem. J.,* **68,** 18 (1958).
133. Verkade, P. E., J. C. Stoppelenburg, and W. D. Cohen, *Rec. trav. chim. Pays-Bas,* **59,** 886 (1940).
134. Wagenknecht, A. C., *Science,* **126,** 1288 (1957).
135. Wallach, D. F. H., and J. E. Garvin, *J. Am. Chem. Soc.,* **80,** 2157 (1958).
136. Weinman, E. O., I. L. Chaikoff, C. Entenman, and W. G. Dauben, *J. Biol. Chem.,* **187,** 643 (1950).
137. Westley, J., J. J. Wren, and H. K. Mitchell, *J. Biol. Chem.,* **229,** 131 (1957).
138. Wheeler, D. H., *Prog. in Chem. Fats Lipids,* **2,** 268 (1954).
139. Wittenberg, J. B., S. R. Korey, and F. H. Swenson, *J. Biol. Chem.,* **219,** 39 (1956).

4

Phosphoinositides

The occurrence of carbohydrates as structural components of certain lipides of plants, animals, and bacteria is now a well-established fact. Indeed, one of the primary components of most lipides, glycerol, in its free form could be classified as a carbohydrate. Perhaps the best examples of carbohydrates as integral components of lipides are galactose in the sphingolipides (cerebrosides) and inositol in the phosphoinositides. At this point, attention will be focused on the chemistry of the phosphoinositides.

In 1930, Anderson[1] obtained the first evidence for the presence of this compound in naturally occurring lipides (tubercle bacillus). Further studies by Anderson and his colleagues led to the isolation of manninositose phosphate[2] and glycerol inositolphosphoric acid[14] from tubercle bacilli. Klenk and Sakai[28] reported inositol to be present as a phosphate in the phospholipides of soybean. Subsequently, Folch and Woolley[22] found inositol as a component of brain phospholipides. While the above reports were concerned mainly with hydrolysates of lipide fractions, it is now certain that inositol is an integral structural component of lipides. As has been stated before, progress in most areas of lipide chemistry has been hampered by inadequate methods of isolation and purification, and lack of information on the stability of these compounds in the preparative and structural procedures. Consequently, it is only recently that sufficient evidence has accumulated to support the assignment of definite structures to the inositol containing lipides.

SOME FACETS OF THE CHEMISTRY OF MYO-INOSITOL

Inositol is a hexahydroxycyclohexane (or a cyclitol), of which there are nine possible stereochemical forms, two of which are optical enantiomorphs. However, the major form present in lipides is the optically inactive *myo*-inositol (I). This is not surprising when one considers the specificity of nature in the synthesis and utilization of specific forms of compounds, i.e., the D-sugars and the L-amino acids. No completely uniform nomenclature and numbering system has been adopted for the inositols. In the main, the system described by Lardy [29] will be followed here.*

In assigning a stereochemical configuration to *myo*-inositol, the planar structure (I) does not completely represent the correct positioning of the hydroxyls in space and certainly does not indicate any possible differences in chemical reactivity of these substituents. On the basis of thermodynamical calculations [4] and by electron diffraction measurements,[25] the cyclohexanes have been assigned the chair form as their most stable conformation. While some question exists as to the exact extension of this reasoning to the inositols and their derivatives, it is considered that these compounds also would have a chair form (II) as their preferred conformation.† As illustrated in II, five

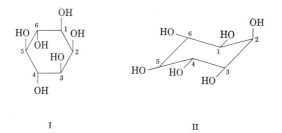

I   II

---

* A more extensive discussion of the chemistry of the inositols and related compounds is presented by R. L. Lohmar in *The Carbohydrates. Chemistry, Biochemistry, Physiology,* edited by W. Pigman, p. 241, Academic Press, New York (1957).

† Primarily for convenience and simplicity, the perspective formula, as shown in I, will be used most often here. The correct conformation of this molecule, as depicted in II, is best illustrated through the use of molecular models.

of the hydroxyls of *myo*-inositol (at 1, 3, 4, 5, 6) are considered as equatorial types (projecting out from a plane passing through the center of the molecule), while the hydroxyl at the 2 position is considered as an axial type (perpendicular to the plane). A twist of the model through a single plane to the opposite chair form changes the axial into an equatorial group and the equatorial groups to axial groups.

A most important aspect of the characterization of any complex organic compound is the absolute identification of its individual components. In the case of *myo*-inositol there are now several approaches to its qualitative and quantitative identification, and while perhaps not as rigorous as desired (especially as regards quantitative methods), they are adequate for most purposes. Thus, *myo*-inositol may be isolated and identified by direct crystallization, paper and column chromatography, and by biological and enzymatic assay.

Isolation and Identification

Before using any of the identification procedures cited here, it is necessary to liberate *myo*-inositol from the lipide by hydrolytic attack. The most reliable means for accomplishing this degradation is through refluxing of the phosphoinositide in 2 to 6N HCl for 48 hours or heating at 120° in a similar media in a sealed tube for 15 hours. At the end of this hydrolysis, the fatty acids are removed by ether extraction and the water soluble fraction is used for the procedures described below.

Crystallization. This water soluble fraction is evaporated to dryness for removal of most of the acid (a considerable amount of glycerol, but no inositol, is lost by this treatment). The residue is then dissolved in water and passed through sufficient Dowex 1, 50 to 100 mesh (—OH cycle) to remove glycerophosphate and any traces of inositol phosphate and mineral acid. The eluate, containing only inositol and glycerol in the case of the mammalian phosphoinositides, is concentrated to a small volume and alcohol is added until turbidity is produced. Crystallization of the inositol is induced by storage at 4° Upon recrystallization under the same conditions, pure *myo*-inositol, in yields of 60 to 80%, can be obtained (m.p. 225°). A slightly different approach to the isolation of *myo*-inositol was reported by Charalampous and Abrahams.[10] In their procedure, the water soluble fraction from an acid hydrolysis was evaporated to dryness, dissolved in water, and neutralized with KOH. This solution was deionized by passage first through a column of Dowex 1, $\times$8 (CH$_3$COO$^-$ form) and next a column of Amberlite IR-120 (H^+ form). The eluates were evaporated and the inositol isolated by alcohol crystallization as described above.

Chromatographic Procedures. Both paper and column chromatographic procedures have been outlined for the detection of *myo*-inositol.

Through chromatography on Whatman No. 1 paper in 80% *n*-propanol, inositol can be detected by reaction at room temperature with the $AgNO_3$—NaOH reagent of Trevalyan et al.[39] In this system, well-defined black spots on a white background are obtained; glycerol also gives a reaction with this system but it has a decidedly different R_F value. In the usual hydrolytic procedure employed for release of inositol, some inositol phosphate remains. This can be distinguished from free inositol by ascending chromatography in propanol-ethanol-water (50:30:20) and detection by the spray reagent of Trevalyan et al. In this case the color develops much more slowly and the reaction is much less sensitive for the phosphate ester. The R_F values of some of the most commonly occurring substances are: inositol monophosphate, 0.08; free inositol, 0.17; glucose, 0.44; and glycerol, 0.67.[24]

A column chromatographic method has been developed for the separation of inositol from a mixture of common sugars. When a mixture of sucrose, ribose, inositol, fructose, and glucose in $0.002M$ potassium tetraborate was absorbed on Dowex 1, $\times 8$ (borate form), elution with increasing concentrations of potassium tetraborate allowed a reasonable separation of these compounds in the above-mentioned sequence. This procedure has proved particularly useful in studies on the biosynthesis of C^{14} *myo*-inositol, where radioactive contamination is an important problem in the purification process.[10]

Quantitative Assay. The most effective and reproducible means for the quantitative assay of *myo*-inositol is by use of the well-known microbiological assay or a more recent enzymatic technique. While chemical methods have been proposed for determination of inositol, they are neither as sensitive nor as dependable as the methods cited below. Even on a qualitative basis, the well-known Scherer test for inositol does not represent as reproducible or sensitive a color test as desired.

Bio-assay. The use of a definite "biological" system for detection of a suspected growth substance is a time-honored practice in biochemistry. Some time ago it was recognized that *myo*-inositol exhibited growth promoting activity in certain yeasts and other microorganisms.

The bio-assay for *myo*-inositol takes advantage of the same principle involved in any microbiological determination, namely the cell count increase of an organism grown in a medium containing all of its nutritional requirements except the one under test. Subsequently, this latter component is added as unknown and the growth is recorded, for example, by a turbidimetric measurement. As in all these assays, it is necessary to run a complete standard curve with graded amounts of known substance added to the medium. In many of the organisms suggested for inositol assay, a base line growth (without added inositol) results and causes some error in estimation of small amounts of inositol. This can be avoided by using an organism, such as *Kloeckera apiculata*, which has an absolute requirement for *myo*-inositol and hence shows no base line growth. Consequently, any growth can be attributed to the presence of inositol. In addition, this organism apparently is not adversely affected by choline, as are some other test organisms. A typical growth curve obtained with this organism plus *myo*-inositol is shown in Fig. 4.1. The range of this method is 1 to 20 μg. It was found that inositol monophosphate does have some growth promoting ability and causes a response to the extent of 10% of theory. This is in agreement with the previous observations of Mc-Kibbin,[32] who found that an inositol monophosphate fraction obtained from horse and dog liver phosphoinositide caused a response of 30% in his microbiological assay system.

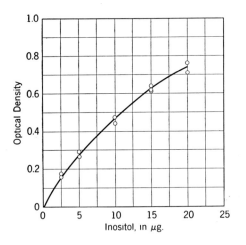

Fig. 4.1. Growth response curve of *Kloeckera apiculata* to added *myo*-inositol Incubated 20 hours at 28°C.

Woolley [43] reported the results of a study on the relative ability of various inositols and related compounds to induce growth in a yeast (*Saccharomyces cerevisiae*). With the exception of the monomethyl ether of *myo*-inositol, and *myo*-inositol, which gave 10% and 100% (reference) response respectively, all the other available forms of inositol were inactive in growth promotion. While not particularly related to the quantitative assay of inositol, it is pertinent to mention the observations of deRobichon-Szulmajster.[13] It was noted that certain strains of *Saccharomyces cerevisiae*, dependent on pyrimidine for their growth, also required *myo*-inositol for growth in the presence of uracil and orotic acid, but not in the presence of cytosine, uridine, and uridylic acids. In the system under study, *myo*-inositol could be replaced only by *scyllo*- and *epi-myo*-inosose. While many other compounds, including several sugars, sugar alcohols, and inositol derivatives were tested, none, except the three noted above, gave any response.

Enzymatic action. In part the evidence leading to the proposal of a non-planar form for *myo*-inositol was obtained from studies on the selective oxidative attack of this compound by resting cells of *Acetobacter suboxydans*. In a convincing manner, Magasanik and Chargaff [34] showed that this oxidation could yield monoketo and/or diketo derivatives. Later, cell-free systems capable of catalyzing this oxidation were obtained from this organism. The following reaction was found to occur with *myo*-inositol:

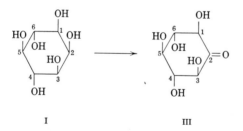

I   III

Thus *Acetobacter suboxydans* was able to specifically oxidize one of the hydroxyls (the 2-axial) on *myo*-inositol (I) to give *myo*-inosose-2 (III). Hence, the proposed conformation (II) of the inositol supplied a good basis for the explanation of enzymatic behavior. The various isomeric forms of the inositols reacted differently towards this organism, and this subject is ably discussed in a review by Magasanik.[34]

At the same time, Carter and his associates [7] reported that the fermentation of *myo*-inositol by *Acetobacter suboxydans* yielded *myo*-inosose-2 as the major product of oxidation. Although various strains of the organism were employed and the fermentation times varied, no other product was obtained in any significant quantity. While this inosose was found to yield an osazone on prolonged treatment with phenylhydrazine, the sodium salt of the oxime derivative was more convenient and stable for characterization purposes.

In the consideration of an enzymatic approach to the assay of inositol by an oxidation reaction as above, two organisms, *Acetobacter suboxydans* and *Aerobacter aerogenes*, are possible choices. Whereas the former organism causes formation of only *myo*-inosose-2 (III), the latter organism is capable of carrying the oxidation beyond this stage. Nevertheless, cell-free extracts from both organisms have been used in assay systems.

When the inositol dehydrogenase of *Acetobacter suboxydans* was prepared, Charalampous and Abrahams [10] were successful in developing a quantitative colorimetric assay for *myo*-inositol. The organism was grown first on an inositol medium and the cells ultimately harvested and ruptured by grinding with alumina. The cell-free extract, containing the dehydrogenase, was obtained by high-speed centrifugation. In the assay, the inositol dehydrogenase, coupled with pig heart diaphorase, reduced 2,6 dichloroindophenol under anaerobic conditions in the presence of *myo*-inositol. The disappearance of the blue color can be followed by colorimetric means. The range of the method is 0.03 to 0.14 μmole (5.4 μg. to 25.2 μg.) *myo*-inositol per ml. incubation mixture. Perhaps the major drawback to this technique is the requirement for anaerobic conditions, which Magasanik also noted in his studies on this subject with extracts of *Aerobacter aerogenes* (previously grown on *myo*-inositol). Larner et al. [30] attempted to adopt this DPN-linked dehydrogenase to the direct spectrophotometric assay for *myo*-inositol, but were not particularly successful. In a recent reinvestigation of this source of the inositol dehydrogenase, Weissbach [42] reported that this enzyme could be obtained in good yields from cells grown on *myo*-inositol as the sole source of carbon, by a technique similar to that described above. The reduction of DPN was followed directly by spectrophotometric measurement at 340 mμ. Under the conditions of the assay, maximum reduction of the DPN by *myo*-inositol was proportional to *myo*-inositol concentration. However, stoichiometric reduction of DPN was not observed and this was interpreted as due possibly to the presence of the DPNH oxidase which may influence the later phases of the reaction. The range of the method is 0.02 to 0.12 μmole (3.6 to 21.6 μg.) *myo*-inositol per ml. incubation mixture and the maximum optical density values are obtained within 3 to 4 minutes after the addition of enzyme. In subsequent periods of time a decrease in optical density occurred. A variety of the commonly encountered sugars and isomers of inositol gave no reaction. However, glycerol, a commonly encountered component, was not tested and it might be expected to react. The only inositol derivative capable of undergoing oxidation was sequoyitol. Colchicine was a potent inhibitor of the reaction. Cell-free extracts stored at −20° were stable for at least 4 months.

If this latter technique proves as sensitive and reproducible as reported by Weissbach, it undoubtedly will replace the time-consuming and less accurate microbiological assay techniques.

CHEMISTRY OF THE NATURALLY OCCURRING PHOSPHOINOSITIDES

Inasmuch as the exact structure of the naturally occurring inositol lipides has not been determined, it seems best for the present to continue the use of the trivial name, phosphoinositide, as the one most descriptive of these compounds. Primarily on the basis of the occurrence of either inositol monophosphate or diphosphate in the hydrolysates of phosphoinositides, the terms "monophosphoinositide" and "diphosphoinositide" have been used to describe certain of the simpler parent compounds. It is of interest to note that only one source, brain lipides, has yielded inositol diphosphate; in all other sources the monophosphate is found.

As has been repeatedly emphasized, the present status of our knowledge of the chemistry of these inositol lipides is rather limited and may be attributed in large degree to the difficulties associated with their isolation and purification. Actually it is only within the past ten years that phosphoinositides have been obtained in a sufficiently pure state for structure studies. Inasmuch as no synthetic route to these compounds has been devised and as no model compounds are available for comparison, studies on structure have been limited mainly to degradative procedures. Obvious difficulties, i.e., migration of phosphate and acyl groups, ensue and make it necessary that the proper precaution is exercised in the assignment of groupings to their exact positions in the molecule.

As interest and progress in this area have developed, it has become increasingly apparent that three different types of inositides can exist in nature and may be categorized as follows: 1. simple monophosphoinositides, 2. diphosphoinositides, and 3. complex phosphoinositides. Attention is focused on these groups of compounds in the following section.

Simple Monophosphoinositides

The current thoughts as to the most probable structure of these compounds may be summarized in the following formula, which is an example of a diacyl ester of glycerylphosphorylinositol:

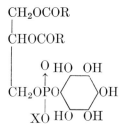

In view of its close relation to the phosphoglycerides (Chapter 3), this type of compound can be designated as phosphatidyl inositol. As these inositides are acidic substances, they are most usually found in natural sources as a mineral salt (X = Na, Mg, K, or Ca). There is little doubt now that any nitrogen associated with these compounds must be considered as a contaminant. These inositides are present in rat, beef, and pig liver, yeast, soybean, wheat germ, and cardiac muscle, where they constitute approximately 5 to 10% of the total phospholipides.

Isolation and Purification. Several different isolation procedures may be used: neutral solvent fractionation (brain),[20] cellulose acetate chromatography (liver),[15] acid solvent fractionation (green pea),[41] silicic acid chromatography (liver, yeast),[24] a combined salt, solvent fractionation (wheat germ, cardiac muscle, soybean),[18,19,38] and recently aluminum oxide chromatography (liver).[23] At present the most satisfactory route to the isolation of the monophosphoinositides, free of nitrogen, and in high yields, is through chromatography on silicic acid. Although a reasonable purification of the inositol lipides is accomplished by a single passage through a silicic acid column, nitrogen contaminants of the order of 20% may be present. Rechromatography on silicic acid will completely remove these substances and allow a satisfactory recovery of the purified phosphoinositide.[24] Recently, the use of aluminum oxide was investigated as a possible fractionation medium for these compounds.[23] When the mixed phospholipides from mammalian liver were passed through aluminum oxide in chloroform-methanol (1:1, v/v), the choline containing phospholipides passed through practically with the solvent front. Subsequent development of the column with ethanol-chloroform-water (5:2:1, v/v/v) eluted phosphatidyl ethanolamine and similar compounds and then ethanol-chloroform-water (5:2:2, v/v/v) removed the phosphoinositide. Recoveries were of the order of 95 to 98% of the applied lipide phosphorus. A typical chromatogram is outlined in Fig. 4.2. In many runs the inositide fraction has been obtained devoid of nitrogen; in others a nitrogen contaminant of the order of 5 to 20% has been found. (Rechromatography on silicic acid usually will remove these contaminants.) The particular advantage of this method over silicic acid is

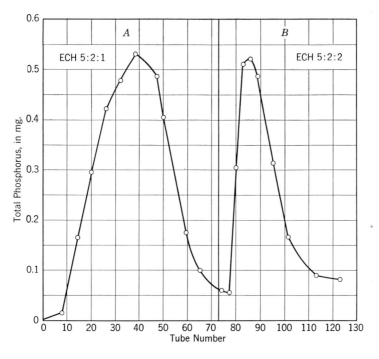

Fig. 4.2. Fractionation of non-choline containing phospholipides of beef liver on an aluminum oxide column. Solvents were ethanol-chloroform-water (5:2:1, v/v/v) and ethanol-chloroform-water (5:2:2, v/v/v). Fraction A was phosphatidyl ethanolamine (and serine) and B was phosphatidyl inositol.

that it is rapid, with the entire fractionation accomplished in one-half to one-third the time usually required with the silicic acid. While this procedure has worked well for the bulk isolation of the phosphoinositide, it can also be used as an analytical method for the estimation of the three different types of phospholipide components, i.e., the choline containing phospholipides, phosphatidyl ethanolamine and serine, and the phosphoinositides.

Questions on the Structure of Phosphatidyl Inositol. Although the data supplied in Table 4.1 and the recognition of the presence of ester linkages through hydrolysis studies support the phosphatidyl inositol

Table 4.1

Composition of Typical Simple Monophosphoinositides

Component	Wheat Germ *	Cardiac Muscle *	Rat Liver †	Beef Liver †
		Source		
P, %	3.56	3.38	3.23	3.40
N, %	0.09	None	0.05	0.09
Inositol, %			17.6	19.7
Glycerol, %			9.4	10.2
N/P, molar ratio	0.056	<0.02	0.01	0.06
Inositol/P, molar ratio			0.94	1.00
Glycerol/P, molar ratio	0.96		0.97	1.00
Inositol/glycerol, molar ratio	1.05	1.00		
Fatty acid, total %			49.0	55.3
Neutral equivalent			254.0	250.0
Fatty acid/P, molar ratio	2.10	2.03	1.90	2.00
Iodine uptake	56 ‡	84 ‡	1.90 §	1.77 §
Ash, %			10.2	10.92
Na/P, molar ratio			1.14	0.70
Mg/P, molar ratio				0.33
$[\alpha]_D^{25°}$			+5.6°	+5.86°

* As sodium salt; data from Faure and Morelec-Coulon.[18, 19]
† Taken from Hanahan and Olley.[24]
‡ Iodine number.
§ Unsaturation, double bond/mole fatty acid.

Table 4.2

Composition of Acid Hydrolysates of Phosphoinositides *

Samples heated at 98° in 2N HCl for 5 minutes. The results are
expressed as per cent of theory.

Fraction	Beef Liver †		Rat Liver	Yeast
	(1)	(2)		
Ether soluble				
Fatty acids as free acids	34	37	22	13
Diglyceride	43	47	47	50
Monoglyceride	17	15	23	18
Phosphatidic acid	14	11	8	18
Unhydrolyzed sample	1			
Water soluble				
Inositol, free	20	17	7	7
Inositol phosphate	80		70	70
Glycerol, free	15	11	18	16
Glycerophosphate	8		4	10
P_i	0	0	0	0

* Taken from Hanahan and Olley.[24]

† In a 30-minute hydrolysis period, the composition of the water soluble
fraction was inositol, free, 17; inositol phosphate, 82; glycerol, free, 29; glycerophosphate, 14; P_i, 2.

structure as depicted above, there still remain questions on the exact
types of linkages involved and the position of certain groupings within
the molecule.

Location and nature of fatty acyl groups. While it might be expected, when compared with the typical phosphoglycerides, that the
fatty acids of the inositides would be esterified to the glycerol portion
of the molecule, there was no assurance that such was the case. There
was an equal possibility that they might be associated with the inositol
portion of the molecule. However, in a study of the short-term acid
hydrolysis (5 minutes at 98° in 2N HCl) of the phosphoinositides of
rat liver, beef liver, and yeast, a preferential attack at the glycerol-
phosphate bond resulted in the release of glycerides and inositol monophosphate (Table 4.2). On the basis of the high recovery of glycer-

ides it was apparent that the fatty acids were attached to glycerol rather than inositol.

In studies on the phosphoinositides of wheat germ, Faure and Morelec-Coulon [18] reported that the fatty acids had an average molecular weight of 263 and an iodine number of 56. Apparently on the basis of the iodine values, they estimated an equimolar amount of palmitic and linoleic acid (C_{18} unsaturated acid) to be present. In heart muscle,[19] the fatty acids were observed to have an iodine value of 84 (no neutral equivalent reported), which was estimated to resemble a mixture of stearic acids and a highly unsaturated fatty acid. At best, the use of iodine values is an inadequate approach to the composition of a mixture of fatty acids.

During the course of an investigation on the metabolism of long-chain fatty acids in adult rats, Dittmer [16] subjected the fatty acids of the phosphoinositides of the liver to reversed phase chromatography. The distribution of fatty acids so obtained is recorded in Table 4.3. While there is some possibility of an "asymmetric" arrangement of the fatty acids on these molecules, it is particularly noteworthy that very high amounts of stearic acid, as compared to other phospholipides in liver, are found. That these observations were of significance and warranted further attention was shown by experiments with stearic acid-1-C^{14}. When this compound was fed to adult rats, Dittmer observed that there was always a high incorporation of this acid into the phosphoinositides, in fact much higher than with any other long-chain fatty acid and with any of the other lipide fractions. Whether

Table 4.3

Fatty Acid Composition of Monophosphoinositides of Rat Liver *

Fraction	Moles Per Cent		
	a	*b*	*c*
Stearic acid	27.9	36.9	34.9
Palmitic acid	8.3	8.9	7.9
Oleic acid	5.7	5.9	5.4
"Linoleic" acid †	58.1	48.3	49.7

* Taken from Dittmer.[16]

† In addition, this fraction can contain arachidonic, linoleic, palmitoleic, and myristic acids.

these inositides in liver are specific "carriers" of stearic acid is unknown.

Position of attachment of phosphate group.

HYDROLYSIS STUDIES. Most of the information regarding the structure of the monophosphoinositides has been derived from studies of the chemical nature of hydrolysis products.[20, 24, 27, 32] Until very recently, the exact position of the phosphate ester on the *myo*-inositol, as well as on the glycerol, remained uncertain. If recognition is made of the possible alterations of the products of hydrolysis, certain definite conclusions can be drawn as to their relation to the original structure. While much of this information has come from use of rather diverse sources of materials, the conclusions and ideas are of general interest.

GENERAL COMMENTS. On the basis of the observations of Pizer and Ballou[37] (see below) and others, the historically prevalent idea that the distances between hydroxyls in the *myo*-inositol phosphates were too great for cyclic ester formation must be abandoned. In part this proposal was based on the assumption that *myo*-inositol and its derivatives will exist in the classical chair form. However, as will be discussed in the succeeding sections, this is not completely correct.

At this point it seems appropriate to mention briefly certain ideas concerning the stereochemistry of inositol and related derivatives. As discussed previously, the assumption that *myo*-inositol will exist in a chair form was based in part on the similarity of this compound to the cyclohexanes, which have been shown to exist preferentially in the chair form. While in general, in assigning a preferred conformation to a molecule, this assumes the maximum possible staggering of the bonds (for reduction of non-bonded interactions), some qualifications may be necessary for the inositol phosphates. Thus, certain intramolecular forces, i.e., hydrogen bonding, electrostatic effects, etc., may significantly alter the conformation and hence distances between the hydroxyl positions. Particularly pertinent to this subject are the observations and comments of Angyal and Macdonald[3] on the stereochemistry of the isopropylidene cyclitols. As emphasized by these authors, the differences in the reactivity of the *cis* and *trans* hydroxyls (*cis* greater than the *trans* form) in acetal formation must involve a deformation of the molecule during the reaction. In essence, it was considered that a deformation bringing an equatorial and an axial bond together is relatively easy, but a deformation bringing two equatorial bonds together requires considerable energy. The former type of deformation decreases puckering and increases the distances between polar groups, while the latter condition increases puckering and polar groups are moved nearer other polar groups. Other facets of the reactivity of the cyclitols in certain instances are ably outlined by Angyal and Macdonald and are of obvious importance and concern in any structural studies on naturally occurring or synthetic inositol derivatives. On a comparable basis, Eliel and Pillar [17] observed a more rapid oxidation (by lead tetraacetate) of the *cis* forms of hydrindane diols than with the *trans* forms of these diols. These results were attributed to a difference in the degree of deformation of the two diol molecules. Consequently, extrapolation from the preferred conformations of the cyclohexanes and derivatives to inositol and thence to the inositol phosphates and derivatives may not be completely valid, so further attention to this most important problem is warranted.

STUDIES ON MODEL COMPOUNDS. Pursuant to the question of the structure of the inositol phosphates as revealed by hydrolysis studies, the observations of Brown and Higson [6] on the problem of migration of phosphates are of interest and importance. On the basis of the preparation of isopropylidene and cyclic sulfite derivatives of both *cis* and *trans* cyclohexane 1:2-diol, Brown and Higson [6] felt that phosphoryl migration could be a distinct possibility on the inositol molecule. Consequently *cis* and *trans*-2-hydroxy cyclohexyl phosphates and their benzyl esters were prepared and subjected to hydrolysis. In alkali or acid at reflux temperatures, hydrolysis of these esters yielded the diol phosphates and in each case proceeded much more readily than that of the dialkyl phosphates lacking a vicinal hydroxyl function. Evidence was secured for the occurrence of *cis* and *trans* cyclic phosphates as intermediates in the hydrolysis; comparable synthetic compounds behaved in a similar manner. Of interest, *cis*-1:3 cyclohexylidene phosphate was very stable to acid or alkali:

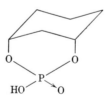

This high stability was interpreted as strong indication that no participation by a *cis* 3-hydroxyl group was evident in the hydrolysis of cyclohexyl alkyl phosphates. Since cyclic ester formation requires a 1:3 diaxial conformation, it is even less likely to occur in the *myo*-inositol series where five oxygen atoms would then be required to be axially disposed. Finally, it was noted that hydrolysis proceeded at a faster rate in the *cis* than in the *trans* series, probably due to a deformational strain in the cyclohexane ring in the formation of the bicyclic intermediate. Of added interest in this connection is the observation that migration has been noted in the case of the 5-phosphate of shikimic acid, which is a trihydroxy cyclohexane carboxylic acid derivative.

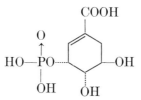

In a more recent report Brown et al.[5] investigated the direction of acid or alkaline cleavage of glycerol-1-(*cis*-2 hydroxy) cyclohexyl phosphate, which yielded mainly 2-hydroxy cyclohexyl phosphate (~85%) whereas the *trans* isomer gave mainly glycerol phosphate (~75%). However, the rates of alkaline hydrolysis were similar although appreciably greater than those found for benzyl *cis* and *trans*-2-hydroxyl cyclohexyl phosphate and glycerol-1-(benzyl phosphate). In each case the reaction was first order in ester. In the course of this investigation it was necessary to prepare glycerol-1-(*cis*-2 hydroxy) cyclohexyl phosphate (III), which was accomplished by the following reaction:

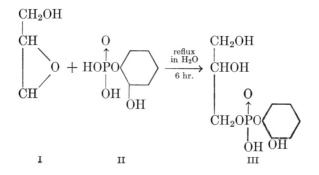

Thus, depending on the particular isomer of II (*cis* or *trans*) used in reaction with glycidol (I), the *cis* or *trans* isomer of III can be prepared. As described above the hydrolysis of III can proceed as follows in an acid medium:

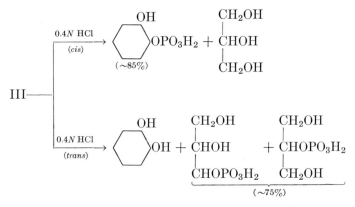

In an alkaline medium the following was found to hold:

$$cis\text{-ester} \rightarrow 85\% \text{ diol phosphates}$$

$$trans\text{-ester} \rightarrow 75\% \text{ glycerol phosphates}$$

In these reactions the data were found consistent with P—O fission in the rate determining step, which must involve formation and not hydrolysis of the cyclic phosphate. Also the removal of a proton from a vicinal hydroxyl group ($pK_a > 14$) is indicated and must occur before or simultaneously with the unimolecular rate determining step in which the cyclic phosphate is formed. Thus hydrogen bonding may then assist the reaction by stabilizing the ejected anion or by facilitating attack on the phosphorus atom. Brown et al. then concluded that the only factor governing hydrolysis of phosphoinositides based on glycerol-phosphorus-inositol structure is the *cis* or *trans* orientation of the hydroxyl groups. In agreement with these above arguments on the mode of hydrolytic attack, Hanahan and Olley [24] observed that highly purified monophosphoinositides of liver were hydrolyzed very rapidly in acid to a mixture mainly composed of glycerides and inositol monophosphate. These results, shown in Table 4.2, support a phosphate ester linkage between the glycerol and inositol portion of the molecule and also illustrate the mode of attack of acid on these phosphate esters. In this case one might suspect that the acyl groups could block any initial phosphate action on the glycerol portion of the molecule and force the reaction towards the inositol unit. Thus, conceivably with glycerylphosphorylinositol, acid hydrolysis might be expected to proceed with the predominant formation of glycerophosphate and free inositol. However, Brown et al.[5] concluded that the only factor governing the hydrolysis of this type of structure would be the *cis-trans* orientation of the inositol hydroxyls. This point remains to be clarified. In an alkaline medium under reflux, these same monophosphoinositides, as expected, yielded primarily glycerophosphate (59%) and inositol monophosphate (35%).

On the basis of the L-α configuration of the other phosphoglycerides, it would seem probable that the site of esterification of the phosphate to the glyceride portion of the molecule would be at the α(C-3) carbon. Also, by comparison of the optical activities of these phosphoinositides $[\alpha]_D^{25}$ +5.5° with those of synthetic phosphoglycerides $[\alpha]_D^{25}$ +6.0°, it is provocative to consider this as added proof for support of this proposition. However, as is obvious, this type of data, insofar as it concerns the phosphoinositides, is not sufficient for complete structure proof.

STRUCTURE OF *Myo*-INOSITOL PHOSPHATE FROM NATURALLY OCCURRING PHOSPHOINOSITIDES. In a recent excellent article, Pizer and Ballou [37] have presented the first sound and quite conclusive evidence as to the positioning of the phosphate on the inositol of naturally occurring monophosphoinositides (phosphatidyl inositol). On alkaline hydrolysis of soybean inositide an optically active *myo*-inositol-1-phosphate was obtained as the major inositol phosphate. This strongly suggested that the phosphate ester linkage in the phosphoinositides is to position 1 of the inositol molecule. Thus, this report weakens considerably the older arguments that the axial hydroxyl (position 2) would be the most likely site of esterification. Furthermore, Pizer and Ballou reported that *myo*-inositol-1- and 2-phosphates were readily interconverted by acid catalyzed phosphate group migration, while the 5-phosphate did not undergo such migration as readily. Also, alkaline hydrolysis of a cyclic 1,2 diphosphate of *myo*-inositol yielded mainly the 1-phosphate, which explains the reason for the predominance of the 1-phosphate in base hydrolysis of the phosphoinositides. Certain details of this investigation are outlined below.

Pizer and Ballou isolated their starting material from soybean phospholipides by the procedure of Hawthorne and Chargaff.[27] Unfortunately, for some reason, no data were supplied as to the composition of the final product. Also, low yields (10 to 15%) of inositol-1-phosphate were recorded. However, similar results were obtained with the phosphoinositides from wheat germ, beef heart, and liver. Upon base hydrolysis of soybean phosphoinositide, *myo*-inositol phosphate was isolated as a crystalline cyclohexylamine salt. On the basis of infrared spectra, chromatographic properties, rate of periodate oxidation, and melting points, this substance differed from the 2- and 5-phosphates and was considered to be a single component. Furthermore it was optically active $[\alpha]_{589}^{25} + 3.4°$ (c 3, *p*H 9.0), $-9.8°$ (c 3, *p*H 2). Thus they argued that it must be the 1(3)- or 4(6)-phosphate—the numbers in the parentheses being the equivalent, but enantiomeric, positions. From the crude mother liquor of the base hydrolysis, a small amount of inositol-2-phosphate was identified by chromatographic inspection. Since this type of hydrolysis most probably proceeds via a cyclic phosphate involving two adjacent hydroxyls of inositol, at least two different monophosphates should result. As this is the case, the cyclic intermediate must involve the 1 and 2 positions as follows:

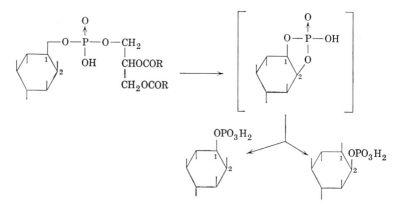

The choice as to which of the two positions was involved in the linkage in the phosphoinositides was suggested by the fact that one of the major products of hydrolysis was optically active. Since both the 1- and 2-phosphates were found in the hydrolysates, this would result from the cyclization and reopening of a phosphate group originally on position 1, as this intermediate cyclic phosphate would retain its asymmetry. Unless the glycerol portion of the molecule influenced the reaction, this would not be the case with a phosphate originally on the 2 position. This was conclusively shown by cyclization of *myo*-inositol-2-phosphate with dicyclohexylcarbodiimide and subsequent mild acid or base hydrolysis. Two monophosphates, the 1 and 2, were obtained, but both were optically inactive. This would be expected if the 2-phosphate were converted to racemic ($\pm$) *myo*-inositol-1-phosphate by forced migration. As only two products were produced, one identical with the starting material, it appeared most unlikely that the phosphate group migrated around the ring. Alkaline hydrolysis of a cyclic 1,2 diphosphate gave 80 to 90% of the 1-phosphate and 10 to 20% of the 2-phosphate. This indicated that the 2 position was the more susceptible to attack. Finally a racemic *myo*-inositol-1-

phosphate was prepared by synthesis and compared exactly in all respects, except of course in optical activity, with the *myo* 1-phosphate from phosphoinositide hydrolysis.

A point of considerable interest was the influence of acid (1*N* HCl at 80°) on the migration of the phosphate groups. While under similar conditions *myo*-inositol-1- and 2-phosphates were readily interconverted, a 5-phosphate was not affected. This indicated that acid catalyzed migration across *trans* hydroxyls in the ring was difficult and would suggest that the 4-phosphate (containing *trans* hydroxyls on either side) would also have resistance to acid migration. Of interest was the observation that no migration occurred in the 1- and 2-phosphates at 50° for as long as 60 hours. On the other hand, the soybean monophosphate in a *p*H 2 medium at 100° showed a distinct change in optical activity with little migration. However, in the latter case, changes in optical activity could be accounted for by formation of free inositol and inorganic phosphate. These observations illustrate very clearly the influence of *p*H and temperature on the direction of hydrolysis.

In performing periodate oxidations on the inositol phosphates, Pizer and Ballou noted that inositol-1-phosphate (from soybean phosphoinositide) as well as racemic inositol-1-phosphate oxidized at rates indistinguishable from the 2-phosphate, but definitely slower than the 5-phosphate. This is comparable to the observations of Angyal and McHugh, who found that 1- and 2-monomethyl ethers of inositol oxidized at slower rates than the 4- and 5-monomethyl ethers. Apparently the reaction is dependent on which of the *cis* hydroxyls is substituted.

OTHER ROUTES. Several possible lines of endeavor, briefly outlined below, could conceivably lead to the exact location of the phosphate esters and thus aid in the total elucidation of the structure.

Derivative Formation. Only limited success has been achieved to date in the area of direct derivative formation on the intact phosphoinositide. In this manner, groups could be stabilized and migration effects could be minimized. Okuhara and Nakayama [36] subjected a "purified" soybean monophosphoinositide to exhaustive methylation and then through hydrolysis isolated in low yields a compound considered to be pentamethyl inositol. This result was interpreted as evidence for the attachment of the phosphate at only one position on the inositol molecule. Notwithstanding the low yield and the concomitant possibility of other points of attachment of the phosphate, this type of approach, either with the ether derivative or a compound of similar stability, should provide valuable information on the structure of the inositides.

Specific Oxidative Degradation. Perhaps one of the more useful reagents for specific oxidative attack is periodic acid. Thus under controlled conditions with positive identification of the products of the reaction, quite definitive information on the structure should be obtained. Thus, if the proposed structure for the monophosphoinositide is correct, periodic acid under proper conditions of attack should require 4 moles of oxidant, with the release of 3 moles of formic acid and a malondialdehyde phosphate derivative, which should be attacked by periodate with ultimate release of the phosphate. Although phosphate migration is possible, it is rather unlikely under the usual conditions employed.

Again, only limited application has been made of this technique to the problem of monophosphoinositide structure. Faure and Morelec-Coulon [18,19] reported that periodic acid could cause complete destruction of the inositol portion of the wheat germ and cardiac muscle phosphoinositides. However, no explanation of the conditions employed or the nature of the products was supplied and hence this report cannot be interpreted as contributing any significant information to knowledge of the phosphoinositide structure. As will be described below, Folch [20] used periodate oxidation for structure proof studies on the inositol phosphates from brain diphosphoinositide. Similarly, Hawthorne and Chargaff [27] investigated briefly the periodate oxidation of intact diphosphoinositide.

Enzymatic (and Non-Enzymatic) Degradation. Through the use of enzymes capable of attacking specific linkages in a molecule, considerable information on relatively labile structures can be gained. Until recently, no enzymatic activity towards the monophosphoinositides had been described, but it was evident that phospholipase A (lecithinase A) apparently had no action on this compound.[24] However, Dawson [12] has noted recently that monophosphoinositides could be rapidly attacked by a *Penicillium notatum* enzyme system, with liberation in equimolar proportions of acid soluble phosphorus and water soluble combined inositol. Subsequently a water soluble phosphorus ester was isolated by chromatography and contained glycerol and inositol in equimolar proportions. It appeared to be identical with glycerylphosphorylinositol prepared by mild alkaline hydrolysis of monophosphoinositides and distinctly different from that of inositol monophosphate. Fatty acid titration indicated the liberation of two acyl units per atom of water soluble phosphorus formed in the reaction. This can be described by the following reaction:

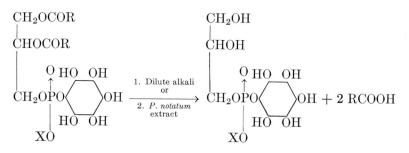

As mentioned above, the use of a mild alkaline hydrolysis, as described by Dawson,[11] will allow deacylation of compounds such as L-α-lecithin to give L-α-glycerylphosphorylcholine and free fatty acids and monophosphoinositides to yield glycerylphosphorylinositol and free fatty acids. This very useful and gentle technique is carried out in $1M$ NaOH in methanol at 37° for 15 minutes, at which time the deacylation is complete (with no loss of N base). Specifically, with lecithin no stereochemical alteration occurred as only L-α-glycerylphosphorylcholine was formed. While the proof of structure of glyceryl-phosphorylinositol is not complete, it is probable that the original stereochemical form of this compound is maintained throughout the reaction.*

Diphosphoinositides

Diphosphoinositide is the name applied to the inositol lipides found primarily in brain tissue. When a neutral solvent fractionation was employed, Folch[20] was able to isolate this acidic phospholipide as a calcium and magnesium salt. The major constituents were fatty acid,

---

* Recently, H. Brockerhoff and D. J. Hanahan [*J. Am. Chem. Soc.*, **81**, 259 (1959)] subjected a phosphatidyl inositol preparation (3.34% P; N/P, 0.05; inositol/P, 1.05) from beef liver to a mild alkaline hydrolysis at 37°. The resultant glyceryl-phosphorylinositol as the free acid had an $[\alpha]_D^{25}$ $-18.7°$ and as the cyclohexylamine salt an $[\alpha]_D^{25}$ $-13.5°$. The two vicinal glycol groups on the glycerol were still intact. Upon selective oxidation of the cyclohexylamine derivative with periodate, the glycol-aldehyde phosphoryl inositol (as the cyclohexylamine salt) had an $[\alpha]_D^{25}$ $-13.2°$. These results strongly suggest that the main point of attachment of the phosphate to the inositol was at the 1 or 4 position and to the glycerol at the α or 3 position. J. N. Hawthorne and G. Hübscher [*Biochem. J.*, **71**, 195 (1959)] isolated glyceryl-phosphorylinositol by an ion exchange chromatographic procedure and found it to have an $[\alpha]_D^{20}$ $-18 \pm 2°$.

glycerol, inositol, and phosphorus in a molar ratio of 1:1:1:2. If the fatty acid is esterified to the glycerol, then only a monoglyceride, in contradistinction to the usual diglyceride found in the monophosphoinositides, is present.

Among the products of acid hydrolysis (at reflux) of the diphosphoinositide from brain, Folch [20] isolated an inositol diphosphate. Through elementary analyses, titration data, and periodate oxidation results, it was firmly established that this derivative was an inositol metadiphosphate. The exact positions occupied by the remainder of the components of the molecule have not been established. Although this argument remains to be settled, there is still the question of the behavior of the two phosphoryl groupings under the conditions of the hydrolytic procedure. While the evidence secured by Pizer and Ballou [37] for the monophosphates would tend to minimize any changes due to migration, this point must still be proved for the more complicated diphosphate molecule.

It is evident that additional information must be supplied before a concise structure can be described for this compound. Folch has proposed the structure of the diphosphoinositide to be pictured in part by formula A, while Hawthorne [26] proposed a 12-membered ring structure (B) to explain his observations on brain diphosphoinositide reactivity. However, the occurrence and stability of 12 membered rings cause some question to be made of this latter proposal. There is the possibility, as suggested by Folch and LeBaron,[21] that the diphosphoinositide might actually be polymeric in nature. Another possibility is that it is linked to another substance in the tissue and in the process of isolation this rather labile linkage is ruptured.

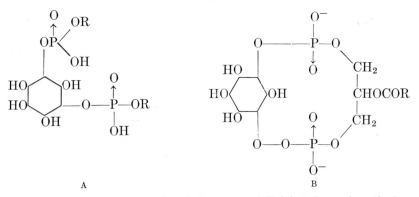

A   B

As regards this latter point, LeBaron and Folch [31] have described a new, second type of inositol lipide derivative in brain tissue. This component occurred in a trypsin resistant protein fraction, which had been isolated by neutral solvent extraction and subsequent treatment with the proteolytic enzyme. In addition to protein and inositol, this fraction contained phosphate (as inositol phosphate) and fatty acids, with the latter components considered to be present as a diphosphoinositide. The exact chemical nature of the bond between the protein and inositide is unknown, but is thought to be a salt-like linkage.

Complex Phosphoinositides

It has become increasingly apparent over the recent years that phosphoinositides more complex than those described above do exist in nature. Insofar as present evidence indicates, the more complex inositides are found almost exclusively in plants (or seeds); at least, no report has been made of their occurrence in mammalian tissues.

Phytoglycolipides. In an investigation of the inositol lipides of soybean, Carter and associates [8] detected the presence of a long-chain base, which they designated phytosphingosine, and determined its structure. Subsequently Carter et al.[9] were able to show the existence in corn and other plant seed phospholipides of a complex inositol-phytosphingosine containing lipide, termed phytoglycolipide. Through the use of mild alkaline hydrolysis (for removal of any contaminant lecithins, etc.) and countercurrent distribution and chromatographic separation, a highly purified lipide fraction was obtained in good yields. This material contained phytosphingosine, fatty acid, phosphate, inositol, glucosamine, hexuronic acid, galactose, arabinose, and mannose. Through alkaline hydrolysis of this material the following products were obtained:

$$\text{Phytoglycolipide} \xrightarrow[\text{reflux}]{\text{Ba(OH)}_2} \left[\begin{array}{l} \rightarrow \text{CHCl}_3 \text{ soluble} \begin{cases} \textit{Ceramide phosphate} \text{ (A)} \\ \text{Unknown fragments} \end{cases} \\ \rightarrow \text{Water soluble} \begin{cases} \text{P-containing oligosaccha-} \\ \quad \text{ride (unstable)} \\ \textit{P-free oligosaccharide} \text{ (B)} \end{cases} \end{array} \right.$$

The ceramide phosphate (A) was isolated as its dipotassium salt. On the basis of analytical data, infrared and periodate oxidation which yielded pentadecanal, and formation of a phosphate containing fraction from which serine could be obtained, the structure of (A) was considered to be as follows:

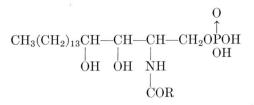

where R is a long-chain fatty (acyl) group.

The P-free oligosaccharide (B) was obtained as a white amorphous powder which contained inositol, glucosamine, hexuronic acid (now established as glucuronic acid), galactose, arabinose, and mannose. It appeared to be a single oligosaccharide, which on mild acid hydrolysis lost galactose, arabinose, and mannose and after chromatography of this hydrolysate on cellulose, a crystalline compound containing inositol, glucosamine, and hexuronic acid. When this latter "trisaccharide" was further hydrolyzed it yielded inositol, glucosamine, and a "disaccharide" containing only glucosamine and hexuronic acid. On a preliminary basis this dissacharide appeared to hylabiuronic acid. Hence the trisaccharide is possibly an inositol glycoside of hylabiuronic acid.

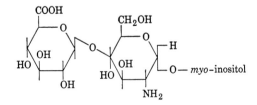

Thus, on this evidence, Carter et al. proposed the following partial structure:

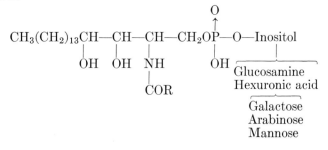

On the basis of more recent evidence from periodate oxidation studies (H. E. Carter, private communication), it is now thought that mannose is attached either to inositol or hexuronic acid. Also, the hexuronic acid must be attached to inositol with glucosamine being attached to the hexuronic acid and the arabinose-galactose units being attached in an as yet unknown manner to glucosamine.

It is of interest to mention the observations of Malkin and Poole [35] on the occurrence of a "glycerinositophosphatide" in ground nut (peanut). On the basis of somewhat limited evidence, they proposed that this compound was best represented as an N-glycosyl derivative of the ethanolamine ester of phosphatidyl inositol phosphate. No further evidence on the structure of this substance has been reported. On the other hand, Carter and associates (private communication) have isolated phytoglycolipides in good yields from peanut.

Microbial Inositides. Vilkas and Lederer [40] separated by silicic acid chromatography the phospholipides of a streptomycin resistant mutant of H37 R_v (tubercle bacillus) into two principal fractions, which differed in their solubility in chloroform-methanol (1:1). One component was apparently the magnesium salt of a phosphatidic acid and the other component was described as the magnesium salt of a phosphatidyl inositol-di-D-mannoside. The latter compound could be represented by the following tentative formula:

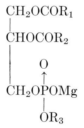

$$CH_2OCOR_1$$
$$CHOCOR_2$$
$$O$$
$$CH_2OPOMg$$
$$OR_3$$

where R_1CO- and R_2CO- are long-chain fatty acyl groups and R_3 may be:

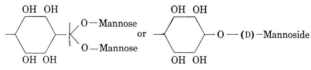

The mannose was identified through its phenylhydrazone. Glycerophosphate and inositol phosphate were detected through paper chromatographic techniques, as was a component described as glycero-phosphoryl inositol. However, on the basis of the evidence presented in this report, additional information must be supplied before any final structure can be assigned to this compound.

REFERENCES

1. Anderson, R. J., *J. Am. Chem. Soc.,* **52,** 1607 (1930).
2. Anderson, R. J., W. C. Lothrop, and M. M. Creighton, *J. Biol. Chem.,* **125,** 299 (1947).
3. Angyal, S. J., and C. G. Macdonald, *J. Chem. Soc.,* **1952,** 686.
4. Beckett, C. W., K. S. Pitzer, and R. Spitzer, *J. Am. Chem. Soc.,* **69,** 2488 (1947).
5. Brown, D. M., G. E. Hall, and H. M. Higson, *J. Chem. Soc.,* **1958,** 1360.
6. Brown, D. M., and H. M. Higson, *J. Chem. Soc.,* **1957,** 2034.
7. Carter, H. E., C. Belinskey, R. K. Clark, Jr., E. H. Flynn, B. Lytle, G. E. McCasland, and M. Robbins, *J. Biol. Chem.,* **174,** 415 (1948).
8. Carter, H. E., W. D. Celmer, W. E. M. Lands, K. L. Mueller, and H. H. Tomizawa, *J. Biol. Chem.,* **206,** 213 (1954).
9. Carter, H. E., R. H. Gigg, John H. Law, T. Nakayama, and E. Weber, *J. Biol. Chem.,* **233,** 1309 (1958).
10. Charalampous, F. C., and P. Abrahams, *J. Biol. Chem.,* **225,** 575 (1957).
11. Dawson, R. M. C., *Biochim. et Biophys. Acta,* **14,** 375 (1954).
12. Dawson, R. M. C., *Biochim. et Biophys. Acta,* **27,** 227 (1958).
13. deRobichon-Szulmajster, H., *Biochim. et Biophys. Acta,* **21,** 313 (1956).
14. deSuto-Nagy, G. I., and R. J. Anderson, *J. Biol. Chem.,* **258,** 33 (1939).
15. Dils, R. R., and J. N. Hawthorne, *Biochim. et Biophys. Acta,* **25,** 424 (1957).
16. Dittmer, J. C., Ph.D. Thesis, University of Washington (1958).
17. Eliel, E. E., and C. Pillar, *J. Am. Chem. Soc.,* **77,** 3600 (1956).
18. Faure, M., and J. Morelec-Coulon, *Compt. rend.,* **236,** 1104 (1953).
19. Faure, M., and J. Morelec-Coulon, *Compt. rend.,* **238,** 411 (1954).
20. Folch, J., *J. Biol. Chem.,* **177,** 497, 505 (1949).
21. Folch, J., and F. N. LeBaron, *Can. J. Biochem. and Physiol.,* **34,** 305 (1956).
22. Folch, J., and D. W. Woolley, *J. Biol. Chem.,* **142,** 963 (1942).
23. Hanahan, D. J., unpublished observations.
24. Hanahan, D. J., and J. N. Olley, *J. Biol. Chem.,* **231,** 813 (1958).
25. Hassel, O., and B. Ottar, *Acta Chem. Scand.,* **1,** 99 (1947).
26. Hawthorne, J. N., *Biochim. et Biophys. Acta,* **18,** 389 (1955).
27. Hawthorne, J. N., and E. Chargaff, *J. Biol. Chem.,* **206,** 27 (1954).
28. Klenk, E., and R. Sakai, *Z. physiol. chem.,* **258,** 33 (1939).
29. Lardy, H. A., in *The Vitamins,* Vol. II, by Sebrell and Harris, p. 323, Academic Press (1954).
30. Larner, J., W. T. Jackson, D. J. Graves, and J. R. Stamer, *Arch. Biochem. Biophys.,* **60,** 352 (1956).
31. LeBaron, F. N., and J. Folch, *J. Neurochem.,* **1,** 101 (1956).
32. McKibbin, J. M., *J. Biol. Chem.,* **220,** 533 (1956).
33. Magasanik, B., in *Essays in Biochemistry,* edited by S. Graff, p. 181, Wiley (1956).
34. Magasanik, B., and E. Chargaff, *J. Biol. Chem.,* **174,** 173 (1948).
35. Malkin, T., and A. G. Poole, *J. Chem. Soc.,* **1953,** 3470.
36. Okuhara, E., and T. Nakayama, *J. Biol. Chem.,* **215,** 295 (1955).
37. Pizer, F. L., and C. E. Ballou, *J. Am. Chem. Soc.,* **81,** 915 (1959).

38. Scholfield, C. R., and H. J. Dutton, *J. Biol. Chem.*, **208**, 461 (1954).
39. Trevalyan, W. E., D. P. Proctor, and J. S. Harrison, *Nature*, **166**, 444 (1950).
40. Vilkas, E., and E. Lederer, *Bull. soc. chim. biol.*, **37**, 111 (1956).
41. Wagenknecht, A. C., and H. E. Carter, *Federation Proc.*, **16**, 266 (1957).
42. Weissbach, A., *Biochim. et Biophys. Acta*, **27**, 608 (1958).
43. Woolley, D. W., *J. Biol. Chem.*, **140**, 461 (1941).

5

by Irving Zabin

Sphingolipides

Sphingolipides, a term proposed by Carter et al.,[22] are defined as those lipides which contain the long-chain amino-alcohol, sphingosine. Recently, several other long-chain amino-alcohols, dihydrosphingosine, phytosphingosine, and dehydrophytosphingosine, have been discovered, and these compounds and their derivatives are also classified in this group. Complex sphingolipides containing sphingosine and dihydrosphingosine have been found so far only in animal tissues, while phytosphingosine and dehydrophytosphingosine appear to occur only in plant sources. Animal sphingolipides are present in particularly high concentrations in brain and nerve tissue, and in lower concentrations in other tissues. These materials, which include the sphingomyelins, cerebrosides, and more complex substances, often accumulate in various organs in certain metabolic lipide disorders (lipidoses). Attempts to understand the chemistry and the causes of the variations in these disease states have stimulated investigations in this area. Another impetus for these studies has been an increased emphasis on experimentation aimed towards an understanding of brain chemistry, metabolism, and function. A number of reviews [17, 18, 28, 68, 116] are pertinent to this subject.

SPHINGOSINE AND DIHYDROSPHINGOSINE

Sphingosine was first obtained by Thudicum [120] from brain lipides in 1901. Subsequent studies by Levene and West [72,73] and Lapworth [67] established the fact that this compound was a long-chain dihydroxyamine with a double bond at the 4–5 position; a 17-carbon structure was assigned. However, Klenk [52] obtained myristic acid after chromic acid treatment of sphingosine, and palmitic acid on chromic acid treatment of the saturated derivative. The beautifully crystalline triacetyl sphingosine prepared by Klenk was of further aid in establishing the correct empirical formula of sphingosine as $C_{18}H_{37}NO_2$. At first, the relative positions of the two hydroxyl groups and the amino group were thought to be 1,2 dihydroxy-3 amino, but the correct structure was conclusively established by Carter and his co-workers [19,20] with the demonstration that N-benzoyl sphingosine (I) does not react with periodate.

$$CH_3(CH_2)_{12}CH{=}CHCH{-}CH{-}CH_2 \xrightarrow{IO_4^-} \text{No reaction}$$

$$\begin{array}{ccc} & | & | & | \\ & OH & NH & OH \\ & & | & \\ & & C{=}O & \\ & & | & \\ & & C_6H_5 & \\ & & \text{I} & \end{array}$$

Since periodate oxidation of the saturated derivative of sphingosine (II) results in the formation of one equivalent each of formaldehyde, formic acid, ammonia, and palmitaldehyde, sphingosine must be 1,3 dihydroxy-2-amino octadecene-4 (III):

$$CH_3(CH_2)_{14}CH{-}CH{-}CH_2 \xrightarrow{IO_4^-}$$

$$\begin{array}{ccc} | & | & | \\ OH & NH_2 & OH \end{array}$$

$$CH_3(CH_2)_{14}CHO + NH_3 + HCO_2H + HCHO$$
$$\text{II}$$

$$CH_3(CH_2)_{12}CH{=}CHCH{-}CH{-}CH_2$$

$$\begin{array}{ccc} | & | & | \\ OH & NH_2 & OH \end{array}$$
$$\text{III}$$

Stereochemistry

The stereochemistry of sphingosine appears also to be firmly established. The D-configuration was assigned to carbon 2 by Carter and

Humiston [23] on the basis of the fact that N-acyl derivatives of L and D amino acids show characteristic changes in optical rotation on dilution of dioxane and acetic acid solutions with water. Known acyl amino acids were compared to N-benzoyl α-amino stearic acid (IV) obtained by conversion of triacetyl sphingosine (V) to diacetyl sphingine (VI) and oxidation of N-benzoyl sphingosine (VII) to the acid.

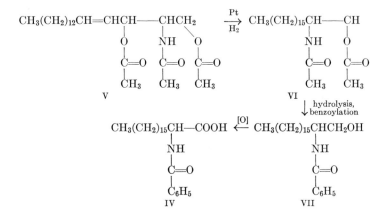

Further evidence for the D-configuration of carbon 2 has been obtained by Kiss, Fodor, and Banfi,[48] who obtained by ozonolysis of triacetyl sphingosine a four-carbon fragment which was compared to known derivatives of α-amino-β,γ-dihydroxybutyric acid. Klenk and Faillard [58] also treated triacetyl sphingosine with ozone and converted the acetylated product by further reactions to L-serine.

The configuration of carbon 3 has been studied, and the evidence indicates that this bears an *erythro* relationship to carbon 2. Carter, Shapiro, and Harrison [27] prepared the *erythro* (VIII) and *threo* (IX) α-amino-β-hydroxystearic acids and converted the esters of these, by reduction with Raney nickel or hydrogen or with lithium aluminum hydride, to the corresponding dihydrosphingosine compounds (X, XI). Only the synthetic *erythro* base (X) gave a crystalline tribenzoyl derivative, while benzoylation of the *threo* compound (XI) under a variety of conditions yielded only an oil.

$$CH_3(CH_2)_{14}CH\!-\!CH\!-\!COOH \xrightarrow[\text{or LiAlH}_4]{\text{Raney Ni,}\ H_2} CH_3(CH_2)_{14}CH\!-\!CH\!-\!CH_2$$

with OH, NH$_2$ below left (VIII) and OH, NH$_2$, OH below right (X).

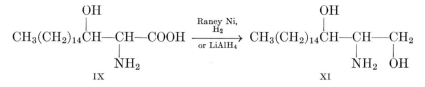

$$CH_3(CH_2)_{14}\overset{\overset{\displaystyle OH}{|}}{C}H—\underset{\underset{\displaystyle NH_2}{|}}{C}H—COOH \xrightarrow[\text{or LiAlH}_4]{\text{Raney Ni,}\ H_2} CH_3(CH_2)_{14}\overset{\overset{\displaystyle OH}{|}}{C}H—\underset{\underset{\displaystyle NH_2}{|}}{C}H—\underset{\underset{\displaystyle OH}{|}}{C}H_2$$

IX   XI

The tribenzoyl derivative of dihydrosphingosine obtained by reduction of naturally occurring sphingosine is similarly crystalline, and the melting points are identical. Resolution of the synthetic material to give the D-*erythro* base yielded an isomer identical in all its properties to the natural form. Kiss et al.[48] showed that the four-carbon compound resulting from the ozonolysis of triacetyl sphingosine was of the *erythro* configuration. Stereospecific syntheses of sphingosine and dihydrosphingosine (see below) have completed the proof for the structure of sphingosine as *trans* D-*erythro* 1,3 dihydroxy-2-amino octadecene-4.

These studies on the structure of naturally occurring sphingosine have been carried out on material obtained by hydrolysis of complex lipides, the sphingomyelins or cerebrosides, because little, if any, free sphingosine is present in tissues. The *trans* configuration of the double bond has been established by the infrared studies of Mislow [77] and of Marinetti and Stotz [76] not only on free sphingosine but on that in intact sphingomyelin and cerebroside. It is possible, however, that sphingosine as it exists in the native compounds may be the *threo*, not the *erythro*, form. Inversion of 1,2 amino alcohols is, in fact, known to occur during hydrolysis of N-acyl derivatives by acidic reagents, although the extent of inversion of *erythro* to *threo* is greater than the reverse.[124] The *threo* isomer of sphingosine has been isolated by Seydel [100] from aqueous methanolic hydrolysates of cerebrosides, and Carter et al.[24] have obtained both the *threo* and *erythro* O-methyl ethers of sphingosine from methanolic sulfuric acid hydrolysates of cerebrosides.

In order to obtain evidence on the exact structure of sphingosine as it exists in sphingolipides, Carter and Fujino [16] prepared a pure cerebroside and removed the fatty acid by a modification of Klenk's barium hydroxide procedure.[50] The resulting compound, galactosidosphingosine, which is also called psychosine, was catalytically reduced and then hydrolyzed with aqueous ethanolic hydrogen chloride to give an excellent yield of *erythro* dihydrosphingosine. Since no inversion would be expected by this procedure, this evidence strongly supports the conclusion that the configuration of sphingosine, at least in cerebrosides, is of the *erythro* form.

Evidence which indicates that biologically formed sphingosine is also of the *erythro* configuration has been obtained by Zabin.[129] From suitably supplemented homogenates of brain tissue of young rats and 3-C[14] serine as tracer, radioactive sphingosine has been isolated without hydrolysis. Addition of carrier *erythro* sphingosine to the enzymatically formed radioactive sphingosine and conversion of the mixture to tribenzoyldihydrosphingosine gave a crystalline radioactive product whose specific activity did not decrease on recrystallization, and whose total activity was equivalent to that in the radioactive sphingosine. Since *erythro*, but not *threo*, dihydrosphingosine forms a crystalline tribenzoyl derivative, it is evident that *erythro* sphingosine was formed under the conditions of these biological experiments.

One experimental finding which does not fit the chemical and biological evidence stated above is that of Sribney and Kennedy,[105] who showed that N-acetyl *threo* sphingosine, but not N-acetyl *erythro* sphingosine, reacts with cytidine diphosphate choline in the presence of an enzyme preparation obtained from chicken liver to form a sphingomyelin. This unexpected result suggests that the natural form of sphingosine, as it exists in the sphingomyelins, is in the *threo* configuration. While it is possible that the stereochemical structure of sphingosine in the sphingomyelins is different from that in the cerebrosides, this would seem most improbable or unlikely. An alternative explanation may be to assume that the results of Sribney and Kennedy are due to an "enzymatic artifact." It may be that under the conditions of these *in vitro* experiments the *threo* derivative might reach the enzyme site, but in the cell under different solubility conditions the *erythro* derivative is the physiologically active compound. It would also be of considerable importance to determine the configuration of sphingosine in the enzymatically formed sphingomyelin, since it is conceivable that an inversion at carbon 3 takes place during the course of the enzymatic reaction, possibly through a keto intermediate.

Dihydrosphingosine, which is readily formed by catalytic reduction of sphingosine, is also a naturally occurring base and was first shown to be present in the larval form (*Cysticercus fasciolaris*) of the tapeworm, *Taenia crassicollis,* of cats by Lesuk and Anderson.[70] Carter and his co-workers [25, 26] found that it is present in the cerebroside fraction of brain and nerve tissue and in considerably higher quantity in spinal cord than in brain.

Isolation and Assay Techniques

Sphingosine is commonly isolated by hydrolysis of sphingolipides with N sulfuric acid in methanol under reflux for 6 hours, or $2N$ HCl in methanol under reflux for 24 hours. After removal of fatty acids with petroleum ether, the aqueous methanolic solution is neutralized and the crude base fraction is extracted with ether. The ether is removed, the residue dissolved in ethanol, and the sphingosine bases precipitated with sulfuric acid to give sphingosine and dihydrosphingosine sulfates. These can be separated by fractional crystallization from methanol, in which dihydrosphingosine sulfate is much less soluble. Preparation of other derivatives gives further purification. Triacetyl sphingosine crystallizes nicely from acetone, and tribenzoyldihydrosphingosine is recrystallized from hot ethanol. Brady and Burton [11] have prepared sphingosine from the sulfate by extraction of an alkaline solution with an isoamyl alcohol-heptane mixture. After removal of the organic solvents, free sphingosine was recrystallized from petroleum ether. Sphingosine has been isolated by silicic acid chromatography,[129] and sphingosine and dihydrosphingosine have been separated on paper with pyridine as the developing solvent.[12] A reversed phase partition system using siliconized diatomaceous earth has been developed by Wittenberg [125] for the separation of sphingosine and related compounds after preliminary conversion of these substances to their N-succinyl derivatives.

Several assay methods are available for sphingosine. The McKibbin-Taylor [74] procedure depends on the fact that sphingosine and sphingosine-like materials are extracted into chloroform from acid hydrolysates, while short-chain amines remain in the aqueous phase. The nitrogen in the chloroform layer is then determined. The method of Robins and co-workers [93] involves the preparation of a dinitrophenyl derivative, with dinitrofluorobenzene, after hydrolysis of the sphingolipides.

Chemical Synthesis

A number of chemical syntheses for sphingosine and dihydrosphingosine have been developed. Gregory and Malkin [41] prepared the oxime (XIII) of methyl 3-keto octadecanoate (XII) and reduced this first with palladium on charcoal and hydrogen in the presence of hydrochloric acid to the amine hydrochloride (XIV), then with Adam's catalyst and hydrogen to the hydroxy ester (XV), and finally with lithium aluminum hydride to dihydrosphingosine (XVI). The product was apparently a mixture of racemates.

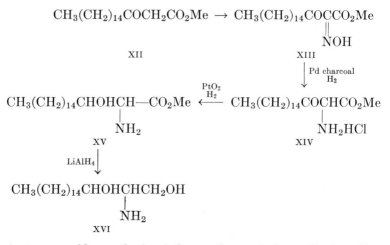

$$CH_3(CH_2)_{14}COCH_2CO_2Me \rightarrow CH_3(CH_2)_{14}COCCO_2Me$$

XII

XIII (with NOH group)

Pd charcoal
H₂

$$CH_3(CH_2)_{14}CHOHCH—CO_2Me \xleftarrow{\text{PtO}_2 \; H_2} CH_3(CH_2)_{14}COCHCO_2Me$$

with NH₂ (XV)

with NH₂HCl (XIV)

LiAlH₄

$$CH_3(CH_2)_{14}CHOHCHCH_2OH$$

with NH₂

XVI

A stereospecific synthesis of the *erythro* and *threo* dihydrosphingosines has been carried out by Jenny and Grob.[46] Reduction of 2-octa-

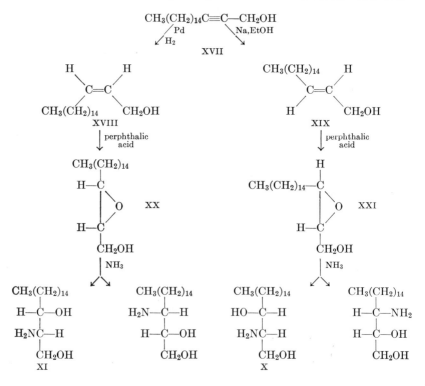

decyne-1-ol (XVII) with palladium and hydrogen gave the *cis*-2-octadecene-1-ol (XVIII) and with sodium in ethanol yielded the *trans* (XIX) compound. Each of these was treated with perphthalic acid to obtain the *cis* (XX) and *trans* (XXI) epoxides. Since a basic attack is from the rear of one of the ring carbons, the configuration of which is therefore inverted, ring opening with ammonia gave two isomeric diols from each epoxide. One of these, from the *cis* epoxide, was *threo* dihydrosphingosine (XI) and one from the *trans* epoxide was *erythro* dihydrosphingosine (X).

Shapiro, Segal, and Flowers [104] prepared dihydrosphingosine by another route. Ethyl palmitoyl acetoacetate (XXII) was coupled with benzene diazonium chloride, and the product was reductively acetylated to an amide (XXIII) which was reduced with lithium aluminum hydride to N-acetyl dihydrosphingosine (XXIV). The pure *erythro* N-acetyl compound was obtained after one recrystallization:

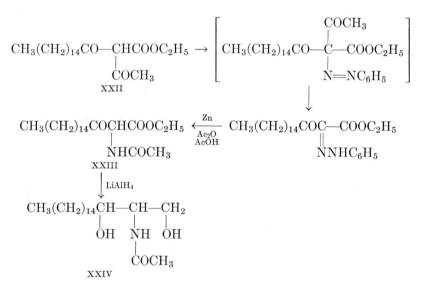

A similar series of reactions has been used by the same investigators for the preparation of DL *erythro* sphingosine.[102, 103]

The *cis* and *trans* forms of DL *threo* sphingosine and of DL *erythro* sphingosine have been prepared by Grob and Gadient.[42] Condensation of 2-hexadecynal (XXV) with nitroethanol gave a mixture of two nitro diols (XXVI), which were separated by fractional crystallization. The higher melting fraction, which was the *threo* form, was reduced to the amine (XXVII) with zinc or aluminum, and the triple bond reduced to a *cis* double bond with palladium inactivated with lead carbonate, or to a *trans* double bond with sodium in butanol or lithium aluminum hydride in tetrahydrofuran. Similarly, the *cis* and *trans* forms of DL *erythro* sphingosine were obtained by reduction of the lower melting nitro diol:

$$CH_3(CH_2)_{12}C \equiv C-CHO \ + \ O_2NCH_2CH_2OH \longrightarrow CH_3(CH_2)_{12}C \equiv C-CHOHCHNO_2$$

$$\underset{CH_2OH}{|}$$

XXV   Zn or / Al   XXVI

$$CH_3(CH_2)_{12}C \equiv CCHOHCHNH_2CH_2OH$$

Pd, PbCO_3 /   XXVII   Na in butanol
/ H_2   or LiAlH_4

cis sphingosine   *trans* sphingosine

PHYTOSPHINGOSINE AND DEHYDROPHYTOSPHINGOSINE

In studies on the hydrolysis products of corn phospholipides, Carter et al.[15] were able to isolate a long-chain base similar to sphingosine. This material is identical to a substance first isolated by Zellner[130] in 1911 from mushrooms, and named cerebrin base. It has also been shown to be present in yeast[91] and molds.[10] The structure of this compound, which is now called phytosphingosine (XXVIII), was established by periodate oxidation. The stereochemistry of carbon atoms 3 and 4 is unknown.

$$C_{14}H_{29}CH-CH-CH-CH_2 \xrightarrow{HIO_4}$$

$$\underset{OH}{|} \ \underset{OH}{|} \ \underset{NH_2}{|} \ \underset{OH}{|}$$

XXVIII

$$C_{14}H_{29}CHO + 2HCO_2H + HCHO + NH_3$$

Dehydrophytosphingosine, isolated so far only from soybean lipides,[78] has been incompletely characterized, but appears to be an unsaturated derivative of phytosphingosine which, based on an absorption peak at 9.7 μ in the infrared, has a *trans* double bond.

A mixture of the racemic forms of phytosphingosine has been synthesized by Prostenik and Stanacev[83] by a series of reactions similar to those used by Shapiro et al.[103] for sphingosine, but with ethyl 2-methoxy palmitoyl acetoacetate as the starting material.

SPHINGOMYELIN

Sphingomyelins are phospholipides in which sphingosine or a closely related base is bound by an amide linkage to a long-chain fatty acid, and by an ester linkage to phosphorylcholine. The name "phospho-sphingoside" has been suggested for these compounds, and the term "diaminophosphatide" is used in the older literature. As early as 1884, Thudicum [119] discovered this class of compounds. It was established by Levene [71] that partial hydrolysis of dihydrosphingomyelin yielded N-lignoceryl dihydrosphingosine. In addition, phosphorylcholine and sphingosine phosphate have been isolated as hydrolysis products,[92, 99] so it is evident that phosphorylcholine must be esterified to one of the hydroxyl groups of sphingosine. The position of attachment of the phosphorylcholine was shown by Marinetti et al.[75] by periodate oxida-tion of sphingosine phosphate (XXIX) obtained by alkaline hydrolysis of sphingomyelin. The product, glycolaldehyde phosphate (XXX), could only be formed from a structure in which phosphate was esteri-fied to the hydroxyl group at carbon atom 1.

$$CH_3(CH_2)_{12}CH{=}CH{-}\underset{\underset{XXIX}{\overset{|}{O}H}}{\overset{|}{C}H}{-}\underset{\overset{|}{N}H_2}{\overset{|}{C}H}{-}CH_2OPO_3H_2 \xrightarrow{IO_4^-}$$

$$CH_3(CH_2)_{12}CH{=}CH{-}\underset{XXX}{CHO} + HC\overset{O}{\underset{}{\diagup\!\!\diagup}}{-}CH_2OPO_3H_2$$

An even better proof was obtained by this same group of investiga-tors [99] by treating intact sphingomyelin (XXXI) with performic acid and then oxidizing the product (XXXII) with periodate. Further treatment of the phosphorylcholine-containing fragment (XXXIII) with permanganate followed by acid hydrolysis yielded serine (XXXIV) as one of the final products. This could result only if the primary hydroxyl group of sphingosine had been protected by esterifica-tion with phosphorylcholine prior to periodate attack.

Thannhauser and Reichel reported [115] that a sphingomyelin ester containing palmitic acid esterified to the hydroxyl group at carbon atom 3 exists in nature; this has since been shown to be due to con-tamination of the preparation with a saturated lecithin.[116] No evidence now exists for the occurrence of 3-substituted sphingosine derivatives. Sphingomyelin from brain has been reported by Thannhauser and

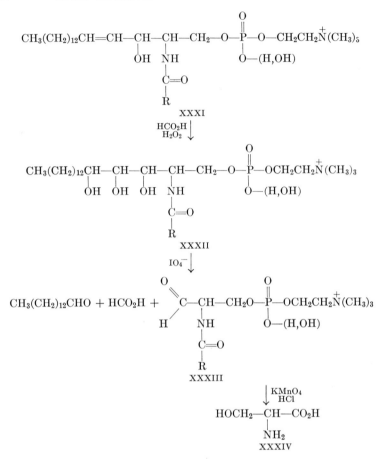

Boncoddo to contain stearic, lignoceric, and nervonic acids,[112] and preparations from lung and spleen [110] had palmitic and lignoceric acids as the constituent fatty acids.

Isolation and Assay Techniques

Most methods for the preparation of sphingomyelin depend on the fact that these compounds are insoluble in ether. Carter and co-workers [22] treated brain or spinal cord first with acetone to remove sterols, and then with anhydrous ether to remove phosphoglycerides. The sphingolipides were next extracted from the residue with hot alcohol, from which, on cooling, a mixture of sphingomyelin and cerebroside was precipitated. This mixture may be partially separated by fractionation from glacial acetic acid or chloroform-methanol, in which sphingomyelin is more soluble, or pyridine, in which cerebroside is more soluble. The last traces of cerebroside can be removed from the preparation by passing a solution in petroleum ether-methanol through an alumina column,[117, 64] and the product in the eluate is recrystallized from ethyl acetate. Since sphingomyelin may be contaminated with ether-insoluble saturated lecithins, Klenk and Rennkamp [64] treated their preparation with sodium ethylate in ethanol under reflux for 1 hour to hydrolyze the lecithin. Although sphingomyelin is relatively alkali-stable, this procedure destroys a part of the desired substance. Thannhauser, Benotti, and Boncoddo [110] have selectively hydrolyzed the hydrolecithin using milder conditions by shaking the mixture for 24 hours at 37° with N aqueous sodium hydroxide.

A simplified preparation of sphingomyelin from a commercial beef heart lecithin fraction has been described by Rapport and Lerner.[90] Most of the phosphoglycerides were removed by hexane-acetone (1:1), and the remaining crude sphingomyelin was freed of phosphoglyceride by the mild alkaline hydrolysis procedure of Dawson [36] involving treatment with N methanolic sodium hydroxide at 37° for 20 minutes. Sphingomyelin was then recrystallized from methanol-ethyl acetate.

An analytical method for sphingomyelin in tissues depends on the assay for choline after total alkaline hydrolysis with barium hydroxide. The total choline minus the choline obtained after a mild alkaline hydrolysis with N alkali at 37° for 24 hours represents sphingomyelin.[35, 43] A direct determination of sphingomyelin as an acetone-insoluble reineckate has been described by Thannhauser, Benotti, and Reinstein.[111] The usual tests for purity of sphingomyelin involve, in addition to the determination of N/P ratios, analysis for the absence of carbohydrate, ester groups or glycerol, plasmalogen, and ninhydrin-reacting substances. Purified sphingomyelins are white crystalline solids which are soluble in benzene, warm ethanol, and hot ethyl acetate, and are insoluble in ether and acetone. Various preparations exhibit optical activities of $[\alpha]^D + 4.9°$ to 7°.

Chemical Synthesis

The synthesis of two dihydrosphingomyelins has recently been described by Shapiro and co-workers.[101] The key intermediate in the preparation was a hydroxymethyl oxazoline (XXXV) in which both the secondary hydroxyl and the amino group were blocked. This compound was treated with β-chloroethylphosphoryl dichloride in the presence of pyridine to yield the phosphate ester (XXXVI). After heating with hydrochloric acid to open the oxazoline ring, acylation with palmitoyl chloride in the presence of sodium acetate gave the amide (XXXVII). This was then treated with trimethylamine and subjected to mild alkaline hydrolysis to obtain palmitoyldihydrosphingomyelin (XXXVIII). The stearoyl derivative was prepared in an identical manner.

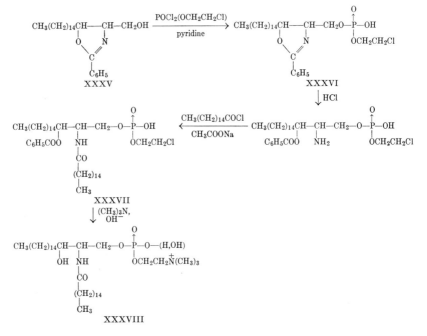

CEREBROSIDES

Cerebrosides contain a nitrogenous base, either sphingosine or dihydrosphingosine, a long-chain fatty acid, and a sugar. They have been variously designated as galactolipins, glycolipides, and glycosphingosides. Thudicum [119] was able to demonstrate the presence of two types of cerebrosides, one of which was called phrenosine, and the other kerasin (cerasin). Later, Klenk and co-workers [51, 60] recognized the existence of additional cerebrosides, nervone, and oxynervone. Kerasin (cerasin) contains lignoceric acid $(CH_3(CH_2)_{22}COOH)$; phrenosine, also called cerebron by Thierfelder,[118] has cerebronic acid $(CH_3-(CH_2)_{21}CHOHCOOH)$; nervone has nervonic acid, *cis* 15-16-tetracosenoic acid; and oxynervone contains as the fatty acid oxynervonic acid, which is a hydroxynervonic acid with the position of the OH group uncertain. Other fatty acids are present also. Chibnall and co-workers [31] showed that the fatty acid mixture obtained from a yeast cerebroside preparation consisted primarily of α-hydroxy *n*-hexacosanoic

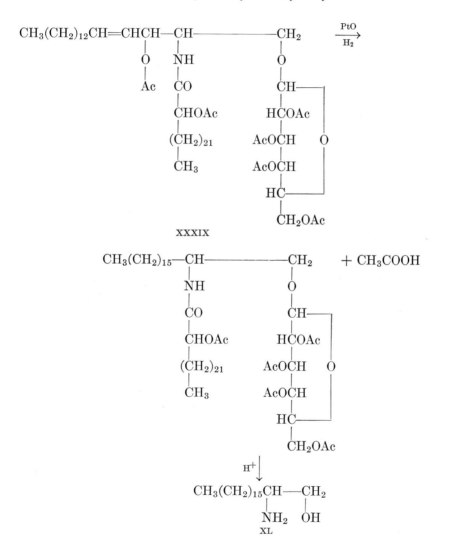

XXXIX

XL

acid. Fatty acids of 22 carbons in length were present in small amounts in the hydrolysis products of cerebrosides from other sources.[30]

Cerebrosides from animal brain contain galactose as the sugar component. In the lipide disorder, Gaucher's disease, which is characterized in part by an accumulation of cerebrosides in the spleen, it has been shown that glucose is the main sugar constituent.[44]

Partial hydrolysis of preparations of cerebrosides by early workers yielded galactosidosphingosine [119, 50] (psychosine) and N-cerebronyl sphingosine.[50] Psychosine did not reduce the ordinary aldehyde reagents and therefore contained a glycosidic linkage. Klenk and Harle [59] showed that only one of the hydroxyl groups of sphingosine was bound by first methylating dihydropsychosine and then isolating a monomethyldihydrosphingosine after hydrolysis with dilute sulfuric acid. Pryde and Humphreys [84, 85] methylated a cerebroside mixture and isolated 2,3,4,6 tetramethyl galactose after hydrolysis, providing further evidence for a galactosidic bond and for a 1,5 pyranose ring.

The position of attachment of galactose to sphingosine remained in doubt until the recent work of Carter and Greenwood.[21] These investigators treated hexaacetyl phrenosine (XXXIX) with platinum oxide and hydrogen, and obtained acetic acid as a hydrogenolysis product, and sphingine (XL) after hydrolysis. Since triacetyl sphingosine reacts in the same manner, the position of attachment of galactose must have been at carbon 1 of sphingosine. Nakayama [79] also reached this conclusion by methylation studies.

An unsolved problem in the proof of structure of cerebrosides is the stereochemical nature of the galactosidic bond. Hamosoto [45] found psychosine sulfate to be hydrolyzed by a β-galactosidase, but Kiss and Jurcsik [49] could observe hydrolysis of cerebrosides only with an α-galactosidase.

Isolation and Assay Techniques.

Like the sphingomyelins, the cerebrosides are insoluble in ether and soluble in hot alcohol. Purification of cerebrosides from crude, cold alcohol-insoluble lipide mixtures can be accomplished by crystallization from hot glacial acetic acid to give a preparation enriched in cerebrosides which still, however, contains phospholipides. Klenk and Leupold [63] dissolved a mixture of cerebroside and sphingomyelin in pyridine, removed the insoluble phospholipides by filtration and any remaining traces of phospholipide by passage through an alumina column. A new procedure for the large-scale preparation of highly pure cerebrosides has been developed by Radin and co-workers.[87, 88] In this method, a mixture of cold alcohol-insoluble sphingolipides is passed through a column of Florisil which removes most of the phospholipides, and then through a mixed bed of cation and anion ion exchange resins for removal of acidic and basic lipides. The cerebrosides in the eluate are 87.5% pure and are further purified by crystallization from chloroform-methanol or by formation of a barium complex. The latter procedure yields a preparation which is 98% cerebroside. Weiss[123] has studied the chromatography of sphingolipides on silicic acid using a gradient elution method with increasing quantities of methanol in chloroform. Cerasin and phrenosin were separated in two distinct bands; this separation was previously accomplished only with difficulty by the procedure of Rosenheim[97] which was based on differential solubility of these compounds in acetone.

Assays for cerebrosides are based on the sugar content after acid hydrolysis.[13, 109] Since lipides other than cerebrosides contain carbohydrate, preliminary purification according to Radin et al.[88] would lead to more accurate analyses. Tests for purity also include determination of the absence of phosphorus, ester groups, and ninhydrin-reacting substances. Iodine numbers[98] have been determined for various cerebroside preparations and are as follows: cerebron, 30.7; cerasin, 30.6; nervone, 62.7. Cerebrosides are white crystalline-appearing solids. They exhibit optical activity, but the values in the literature vary a great deal, and determinations should be repeated on highly purified samples. Cerasin and nervone are reported as levorotatory, while phrenosine is dextrorotatory.

CEREBROSIDE SULFURIC ESTER

In 1933, Blix[1] isolated from beef brain a crystalline sulfur-containing lipide, as the potassium salt, which contained fatty acid (primarily cerebronic acid), galactose, and sphingosine. Nakayama[80] and Thannhauser and co-workers[113] also reported preparation of this substance, and the latter group by methylation studies showed that the sulfate was esterified at the primary hydroxyl group, carbon 6 of galactose, and that carbon 1 was in glycosidic linkage to the remainder of the molecule:

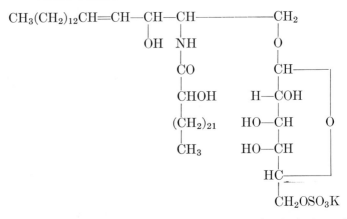

Lees [69] developed a simplified procedure for the isolation of this same substance from brain white matter which gave a much higher yield. Radin and co-workers [86, 89] separated sulfatides from cerebrosides by elution with lithium acetate in chloroform-alcohol-water from a mixed ion exchange column.

DERIVATIVES OF SPHINGOMYELIN AND CEREBROSIDE

A number of relatively small molecular weight derivatives of sphingosine have been isolated from tissues and have been obtained by partial hydrolysis of sphingomyelin and cerebroside. The ceramide, N-lignoceryl sphingosine, has been isolated without prior hydrolysis from spleen,[121] liver,[39] and red cells.[61] This substance has been prepared by hydrolysis with methanolic sodium hydroxide of a pig liver preparation,[114] and Levene [71] isolated lignoceryl dihydrosphingosine as a product of partial hydrolysis of hydrogenated sphingomyelin. N-cerebronyl sphingosine has been obtained by Klenk [50] by partial hydrolysis of the cerebroside, phrenosine, with a mixture of glacial acetic acid and 10% sulfuric acid. The material which has been named psychosine (galactosidosphingosine) by Thudicum [119] has not been observed in tissues. However, it has been isolated by Klenk [50] after barium hydroxide hydrolysis of cerebroside, and an improved modification of this procedure has been developed by Carter and Fujino.[16]

Sphingosylphosphorylcholine has been reported to be present in pancreas,[47] liver,[106] and embryonic tissue,[81] but in a reinvestigation of this problem Dawson [37] could find no evidence for the presence of this substance in a variety of animal tissues. Acid hydrolysis of sphingomyelin yielded some sphingosylphosphorylcholine and sphingosine phosphate. Alkaline hydrolysis of sphingomyelin also gave sphingosine phosphate but none of the choline derivative.[37, 99]

A hydrolysis product from bovine cerebral tissue which had the structure of an O-tetradecylsphingosine was isolated by Niemann.[82] No further information concerning the parent compound from which this was derived is available.

MUCOLIPIDES AND RELATED SUBSTANCES

The term "mucolipides" has been suggested by Rosenberg, Howe, and Chargaff [96] for those complex substances which have in common the presence of sialic acids among their constituents. This group includes gangliosides, strandin, and similar compounds, materials whose chemical structures are only partly known.

Sialic acid is the name given by Blix [2] to a crystalline substance which he isolated first from submaxillary mucin and which he later suggested was also present in a brain lipide fraction [3] on the basis of similar color reactions: a deep red color on heating with Bial's reagent (orcinol and hydrochloric acid) and a marked humin formation with hot aqueous acids. Klenk,[55] using a similar brain lipide fraction, isolated a crystalline acid exhibiting comparable color reactions which he called neuraminic acid. For some time, the relationship between the two compounds was unknown but recent work has clarified this point. The nomenclature now agreed upon by Blix, Gottschalk, and Klenk [4] reserves the name neuraminic acid for the basic unsubstituted compound, and sialic acid as the group name for acylated neuraminic acids. Sialic acids are present not only in mucolipides but also in a variety of mucoproteins, and include the N-acetyl, N-glycolyl, and O,N-diacetyl neuraminic acids.[40, 33]

The first sialic acid of Blix [2] is now known to be O,N-diacetyl neuraminic acid. The compound isolated by Klenk [55] by a procedure involving hydrolysis at 100° with 5% methanolic hydrogen chloride was the methyl glycoside of neuraminic acid, and all acyl groups were lost by alcoholysis.

The synthesis of N-acetyl neuraminic acid, which has been reported to be present in human gangliosides,[5] has recently been accomplished by Cornforth, Firth, and Gottschalk [33] from the reaction of N-acetyl D-glucosamine and oxalacetic acid. The product appeared to be identical to authentic N-acetyl neuraminic acid of natural origin, and the following structure was proposed:

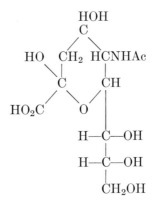

However, Comb and Roseman [32] obtained and purified an enzyme from *Clostridium perfringens* which reversibly converted N-acetyl neuraminic acid to pyruvate and N-acetyl D-mannosamine. N-acetyl D-glucosamine was completely inactive in this enzyme system. These investigators were also able to show that at the alkaline pH (11.0) used in the chemical synthesis, an appreciable quantity of N-acetyl D-mannosamine is formed from N-acetyl D-glucosamine.[94] The N-acetyl hexosamine, therefore, in N-acetyl neuraminic acid is apparently a mannose derivative.

By following the neuraminic acid content, Klenk [55] succeeded in purifying a brain lipide fraction to the extent that it contained 21% neuraminic acid and could be crystallized from hot alcohol as small spherocrystals. He named this material ganglioside because it appeared to be concentrated mostly in ganglion cells. Other constituents were 13% sphingosine or sphingosine-like substances, 20% fatty acids (primarily stearic and nervonic), and 40–43% sugars, mainly galactose, with some glucose. Klenk [57] and also other workers [14, 6, 7] have since found galactosamine to be present in these compounds. The presence in lipides of compounds which resembled cerebrosides and gave color reactions with Bial's orcinol reagent had been recognized much earlier,[66, 122] and Klenk [53, 54] had in fact previously isolated a lipide with the same properties which he called "Substance X," from tissues of individuals with Niemann-Pick's disease and Tay-Sachs' disease. These compounds are water-soluble non-dialyzable colloids, which are insoluble in ether and acetone. They contain no free amino groups, are non-reducing, and are monobasic acids. Svennerholm [108] has proposed the following sequence of constituents:

Ceramide-hexose-hexose-hexosamine-N-acetyl neuraminic acid

Folch and his co-workers [38] in 1951 isolated from gray and white matter of brain a high molecular weight (250,000) water-soluble substance which was named strandin because it was obtained in long birefringent strands. This material, like the gangliosides, was a monobasic acid, with a neutral equivalent of about 1500, and contained a chromogenic group which was a sialic acid.[34,29] More highly purified preparations were shown to be homogenous by electrophoresis and ultracentrifugation and had a neutral equivalent of approximately 1150.[68,95] This material contained 30% sialic acid, 25% galactose and glucose (in a ratio of nearly 2:1), 10–11% galactosamine, and the remainder fatty acids and sphingosine or sphingosine-like substances combined as ceramides. By partial acid hydrolysis followed by dialysis, it was found that sialic acid was combined through its reducing group, and that the galactosamine and the neutral sugars were combined with each other.[68] Bogoch [8,9] has obtained from a strandin preparation after partial hydrolysis a fragment with the composition of a glucocerebroside.

Strandin and gangliosides are similar not only in their constituent materials but in their color reactions and in their solubility properties. They differ in crystalline form, and strandin contains more sialic acid and less sugar than do the gangliosides. Also, strandin has been obtained from brain in higher yields, and appears to be present in immature brain in much larger amounts than the gangliosides. However, these differences might be due to differences in methods of isolation. Whereas strandin is isolated by mild procedures, gangliosides are obtained by treatment with hot glacial acetic acid.[56] When strandin is treated with this latter reagent, the crystalline form changes from strands to spherules, and the content of sialic acid decreases, and the sugars increase. Also, when mucolipides are isolated by procedures more mild than those used for strandin, and less mild than those used for gangliosides, a number of different fractions of varying degrees of hydrolysis can be demonstrated.[107] These observations suggest that strandin may be a polyganglioside.

Many other complex glycosides of sphingosine have been discovered. Yamakawa and Suzuki [126,127] isolated from stroma of horse erythrocytes a lipide which was called hematoside. Hydrolysis of this substance yielded fatty acid, sphingosine, galactose, and a water-soluble aminohydroxy acid, hemataminic acid, isolated as the methoxyl derivative. No galactosamine was present. The parent compound was named prehemataminic acid. Klenk and co-workers [61, 65] confirmed these results and showed that hemataminic acid was the methoxyl derivative of neuraminic acid. Species differences apparently exist, since erythrocyte lipides of the human, sheep, goat, and hog contain hexosamine but no sialic acid, and have been referred to as the "globoside" type.[128] Also, glucosamine instead of galactosamine has been shown to be present in bovine erythrocytes.[62] Radin [86] obtained a very complex pattern of glycolipides after chromatography of human red cell lipides on a cellulose column.

REFERENCES

1. Blix, G., *Z. physiol. Chem.,* **219**, 82 (1933).
2. Blix, G., *Z. physiol. Chem.,* **240**, 43 (1936).
3. Blix, G., *Skand. Arch. Physiol.,* **80**, 46 (1938).
4. Blix, G., A. Gottschalk, and E. Klenk, *Nature,* **179**, 1088 (1957).
5. Blix, G., and L. Odin, *Acta Chem. Scand.,* **9**, 1541 (1955).
6. Blix, G., L. Svennerholm, and I. Werner, *Acta Chem. Scand.,* **4**, 717 (1950).
7. Blix, G., L. Svennerholm, and I. Werner, *Acta Chem. Scand.,* **6**, 358 (1952).
8. Bogoch, S., *J. Am. Chem. Soc.,* **79**, 3286 (1957).
9. Bogoch, S., *Biochem. J.,* **68**, 319 (1958).
10. Bohonas, N., and W. H. Peterson, *J. Biol. Chem.,* **149**, 295 (1943).
11. Brady, R. O., and R. M. Burton, *J. Neurochem.,* **1**, 18 (1956).
12. Brady, R. O., and G. J. Koval, *J. Biol. Chem.,* **233**, 26 (1958).
13. Brand, F. C., and W. M. Sperry, *J. Biol. Chem.,* **141**, 545 (1941).
14. Brante, G., *Upsala Lakareforen Forhandl.,* **53**, 301 (1948).
15. Carter, H. E., W. D. Celmer, W. E. M. Lands, K. L. Mueller, and H. H. Tomizawa, *J. Biol. Chem.,* **206**, 613 (1954).
16. Carter, H. E., and Y. Fujino, *J. Biol. Chem.,* **221**, 879 (1956).
17. Carter, H. E., D. S. Galanos, and Y. Fujino, *Can. J. Biochem. and Physiol.,* **34**, 320 (1956).
18. Carter, H. E., D. S. Galanos, R. H. Gigg, J. H. Law, T. Nakayama, D. B. Smith, and E. J. Weber, *Federation Proc.,* **16**, 817 (1957).
19. Carter, H. E., F. J. Glick, W. P. Norris, and G. E. Phillips, *J. Biol. Chem.,* **142**, 449 (1942).
20. Carter, H. E., F. J. Glick, W. P. Norris, and G. E. Phillips, *J. Biol. Chem.,* **191**, 727 (1951).
21. Carter, H. E., and F. L. Greenwood, *J. Biol. Chem.,* **199**, 283 (1952).
22. Carter, H. E., W. J. Haines, W. E. Ledyard, and W. P. Norris, *J. Biol. Chem.,* **169**, 77 (1947).
23. Carter, H. E., and C. G. Humiston, *J. Biol. Chem.,* **191**, 727 (1951).

24. Carter, H. E., O. Nalbandov, and P. A. Tavormina, *J. Biol. Chem.*, **192**, 197 (1951).

25. Carter, H. E., and W. P. Norris, *J. Biol. Chem.*, **145**, 709 (1942).

26. Carter, H. E., W. P. Norris, F. J. Glick, G. E. Phillips, and R. Harris, *J. Biol. Chem.*, **170**, 269 (1947).

27. Carter, H. E., D. Shapiro, and J. B. Harrison, *J. Am. Chem. Soc.*, **75**, 1007 (1953).

28. Celmer, W. D., and H. E. Carter, *Physiol. Rev.*, **32**, 167 (1952).

29. Chatagnon, C., and P. Chatagnon, *Bull. soc. chim. biol.*, **35**, 1319 (1953).

30. Chibnall, A. C., S. H. Piper, and E. F. Williams, *Biochem. J.*, **55**, 707 (1953).

31. Chibnall, A. C., S. H. Piper, and E. F. Williams, *Biochem. J.*, **55**, 711 (1953).

32. Comb, D. G., and S. Roseman, *J. Am. Chem. Soc.*, **80**, 497 (1958).

33. Cornforth, J. W., M. E. Firth, and A. Gottschalk, *Biochem. J.*, **68**, 57 (1958).

34. Daun, H., *Zur Kenntnis des Folch'schen Strandin*, Dissertation, Cologne, (October 1952).

35. Dawson, R. M. C., *Biochem. J.*, **56**, 621 (1954).

36. Dawson, R. M. C., *Biochim. et Biophys. Acta*, **14**, 374 (1954).

37. Dawson, R. M. C., *Biochem. J.*, **68**, 357 (1958).

38. Folch, J., S. Arsove, and J. A. Meath, *J. Biol. Chem.*, **191**, 819 (1951).

39. Frankel, E., and F. Bielschowsky, *Z. physiol. Chem.*, **213**, 58 (1932).

40. Gottschalk, A., *Yale J. Biol. Med.*, **28**, 525 (1956).

41. Gregory, G. I., and J. Malkin, *J. Chem. Soc.*, **2453** (1951).

42. Grob, C. A., and F. Gadient, *Helv. Chim. Acta*, **40**, 1145 (1957).

43. Hack, M. H., *J. Biol. Chem.*, **169**, 137 (1947).

44. Halliday, N. H., H. J. Deuel, L. J. Tragenman, and W. E. Ward, *J. Biol. Chem.*, **132**, 171 (1940).

45. Hamosoto, Y., *Tohuku J. Exptl. Med.*, **53**, 35 (1950).

46. Jenny, E. F., and C. A. Grob, *Helv. Chim. Acta*, **36**, 1454 (1953).

47. King, E. J., and C. W. Small, *Biochem. J.*, **33**, 1135 (1939).

48. Kiss, J., G. Fodor, and D. Banfi, *Helv. Chim. Acta*, **37**, 1471 (1954).

49. Kiss, J., and I. Jurcsik, *Acta Chim. Acad. Sci. Hung.*, **5**, 477 (1955).

50. Klenk, E., *Z. physiol. Chem.*, **153**, 74 (1926).

51. Klenk, E., *Z. physiol. Chem.*, **157**, 291 (1926).

52. Klenk, E., *Z. physiol. Chem.*, **185**, 169 (1929).

53. Klenk, E., *Z. physiol. Chem.*, **235**, 24 (1935).

54. Klenk, E., *Ber. ges. Physiol. exptl. Pharmakol.*, **96**, 659 (1937).

55. Klenk, E., *Z. physiol. Chem.*, **268**, 50 (1941).

56. Klenk, E., *Z. physiol. Chem.*, **273**, 76 (1942).

57. Klenk, E., *Z physiol. Chem.*, **288**, 216 (1951).

58. Klenk, E., and H. Faillard, *Z. physiol. Chem.*, **299**, 48 (1955).

59. Klenk, E., and R. Harle, *Z. physiol. Chem.*, **178**, 221 (1928).

60. Klenk, E., and R. Harle, *Z. physiol. Chem.*, **189**, 243 (1930).

61. Klenk, E., and K. Lauenstein, *Z. physiol. Chem.*, **288**, 220 (1951).

62. Klenk, E., and K. Lauenstein, *Z. physiol. Chem.*, **291**, 249 (1953).

63. Klenk, E., and F. Leupold, *Z. physiol. Chem.*, **281**, 208 (1944).

64. Klenk, E., and F. Rennkamp, *Z. physiol. Chem.*, **267**, 145 (1941).

65. Klenk, E., and H. Wolter, *Z. physiol. Chem.*, **291**, 259 (1953).

66. Landsteiner, K., and P. A. Levene, *J. Immunol.*, **10**, 731 (1925).

67. Lapworth, A., *J. Chem. Soc.*, **103**, 1029 (1913).

68. LeBaron, F. N., and J. Folch, *Physiol. Rev.,* **37,** 539 (1957).

69. Lees, M. B., *Federation Proc.,* **15,** 298 (1956).

70. Lesuk, A., and R. J. Anderson, *J. Biol. Chem.,* **139,** 457 (1941).

71. Levene, P. A., *J. Biol. Chem.,* **24,** 69 (1916).

72. Levene, P. A., and C. J. West, *J. Biol. Chem.,* **16,** 549 (1913).

73. Levene, P. A., and C. J. West, *J. Biol. Chem.,* **18,** 481 (1914).

74. McKibbin, J. M., and W. E. Taylor, *J. Biol. Chem.,* **178,** 29 (1949).

75. Marinetti, G., J. F. Berry, G. Rouser, and E. Stotz, *J. Am. Chem. Soc.,* **75,** 313 (1953).

76. Marinetti, G., and E. Stotz, *J. Am. Chem. Soc.,* **76,** 1345 (1954).

77. Mislow, K., *J. Am. Chem. Soc.,* **74,** 5155 (1952).

78 Mueller, K. L., M.S. Thesis, University of Illinois (1953).

79. Nakayama, T., *J. Biochem. (Japan),* **37,** 309 (1950).

80. Nakayama, T., *J. Biochem. (Japan),* **38,** 157 (1951).

81. Needham, J., *Biochem. J.,* **31,** 1199 (1937).

82. Niemann, C., *J. Am. Chem. Soc.,* **63,** 3535 (1941).

83. Prostenik, M., and N. Z. Stanacev, *Naturwissenschaften,* **43,** 447 (1956)

84. Pryde, J., and R. W. Humphreys, *Biochem. J.,* **18,** 661 (1924).

85. Pryde, J., and R. W. Humphreys, *Biochem. J.,* **20,** 825 (1926).

86. Radin, N. S., *Federation Proc.,* **16,** 825 (1957).

87. Radin, N. S., J. R. Brown, and F. B. Lavin, *J. Biol. Chem.,* **219,** 977 (1956).

88. Radin, N. S., F. B. Lavin, and J. R. Brown, *J. Biol. Chem.,* **217,** 789 (1955).

89. Radin, N. S., F. B. Martin, and J. R. Brown, *J. Biol. Chem.,* **224,** 499 (1957).

90. Rapport, M. M., and B. Lerner, *J. Biol. Chem.,* **232,** 63 (1958).

91. Reindel, F., *Ann. Chem.,* **480,** 76 (1930).

92. Rennkamp, F., *Z. physiol. Chem.,* **284,** 215 (1949).

93. Robins, E., O. H. Lowry, K. M. Eydt, and R. E. McCaman, *J. Biol. Chem.,* **220,** 661 (1956).

94. Roseman, S., and D. G. Comb, *J. Am. Chem. Soc.,* **80,** 3166 (1958).

95. Rosenberg, A., and E. Chargaff, *Biochim. et Biophys. Acta,* **21,** 588 (1956).

96. Rosenberg, A., C. Howe, and E. Chargaff, *Nature,* **177,** 234 (1956).

97. Rosenheim, O., *Biochem. J.,* **8,** 110 (1914)

98. Rosenmund, K. W., W. Kuhnheim, D. V. Rosenberg-Gruszynsky, and H. Rosetti, *Z. Untersuch. Nahr. Genussm.,* **46,** 154 (1923)

99. Rouser, G., J. F. Berry, G. Marinetti, and E. Stotz, *J. Am. Chem. Soc.,* **75,** 310 (1953).

100. Seydel, P. V., *Zur Kenntnis des Sphingosine.* Dissertation, Eidgenossische Technische Hochschule in Zurich, Zurich (1941).

101. Shapiro, D., H. M. Flowers, and S. Spector-Shefer, *J. Am. Chem. Soc.,* **80,** 2339 (1958).

102. Shapiro, D., and K. Segal, *J. Am. Chem. Soc.,* **76,** 5894 (1954).

103. Shapiro, D., H. Segal, and H M. Flowers, *J. Am. Chem. Soc.,* **80,** 1194 (1958).

104. Shapiro, D., H. Segal, and H. M. Flowers, *J. Am. Chem. Soc.,* **80,** 2170 (1958).

105. Sribney, M., and E. P. Kennedy, *J. Am. Chem. Soc.,* **79,** 5325 (1957).

106. Strack, E., E. Neubaur, and H. Geissendorfer, *Z. physiol. Chem.,* **220,** 217 (1933).

107. Svennerholm, L., *Acta Chem. Scand.,* **8,** 1108 (1954).

108. Svennerholm, L., *Nature,* **177,** 524 (1956).

109. Svennerholm, L., *J. Neurochem.,* **1,** 42 (1956).

110. Thannhauser, S. J., J. Benotti, and N. F. Boncoddo, *J. Biol. Chem.*, **166**, 677 (1946).

111. Thannhauser, S. J., J. Benotti, and H. Reinstein, *J. Biol. Chem.*, **129**, 709 (1939).

112. Thannhauser, S. J., and N. F. Boncoddo, *J. Biol. Chem.*, **172**, 141 (1948).

113. Thannhauser, S. J., J. Fellig, and G. Schmidt, *J. Biol. Chem.*, **215**, 211 (1955).

114. Thannhauser, S. J., and E. Fraenkel, *Z. physiol. Chem.*, **203**, 183 (1931).

115. Thannhauser, S. J., and M. Reichel, *J. Biol. Chem.*, **135**, 1 (1940).

116. Thannhauser, S. J., and G. Schmidt, *Physiol. Rev.*, **26**, 275 (1946).

117. Thannhauser, S. J., and P. Setz, *J. Biol. Chem.*, **116**, 527 (1936).

118. Thierfelder, H., *Z. physiol. Chem.*, **43**, 21 (1904).

119. Thudicum, J. W. L., *A Treatise on the Chemical Composition of Brain*, Bailliere, Tindall, and Cox (1884).

120. Thudicum, J. W. L., *Die Konstitution des Gehirns des Menschen und die Tiere*, Franz Pietzeker (1901).

121. Tropp, C., and V. Wiedersheim, *Z. physiol. Chem.*, **222**, 39 (1933).

122. Walz, E., *Z. physiol. Chem.*, **166**, 210 (1927).

123. Weiss, B., *J. Biol. Chem.*, **223**, 523 (1956).

124. Welsh, L. H., *J. Am. Chem. Soc.*, **71**, 3500 (1949).

125. Wittenberg, J. B., *J. Biol. Chem.*, **216**, 379 (1955).

126. Yamakawa, T., and S. Suzuki, *J. Biochem. (Japan)*, **38**, 199 (1951).

127. Yamakawa, T., and S. Suzuki, *J. Biochem. (Japan)*, **39**, 175 (1952).

128. Yamakawa, T., and S. Suzuki, *J. Biochem. (Japan)*, **39**, 393 (1952).

129. Zabin, I., unpublished results.

130. Zellner, J., *Monatschr. Chem.*, **32**, 133 (1911).

6

Minor phospholipides

While the subject matter of the foregoing chapters has been directed exclusively towards the more abundant and consequently better studied phospholipides, there are several less familiar or minor types worthy of consideration. These are the phosphatidic acids, bis(phosphatidic) acids, cardiolipins, glycol lecithins, and lysolecithins. Although only indirect evidence has been presented for the normal occurrence of many of these compounds in naturally occurring lipides, the increased attention being devoted to the chemistry of these substances should provide valuable information for any subsequent biochemical investigations.

PHOSPHATIDIC ACIDS

These lipides, as represented by the following formula,

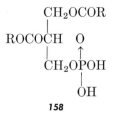

are diacyl-L-α-glycerophosphoric acids. Normally they are found in very small concentrations in most naturally occurring sources. However, this fact does not diminish their importance as a typical phosphoglyceride or as a derivative of the more commonly occurring types (phosphatidyl choline, phosphatidyl ethanolamine). Initially, most of the interest in this type of compound was derived from the report that such acids were present in high concentrations in cabbage leaves.[7] Later this fact was shown to be attributable to the presence of the enzyme, phospholipase (or lecithinase) C,[13] which attacked the fully esterified phosphoglycerides with the release of a nitrogen base and the phosphatidic acid. More recently the activation of this enzyme system by certain organic solvents, commonly used in lipide extraction procedures, added to the complications encountered in the isolation of a native phosphoglyceride from a natural source.[16] However, within the past few years substantial evidence has accumulated as to the probable role of phosphatidic acids in the biosynthesis of lecithins and triglycerides.

Stability

Prior to a discussion of the synthesis or isolation of this lipide, it is important to emphasize certain facets of its stability. Although some reference had been made in the literature to the instability of phosphatidic acids, it was not until the report of Olley [29] that sufficient evidence was presented in support of the hydrolytic decomposition of this compound by an intramolecular attack. Olley noted that synthetic dimyristoyl- and distearoyl-phosphatidic acids underwent hydrolytic decomposition on countercurrent distribution between light petroleum ether and 85% ethanol. Moreover, a sample of distearoyl-phosphatidic acid, maintained for 5 months in the laboratory without special precautions, had almost completely decomposed to free fatty acids and glycerophosphoric acid. Other experiments confirmed the susceptibility of the phosphatidic acids to decomposition under mild conditions.* Sufficient evidence was presented in support of an intra-

* Although the phosphatidic acids appear to be most stable in the salt form, only limited information is available on the properties of these derivatives. In studies on the synthetic saturated phosphatidic acids, Baer [1] reported on the melting points, specific rotation, and solubilities of the choline, ethanolamine, and, to a limited extent, the monopyridine salts. When naturally occurring lecithins were subjected to the action of phospholipase (lecithinase) C, Kates [16] observed that the resulting phosphatidic acids were soluble in diethyl ether and

molecular attack by the phosphoric acid group on the two fatty acyl esters with subsequent formation of free fatty acids and equal amounts of α- and β-glycerophosphoric acid. This latter substance undoubtedly resulted from migration of the phosphate via a cyclic intermediate. No inorganic phosphate was formed.

It is of interest to note that the phosphatidic acids are stable for long periods of time when maintained over P_2O_5 *in vacuo* or stored as the sodium salt. Also as has been noted before, the alkaline hydrolysis of the phosphatidic acids, in contrast to acid hydrolysis, proceeds without migration of the phosphate group.[38]

Thus, in any studies involving these acids, cognizance must be made of the possible instability of these compounds under certain conditions.

Preparation

Direct Synthesis. In common with the other phosphoglycerides, the synthesis of a phosphatidic acid in an unequivocal manner has posed a difficult problem. In reference to much of the early work on this subject, considerable doubt must be cast as to the chemical nature of the products owing to questions on the nature of the starting material, degree of formation of undesirable side products, and the probable decomposition of the acids in the process of isolation and on storage. The following two syntheses represent the most feasible routes to the preparation of known phosphatidic acids in good yields. Again considerable care must be exercised in handling the phosphatidic acids so that the undesirable decomposition of this material may be maintained at a minimum.

99% ethanol. In the latter solvent, the monosodium salt could be formed by addition of dilute alkali in ethanol. The sodium salt was insoluble in ethanol-diethyl ether (4:1) and 99% ethanol, but was soluble in diethyl ether. While the sodium salt could be precipitated from a diethyl ether solution by acetone, the free acid was quite soluble in the latter solvent. Inasmuch as complete data are not available on the stability of the phosphatidic acids and salts, it would seem best to avoid, as a first approximation, subjecting these compounds to pH conditions below 7.

Method (a)

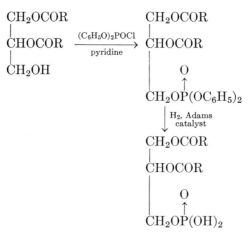

Through the use of D- and L-diglycerides, Baer[1] was able to prepare the desired enantiomeric forms in good yields. However, it is interesting to note that Uhlenbroek and Verkade[38] found the hydrogenolysis step proceeded much more smoothly (and gave a higher melting product) if performed with Pt on charcoal (as the catalyst) in dry ethyl acetate or dioxane. Apparently the Adams catalyst (PtO$_2$) retains a small amount of alkali, which is capable of forming a stable quarter salt with the phosphatidic acid. Use of acid-washed Adams catalyst obviates this difficulty.

Method (b)

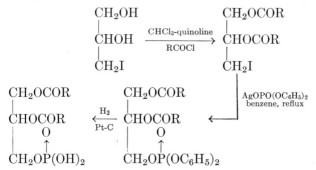

Both Hessel et al.[14] and Baylis et al.[5] have reported the successful use of method (b) for preparation of phosphatidic acids in good yields. However, it should be noted that no stereoisomeric forms of the phosphatidic acids were prepared.

Enzymatic Approach. While this approach requires phosphatidyl choline (lecithin) or phosphatidyl ethanolamine (usually of natural origin) as starting materials, it does allow a convenient route to the preparation of phosphatidic acids. In general, this procedure involves the use of phospholipase (or lecithinase) C for the specific hydrolytic cleavage of fully esterified phosphoglycerides with the resultant formation of phosphatidic acid and a free nitrogen base shown:

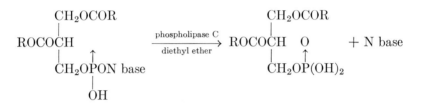

As observed by Kates,[16] this reaction is activated by solvents such as diethyl ether. Further investigation by Kates indicated that this enzyme system could be used for the preparation of phosphatidic acid in good yields. The best source of this enzyme proved to be carrot root chloroplasts; although cabbage or spinach also provided adequate sources, the chlorophyll pigments present in high amounts in these preparations are difficult to remove in a complete manner. Davidson et al.[8] employed an aqueous cabbage leaf enzyme preparation free from chloroplasts and found it capable of degrading synthetic saturated lecithins to give the theoretical yields of desired products. Naturally occurring and synthetic β-lysolecithins are attacked only partially, while the sphingomyelins are unaffected.

Thus this enzymatic procedure can provide a convenient and smooth route to the preparation of phosphatidic acids from naturally occurring as well as synthetic phosphoglycerides. It is interesting to note that Long and Maguire[24] employed enzymatic degradation, by the phospholipase D of *Clostridium Welchii* toxin, for the preparation of a diglyceride and phosphorylcholine. The diglyceride was phosphorylated by method (a) cited above and then converted to a phosphatidic acid. Subsequently this acid was hydrolyzed in an alkaline medium to give only L-α-glycerophosphoric acid, thus substantiating the L-α-configuration of the naturally occurring lecithins. In a similar manner, Kates utilized the specific action of lecithinase C of carrot root chloroplast for the formation of phosphatidic acid from the native lecithins.[16] The resultant phosphatidic acid was shown to possess the properties of an L-α-type.

General Comments

Since the phosphatidic acids are present in such small amounts in most sources and as they are relatively unstable in acid medium, their isolation is not an easy task. Normally the phosphatidic acids would be expected to be extracted along with the other lipides present in a tissue. However, due to the rather high solubility of these acids (and their salts) in acetone, any preliminary fractionation of the mixed lipides by this solvent could result in serious losses of the desired product. The most promising route to their isolation appears to be chromatography on silicic acid, where these compounds should be eluted in the more non-polar solvents. However, depending on the length of time on the column the phosphatidic acids might undergo decomposition, hence proper precautions must be taken to avoid this difficulty. In their studies on the biosynthesis of phospholipides, Kornberg and Pricer [17] found a Dowex column useful in the separation of various phosphate esters. The sample was placed on the column in an isooctane-pyridine-ethanol mixture and eluted with dilute HCl (5×10^{-4} to 2.5×10^{-3} M HCl). In this manner phosphatidic acid could be separated from the other esters. While decomposition of the phosphatidic acid could conceivably occur under these conditions, no note was made of any structural alterations in the phosphate esters. Paper chromatography has been used to some extent as a means of detection and separation of the phosphatidic acids.[15,35] However, in certain instances considerable streaking of the spots was noted and may be attributed to instability of the molecule. It is obvious, though, that more detailed information on the behavior of phosphatidic acids under various isolation procedures and conditions would be of considerable value.

The physical state of the salts of phosphatidic acids, which were isolated from wheat germ (two free hydroxyls per atom P) and from heart muscle (cardiolipin, with one free hydroxyl per atom P), have been investigated in organic solvents.[20] In non-polar solvents (benzene, acetic anhydride), the sodium and potassium salts assumed a micellar state, due to the influence of the inorganic base, and did not diffuse through cellophane bags suspended in the same solvents. The apparent molecular weights of the micelles, which were ascertained by a vapor tension method, were above 12,000. In these same non-polar solvents the salts of organic bases such as quinine and Me_4N^+ remained in monomolecular dispersion and readily diffused through cellophane. In polar solvents (methanol, ethanol, butanol, acetic acid), the sodium and potassium salts remained practically all in the monomolecular state and could diffuse through cellophane.

PHOSPHATIDYL GLYCEROLS

It has become increasingly apparent over the past few years that several different types of nitrogen-free phospholipides are present in many natural sources. A particular example is phosphatidyl glycerol (I), which has been detected in plants and animals:

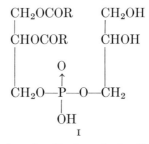

I

These compounds can be classified as derivatives of the phosphatidic acids or more correctly as derivatives of the bis(glyceryl)phosphoric acids.

Maruo and Benson [27, 28] first noted the presence of α,α'-diglycerophosphate [or bis(glyceryl)phosphoric acid] in *Scenedesmus* and suggested the possible occurrence of an acylated derivative of this compound. In a later study, these same investigators incubated *Scenedesmus* in a P^{32} containing medium and ultimately extracted the cells with hot absolute ethanol. Upon paper chromatography of this extract, four distinct phospholipide fractions were obtained. Subsequently the spots were eluted and subjected to several identification procedures. In particular, one spot was found to give reactions expected of phosphatidyl glycerol. Hence by lead tetraacetate oxidation, benzoylation, and acetonation, Benson and Maruo [6] concluded that this unknown was a phosphatidyl glycerol (I). While these results are highly significant, these compounds need to be characterized in much greater detail. Thus, the stereochemical configuration of the molecule, nature of the acyl groups, etc., are of considerable importance. This approach necessitates the isolation of these compounds in fairly large amounts. However, owing to the low concentration present in most tissues, this will be a typically difficult problem of isolation.

While the exact stereochemistry of these phospholipides is unknown, it is reasonable to assume that they would possess an L-configuration. On this basis, Baer and Buchnea [4] prepared by direct synthesis phosphatidyl glycerols of known structure and configuration. The following scheme illustrates the chemical procedures involved in the preparation of the dioleyl(L,L) derivative (yield, 90%):

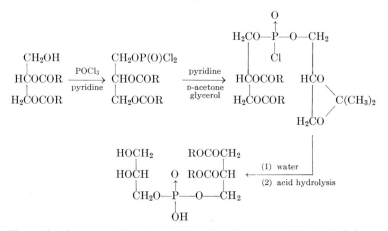

Through the use of appropriate stereoisomers of α,β-diolein and acetone glycerol, the other possible enantiomers can be prepared.

BIS(PHOSPHATIDIC) ACIDS

In the widely used serodiagnostic test for syphilis, the most commonly employed "antigen" consists of beef heart lecithin, cardiolipin (see below), and cholesterol. As is found in actual practice, the reproducible preparation of the first two components from a natural source has proved difficult. While, in general, it is considered that synthetic or highly purified lecithins can replace the beef heart lecithin component,[36, 37] the search for a suitable synthetic substitute for cardiolipin has not been as successful. However, one of the more promising avenues of study implicates the bis(phosphatidic) acids as possible substitutes. Furthermore, a synthetic bis(phosphatidic) acid, tetramyristoyl bis(L-α-glyceryl)phosphoric acid, in the presence of beef heart lecithin was shown to possess a cardiolipin-like activity. In the latter case, the greater activity of the dimyristoyl derivative (as compared to the low activity of the C_{16} and C_{18} derivatives) was thought due, in part, to its higher solubility in water. On this basis it would be important to learn whether the unsaturated analogues, which are usually more soluble, would possess a higher activity in the test system.

Synthesis

In the synthesis of the L-α-lecithins by the procedure of Baer and Kates, one of the by-products of the reaction is a bis(phosphatidic) acid. Subsequent adjustment of the concentration of the reactants, as indicated below, allowed an almost quantitative yield of optically pure bis-acids: [2]

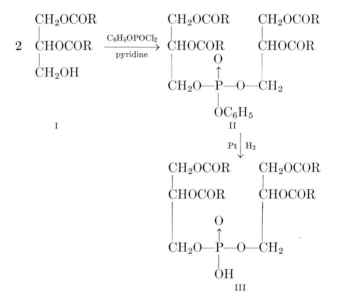

The yield of III, a tetra acyl bis(L-α-glyceryl)phosphoric acid, was in the range of 85 to 90%. The synthesis of the corresponding bis-(L-α-glyceryl)phosphoric acid was reported by Baer and Buchnea.[4] It is of interest to note that Garcia et al.[12] have found a bis(phosphatidic) acid in the flesh of the cod and haddock.

Glycol Analogues

In a somewhat comparable manner to the preparation of the glycerol containing bis(phosphatidic) acids, the glycol analogues can be synthesized by a direct procedure. This can be depicted as follows:

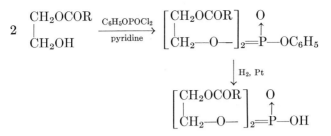

Both the palmitoyl and stearoyl derivatives were prepared by Van der Neut et al.[41] in 70 to 80% yields. The activity of these compounds as haptens in the syphilis test has not been reported. A similar approach to the synthesis of myristoyl, palmitoyl, and stearoyl bis-glycol phosphatidic acids was utilized with success by Van der Gijzen.[40] The mono acyl glycols were prepared by acylation of the tritylated glycols and subsequent removal of the trityl group by hydrogenolysis yielded the desired starting product. The remainder of the procedure was similar to that described above.

CARDIOLIPIN

Closely allied with the above mentioned phosphatidic acids is the substance commonly termed cardiolipin. In 1941, Pangborn[30] reported the occurrence of a complex phosphatidic acid compound in beef heart and affixed the name cardiolipin to it. Apparently this compound represents an essential requirement for the complement binding activity of beef heart extracts with the sera of syphilitic subjects. Later, in 1947, Pangborn[32] reported observations on the chemical nature of the products of partial hydrolysis of cardiolipin as follows:

$$\text{Cardiolipin} \xrightarrow[25°]{\text{KOH, EtOH}} \begin{array}{l} \text{Linoleic, oleic acids} \\ \text{Polyester of} \\ \qquad \text{glycerophosphoric acid} \end{array} \xrightarrow{\text{dil. HCl}}$$

$$\begin{array}{c} \text{glycerophosphoric acid} \\ + \\ \text{glycerol} \end{array}$$

On the basis of these observations, Pangborn proposed the following structure for this substance:

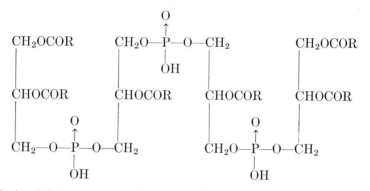

It is of interest to note here that Faure[9] has indicated the phosphatidic acids, prepared from lecithins by carrot enzyme, as active haptens but not at the comparable level of cardiolipin. Furthermore, hydrogenation of the phosphatidic acids as well as cardiolipin[10] produced little or no change in the activity of either compound.

While it is evident that the above formulation for cardiolipin is that of a "poly" phosphatidic acid, the proof of structure of this substance is not complete as yet. Recent information from MacFarlane and Gray[26] would tend to cast some doubt on the validity of the structure as proposed by Pangborn. These investigators obtained cardiolipin (4.1% P, 0.05% N, no inositol) from ox heart muscle by silicic acid chromatography, and also by Pangborn's[31] and Faure and Morelec-Coulon's[11] method. Upon analysis, these three different preparations gave comparable values, namely P:glycerol:fatty acid, 1:1.5:2. These data suggested to MacFarlane and Gray that a revision of the formula of Pangborn (where P:glycerol:fatty acid was 1:1.3:2) could be depicted as follows:

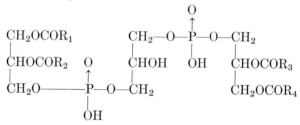

Upon treatment as described below the cardiolipin yielded the indicated products:

$$\text{Cardiolipin} \xrightarrow[\text{(2) } N \text{ HCl, 100°, 15 min.}]{\text{(1) } N \text{ NaOH, reflux}} \begin{array}{l} \text{RCOOH} \\ \text{Glycerophosphoric acid (98\% of P)} \\ \text{Glycerol (30\% of total)} \end{array}$$

If Pangborn's structure is correct, the amount of glycerol released should be 25%, but if MacFarlane and Gray's proposal is right, then the amount should be 33%. Also, in the latter investigators' formula, an alcoholic group susceptible to oxidation was required. Consequently the cardiolipin was subjected to oxidative conditions as follows:

$$\text{Cardiolipin} \xrightarrow[\substack{(2)\ \text{KMnO}_4,\ p\text{H } 5.8 \\ 16\ \text{hr.},\ 38°}]{(1)\ \text{H}_2}$$

Oxidized product
(Fatty acid/P, molar ratio, 2.1;
70% of P recovered)

Methyl glyoxal
(Pyruvaldehyde) $\xleftarrow[100°]{2N\ \text{HCl, 2hr.}}$
12% of theory

No other products of the reaction were identified. Although the data were not conclusive *per se*, these observations cast some doubt on the validity of Pangborn's structure. Of considerable interest was the observation that the mixed fatty acids of cardiolipin (75% by wt.) were composed mainly (95%) of unsaturated fatty acids. Linoleic acid was present to the extent of 72%, oleic acid to 11%, linolenic acid to 8%, and palmitoleic acid to 5.2%.

While these observations are highly interesting and important, there are other possible structural interpretations. The procedures used for glycerol and glycerophosphate assay were not reported by Mac-Farlane and Gray in their preliminary report. If they employed any of the conventional methods for glycerol determination, significant losses of glycerol could have occurred (Chapter 7). Thus this could give rise to low glycerol values. Then, the structural formula of the cardiolipin might more closely represent a bis(phosphatidic) acid (C-III). Also, the occurrence of mainly unsaturated fatty acids might indicate a specific positioning of these acids similar to that found for a lecithin (phosphatidyl choline) molecule. Another possibility, though perhaps less likely, is that of a phosphatidyl glycerol C-IV reported by Maruo and Benson.[28]

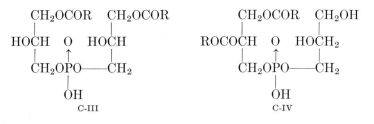

$$\begin{array}{cc}
\text{CH}_2\text{OCOR} & \text{CH}_2\text{OCOR} \\
| & | \\
\text{HOCH} \quad \text{O} & \text{HOCH} \\
| \quad \uparrow & | \\
\text{CH}_2\text{OPO}\!\!-\!\!-\!\!\text{CH}_2 \\
| \\
\text{OH} \\
\text{C-III}
\end{array}
\qquad
\begin{array}{cc}
\text{CH}_2\text{OCOR} & \text{CH}_2\text{OH} \\
| & | \\
\text{ROCOCH} \quad \text{O} & \text{HOCH}_2 \\
| \quad \uparrow & | \\
\text{CH}_2\text{OPO}\!\!-\!\!-\!\!\text{CH}_2 \\
| \\
\text{OH} \\
\text{C-IV}
\end{array}$$

Recently Rice [34] reported the separation of cardiolipin (commercial and laboratory preparations) into several chromatographically distinguishable fractions, each of which possessed biological activity. This chromatographic separation was effected through use of silicic acid with ethanol-chloroform mixtures as the eluting solvents. Subsequently, by a rather lengthy procedure, wherein the long-chain fatty acids were converted to alcohols by the action of lithium aluminum hydride, Rice isolated by fractionational distillation several different alcohols. Rice concluded that this was the expected result if several different fatty acids were present and hence several types of cardiolipins. Thus this was considered as support of the above conclusions of MacFarlane and Gray. This particular approach to proof of the occurrence of several species of cardiolipin appears rather lengthy and could be just as easily accomplished by separation of the fatty acids by reverse phase chromatography.

Although cardiolipin represents the best-defined mammalian lipide hapten, Rapport et al.[33] reported in a preliminary note the isolation of another lipide hapten, called cytolipin H, from human tumor tissue. This water insoluble, complex lipide hapten accounted for the major portion of the anti-lipide reaction noted with most rabbit anti-human tumor sera. This observation was in accord with the well-established fact that rabbit antisera against mammalian tissue fractions can fix complement in the presence of lipide-like material. In the present case, the lipides were isolated from human epidermal carcinoma (grown in rats) and subjected to chromatography on silicic acid and on florisil and finally crystallization of the cytolipin from a pyridine-acetone solution. The cytolipin H was described as a phosphorus-free sphingolipide with four residues: fatty acids (R), sphingosine, glucose, and galactose. If analogous in structure to the "cerebroside" type molecules, this compound may be represented possibly as follows:

$$CH_3(CH_2)_{12}CH=CH-CH-CH-CH_2O-glucose-O-galactose$$

$$\underset{OH}{|} \quad \underset{\underset{COR}{|}}{\overset{|}{NH}}$$

Thus, this hapten is distinctly different from cardiolipin in composition and suggests a totally different mode of action for each of these two lipide haptens.

In connection with studies on abnormal tissues, Kosaki and coworkers [18] claimed the isolation of a new phospholipide, malignolipin, from human malignant tumors, but noted it was never detected in normal tissue. On the basis of preliminary chemical evidence, this phospholipide was found to contain choline, spermine, phosphorus, and fatty acid in equimolar quantities. The following tentative formula was proposed:

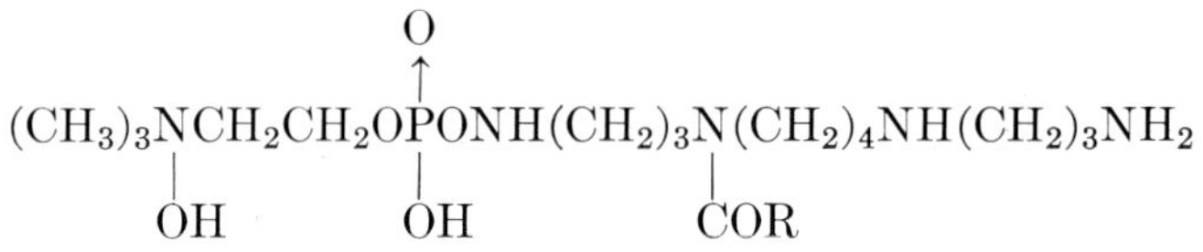

$$(CH_3)_3NCH_2CH_2O\overset{\overset{O}{\uparrow}}{P}ONH(CH_2)_3N(CH_2)_4NH(CH_2)_3NH_2$$
$$\underset{\overset{|}{OH}}{} \quad \underset{\overset{|}{OH}}{} \quad \underset{\overset{|}{COR}}{}$$

Further study is necessary to establish a more exact formulation for this compound.

GLYCOL LECITHINS

These compounds, as shown in the structural formula below,

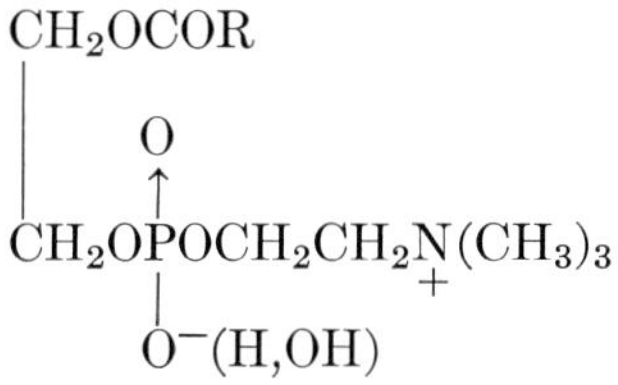

$$CH_2OCOR$$
$$|$$
$$\quad\quad O$$
$$|\quad\uparrow$$
$$CH_2OPOCH_2CH_2\overset{+}{N}(CH_3)_3$$
$$|$$
$$O^-(H,OH)$$

represent a new class of phospholipides, which have been prepared by synthetic procedures only, but not isolated from a natural source. They differ from the more conventional types in containing glycol instead of glycerol and in possessing no positional or stereoisomeric forms. Although not particularly well documented, the isolation of propylene glycol phosphate from sea urchin eggs [22] and in rat liver [23] was interpreted as evidence for the occurrence of an additional alcohol among the phospholipides.

The synthesis of two representative members of the glycol lecithins, stearoyl and palmitoyl, was described by Baer [3] and followed basically the same procedure as previously outlined by Baer and Kates in the preparation of the α-lecithins. In brief, this method involved the phenyl phosphorylation of a mono acyl glycol, followed by treatment with choline chloride and hydrogenolysis of this product to the glycol lecithin. The yields were 80 to 90% of theory.

Both the stearoyl and palmitoyl glycol lecithins exhibited high solubility in water and in addition were soluble in chloroform, methanol, and ethanol, but were insoluble in acetone and diethyl ether. While there was the possibility that these compounds might serve as useful synthetic substitutes in the serodiagnostic test for syphilis, their strong, but not unexpected, hemolytic activity prohibited their use.

LYSOPHOSPHOGLYCERIDES

Classically these phosphoglycerides were recognized first as the major product resulting from the action of venoms on phospholipides such as phosphatidyl choline and phosphatidyl ethanolamine. Also they were early recognized as powerful hemolytic agents, and this property served for many years as an assay system for these compounds. On a chemical basis they may be represented as follows,

$$
\begin{array}{c}
\text{CH}_2\text{OH} \\
| \\
\text{ROCOCH} \quad \text{O} \\
| \quad \uparrow \\
\text{CH}_2\text{OPON base} \\
| \\
\text{OH}
\end{array}
$$

where R is a long-chain fatty acid and the N base is choline or ethanolamine. Perhaps one of the earliest well-defined studies on these compounds was that of Levene and Rolf,[21] who noted that the action of snake venom on egg yolk phospholipides resulted in the formation of lysophosphatidyl choline and lysophosphatidyl ethanolamine. Subsequently these two compounds were separated by solvent fractionation and identified as mono acyl derivatives. While no proof was presented for the position of the fatty acid on the glycerol unit or the stereochemical form of this compound, it was evident that these compounds were derived from diacyl phosphoglycerides. Although under normal circumstances the lysophosphoglycerides are present to a very small extent in most tissues, they have been found in eggs, adrenals, plasma, and other tissues.

Inasmuch as the choline containing lysophosphoglycerides have been investigated more extensively than the ethanolamine counterpart, most attention will be focused on this type here.

Preparation

In general, the majority of the methods for the preparation of the lysophosphoglycerides have centered on the use of a specific enzymatic degradation of the diacyl phosphoglycerides, while the direct synthetic approach has not proved as rewarding as desired.

Enzyme Method. The most profitable approach to the preparation of lysolecithin is through hydrolytic attack by the phospholipase (or lecithinase) A of snake venom on lecithin.[13] This can be illustrated as follows:

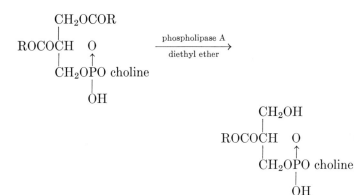

The substrates for this reaction can range from fully saturated to fully unsaturated lecithins and the entire reaction is best carried out in moist diethyl ether. Under these conditions the lysolecithin is insoluble and the fatty acid is soluble. When excess enzyme is used, the reaction can be quantitative. A more extensive treatment of the action of this enzyme system can be found in a recent review.[13]

If the above reaction is quantitative, the ether insoluble lysolecithin can be isolated directly from the reaction mixture. Furthermore, if the product is completely saturated, it can be recrystallized from absolute ethanol, or from chloroform-diethyl ether mixtures. The unsaturated and saturated lysolecithins are insoluble in diethyl ether, petroleum ether, and 100% acetone (cold), and are soluble in chloroform, pyridine, 90% acetone, and water. If the above reaction is not quantitative, then the isolation of the desired product may be most effectively accomplished through chromatography on silicic acid. In this case the ether is removed from the reaction mixture, which is then dissolved in chloroform-methanol (4:1, v/v) or chloroform only, and passed through a silicic acid column. This procedure will remove the free fatty acids and subsequent treatment of the column with chloroform-methanol (1:4) will remove first the remaining lecithin and then the lysolecithin. Lysophosphatidyl ethanolamine can be prepared from phosphatidyl ethanolamine by a similar enzymatic procedure.

However, cognizance must be taken of the possible migration of the acyl group on the lysolecithin in this type of chromatography. Such migrations have been noted for the monoglycerides chromatographed on silicic acid. Also, it is known that the long-chain fatty acid group on the β position of lysolecithin (enzymatically prepared as above) can migrate to the α' position under the influence of dilute acid (0.05N HCl) or an enzyme, a migratase (isomerase) found in pancreas and in *Penicillium notatum*.[39]

The lysophosphoglycerides can be separated from many other phospholipides by chromatography on silicic acid impregnated and non-impregnated paper with solvents such as chloroform-methanol[19] and certain mixtures of ketones and acetic acid,[42] respectively. Also α'- and β-lysolecithin may be distinguished by the ready migration of the β form in a water system, whereas the α' form remains at the origin.[34]

Direct Synthesis. Only very limited success has been attained in the synthesis of the lysolecithins. The following procedure described by Baylis et al.[5] represents the most plausible attempt to date:

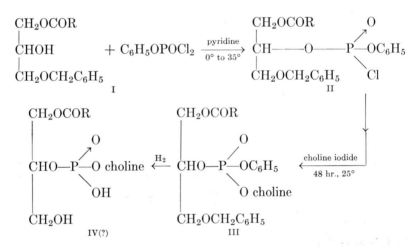

The over-all yield for this reaction was 25%. Although the phosphate group was presumed to be in the 2 position on IV, the possibility was not excluded that this unit could have migrated to the 1 position.

No indication was given of the possible isolation of the stereoisomeric forms of this compound. A lysophosphatidyl ethanolamine was prepared by reaction of compound II (above) with carbobenzoxyethanolamine, followed by hydrogenolysis.

While the above procedure represents a reasonable approach to the synthesis of a lysolecithin (and lysophosphatidyl ethanolamine), the fact still remains that it is highly desirable to have available procedures for the unequivocal preparation of the enantiomeric forms of the lysophosphoglycerides.

Proof of Structure

Inasmuch as no unequivocal synthetic preparation of the lysolecithins is available, it is necessary to adopt a degradation scheme for proof of structure of lysolecithin formed in enzymatic reactions or isolated from natural sources. The most feasible and successful route to selective degradation is afforded by oxidation of the free hydroxyl with potassium permanganate. A typical reaction sequence with a β(C-2 substituted) lysolecithin is described by the following equation:

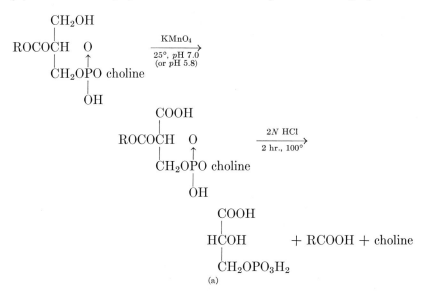

This reaction scheme has been confirmed by Davidson et al.[8] and MacFarlane and Gray.[26] If the acyl had been on the α'(C-1) position, then the following series of reactions would have ensued:

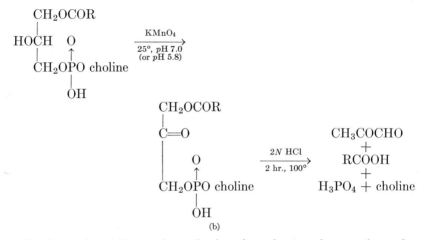

(b)

In the study of the product of migration of an acyl group from the β to the α' position of lysolecithin by enzyme or acid (0.05N HCl) catalysis, Uziel and Hanahan [39] identified the products of the reaction as shown in (b). On the other hand, MacFarlane [25] claims that in a buffered system, at pH 5.8, only phosphorylcholine and fatty acids (and not inorganic phosphate and free choline) would be released under hydrolytic conditions.* However, for the present, these differences have not been resolved.

REFERENCES

1. Baer, E., *J. Biol. Chem.*, **189**, 235 (1951).
2. Baer, E., *J. Biol. Chem.*, **198**, 853 (1953).
3. Baer, E., *J. Am. Chem. Soc.*, **75**, 5533 (1953).
4. Baer, E., and D. Buchnea, *J. Biol. Chem.*, **232**, 895 (1958).
5. Baylis, R. L., T. H. Bevan, and T. Malkin, in *Biochemical Problems of Lipids*, edited by Popjak and LeBreton, p. 91, Interscience (1956).
6. Benson, A. A., and B. Maruo, *Biochim. et Biophys. Acta*, **27**, 189 (1958).
7. Chibnall, A., and H. Channon, *Biochem. J.*, **21**, 233 (1927).
8. Davidson, F. M., C. Long, and I. F. Penny, in *Biochemical Problems of Lipids*, edited by Popjak and LeBreton, p. 253, Interscience (1956).
9. Faure, M., *Bull. soc. chim. biol.*, **31**, 1362 (1949).
10. Faure, M., *Ann. Inst. Pasteur*, **76**, 465 (1949).
11. Faure, M., and M. J. Morelec-Coulon, *Compt. rend.*, **238**, 411 (1954).
12. Garcia, M., J. A. Lovern, and J. Olley, *Biochem. J.*, **62**, 99 (1956).

* The details of additional structure proof studies on C-1(α')- and C-2(β)-lysolecithins are outlined in a recent paper by G. M. Gray [*Biochem. J.*, **70**, 435 (1958)].

13. Hanahan, D. J., *Prog. in Chem. Fats Lipids,* **4,** 141–176 (1957).
14. Hessel, L. W., I. D. Morton, A. R. Todd, and P. E. Verkade, *Rec. trav. chim.,* **73,** 150 (1954).
15. Huennekens, F. M., D. J. Hanahan, and M. Uziel, *J. Biol. Chem.,* **206,** 443 (1954).
16. Kates, M., *Can. J. Biochem. and Physiol.,* **33,** 575 (1955).
17. Kornberg, A., and W. E. Pricer, Jr., *J. Biol. Chem.,* **204,** 345 (1953).
18. Kosaki, T., T. Ikoda, Y. Kotani, S. Nakagawa, and T. Saka, *Science,* **127,** 1176 (1958).
19. Lea, C., D. N. Rhodes, and R. D. Stoll, *Biochem. J.,* **60,** 353 (1955).
20. Legault-Demare, J., and M. Faure, *Bull. soc. chim. biol.,* **33,** 1013 (1951).
21. Levene, P. A., and I. P. Rolf, *J. Biol. Chem.,* **55,** 743 (1923).
22. Lindberg, O., *Arkiv Kemi, Minerali, Geol.,* **16,** No. 15 (1943).
23. Lindberg, O., *Arkiv Kemi, Minerali. Geol.,* **23,** 1 (1946).
24. Long, C., and M. F. Maguire, *Biochem. J.,* **57,** 223 (1954).
25. MacFarlane, M. G., private communication.
26. MacFarlane, M. G., and G. M. Gray, *Biochem. J.,* **67,** 25P (1957).
27. Maruo, B., and A. A. Benson, *J. Am. Chem. Soc.,* **79,** 4564 (1957).
28. Maruo, B., and A. A. Benson, *Federation Proc.,* **17,** 270 (1958).
29. Olley, J., *Chem. Ind.,* **1954,** 1069.
30. Pangborn, M. C., *Proc. Soc. Exptl. Biol. Med.,* **48,** 484 (1941).
31. Pangborn, M. C., *J. Biol. Chem.,* **143,** 247 (1942).
32. Pangborn, M. C., *J. Biol. Chem.,* **168,** 351 (1947).
33. Rapport, M. M., N. F. Alonzo, L. Graf, and V. P. Skipski, *Federation Proc.,* **17,** 293 (1958).
34. Rice, F. A. H., *Science,* **127,** 339 (1958).
35. Rouser, G., G. V. Marinetti, R. F. Witter, J. F. Berry, and E. Stotz, *J. Biol. Chem.,* **223,** 485 (1956).
36. Tonks, D. B., and R. H. Allen, *Brit. J. Venereal Diseases,* **31,** 180 (1955).
37. Tonks, D. B., and R. H. Allen, *Brit. J. Venereal Diseases,* **32,** 253 (1956).
38. Uhlenbroek, J. H., and P. E. Verkade, *Rec. trav. chim.,* **72,** 558 (1953).
39. Uziel, M., and D. J. Hanahan, *J. Biol. Chem.,* **226,** 789 (1957).
40. Van der Gijzen, J., and P. E. Verkade, *Rec. trav. chim.,* **72,** 365 (1953).
41. Van der Neut, J. H., J. H. Uhlenbroek, and P. E. Verkade, *Rec. trav. chim.,* **73,** 365 (1953).
42. Witter, R. F., G. V. Marinetti, A. Morrison, and L. Heicklin, *Arch. Biochem. Biophys.,* **68,** 15 (1957).

7

Simple lipides

Certainly among the most abundant fatty acid derivatives found in animal and plant tissues are the simple (or neutral) lipides. The major components in this class of substances are the glycerides and the cholesterol esters. Although the glyceryl ethers are present in much smaller amounts and have not been as extensively studied, they deserve attention at this point.

GLYCERIDES

The most commonly encountered glycerides may be represented by the following well-known structural formulae:

$$
\begin{array}{lll}
CH_2OCOR_1 & CH_2OCOR_1 & CH_2OH \\
| & | & | \\
CHOCOR_2 & CHOCOR_2 & CHOCOR \\
| & | & | \\
CH_2OCOR_3 & CH_2OH & CH_2OH \\
\quad\text{I} & \quad\text{II} & \quad\text{III}
\end{array}
$$

where R_1, R_2, and R_3 are the long-chain hydrocarbon units of fatty acids (usually in range of C_{14} to C_{22} in mammalian tissues) and the alcohol component is glycerol. While the triglycerides (I) are present to the largest extent, nevertheless the diglycerides (II) and monoglycerides (III) can be isolated from certain tissues and should be noted as possible components of any glyceride preparation. Whether this may be a true reflection of the metabolic state of the tissue in question or possible enzymatic degradation in the isolation procedure is unknown. So far as can be ascertained, glycerol is the only polyhydroxyl alcohol normally found in glyceride fractions.

While the glycerides constitute well over 98% of the lipides of the adipose tissue of the mammal, they comprise only approximately 30% of the plasma and liver lipides, and less than 10% of the lipide of the red blood cell.

In considering the chemistry of the glycerides (tri-, di-, or mono-), the following major topics will be covered: isolation, fractionation, and purification of the glycerides; the analytical estimation of the type of glyceride (glycerol, fatty acid, nature of fatty acids, etc.), and the proof of structure as regards the position and distribution of the acids on the glycerol unit; the synthesis of glycerides of known structure and configuration, and the use of the latter for comparative purposes as substrates for lipolytic enzyme studies and in metabolic investigations.

Chemical Synthesis of Glycerides

Since Malkin and Bevan [53] recently reviewed the major segment of this topic, no attempt will be made to detail the various syntheses reported by these authors. As discussed by Malkin and Bevan, most of the synthetic procedures for other than the monoglyceride types have utilized monoglycerides or diglycerides as the starting material. In these procedures, the usual methods of protection of groups, acylation reactions, migrations, etc., have been utilized. Although nearly all the desired types of glycerides have been synthesized, the unsaturated (or mixed unsaturated-saturated) α,β (1:2) diglycerides, until recently, have resisted unequivocal synthesis.

Consequently, certain information, published subsequent to the above review, on the synthetic routes to the fully or partially unsaturated (1:2) diglycerides, as well as a novel approach to triglyceride preparation, will be described here.

α,β **(1:2) Diglycerides.** Any synthetic approach to these diglycerides immediately poses the problem of the preparation of an optically active compound. In the normal biosynthetic pathway to phosphoglycerides, the optically active D-α,β diglycerides are considered to be an immediate precursor. Consequently, it is of obvious value to have available the D-α,β, as well as the L-α,β, series of glycerides.

Symmetrical, unsaturated types (D-α,β-**diolein**). Recently, Baer and Buchnea [3] reported the successful synthesis of D-α,β-diolein. As outlined by these authors, previously two methods were employed in the synthesis of optically active glycerides: (1) resolution of a racemic intermediate from which an optically active glyceride is obtained by esterification; (2) isolation of a naturally occurring, optically active compound which is converted without racemization into the desired glyceride. As an example of the second approach, which is the more desirable, Baer and Buchnea prepared optically active diolein as follows:

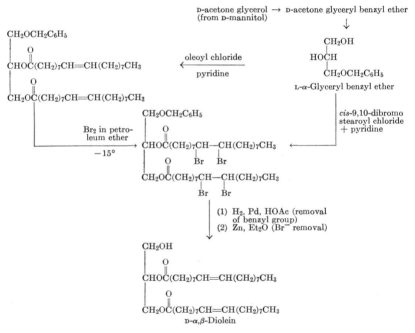

Over-all yields of 60 to 67% of desired diglyceride were obtained from glyceryl benzyl ether (L-α,β-diolein from D-glyceryl benzyl ether). The optical purity was good: $[\alpha]_D^{20}$ −2.8° in CHCl₃, for D-α,β-diolein; $[a]_D^{20}$ +2.7° in CHCl₃, for L-α,β-diolein. Both diglycerides on hydrogenation gave, respectively, in good yields pure D-α- and L-α-distearin.

Other types. An additional route, though more detailed, is possible for the preparation of symmetrical, diunsaturated diglycerides as well as unsaturated, unsymmetrical, and unsaturated-saturated diglycerides.

Essentially this would entail the synthesis of lecithins of known structure and configuration (see Chapter 3) by the following reactions:

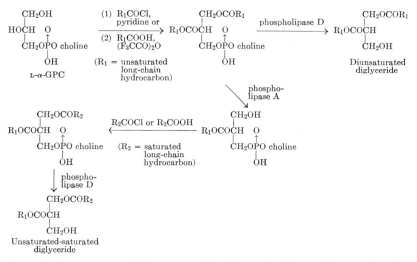

As is obvious, many different combinations of diglycerides can be derived by these series of reactions.

Triglycerides, Symmetrical. A novel and very efficient procedure for the synthesis of symmetrical triglycerides is demonstrated by the trifluoracetic anhydride technique as perfected by Bourne et al.[10] The distinct advantage of this technique is that it allows one to employ the long-chain fatty acid in the free form instead of the acyl chloride or anhydride and a short reaction period, usually no more than 2 to 3 hours at room temperature. Thus, a triglyceride can be synthesized as follows:

$$\text{Glycerol} + \text{RCOOH} \xrightarrow[\text{(25°, 2–3 hr.)}]{\substack{\text{trifluoroacetic} \\ \text{anhydride}}} \text{Triglyceride}$$

The reaction usually proceeds to completion, but even if it does not, the desired product can be isolated via silicic acid chromatography (see Chapter 2). Both unsaturated and saturated long-chain fatty acids can be utilized with equally satisfactory results in this reaction system.

Structure of Naturally Occurring Glycerides

Proposed Rules. The proof of structure of the naturally occurring glycerides resolves itself into a study of the types and location of the fatty acids on the glycerol portion of the molecule. Thus, an analysis of the fatty acids or partial derivatives of a glyceride mixture has been used as a basis for proposals of certain rules concerning the distribution of fatty acids on a glyceride. A detailed discussion of the composition of naturally occurring glycerides is presented in a book by Hilditch [37] and in review articles by Van der Wal [75] and Hilditch.[36] To date, the following four rules have been proposed.

Rule of even distribution. On the basis of his extensive and detailed studies of the fatty acid composition of naturally occurring glycerides, Hilditch [35, 36] proposed that each of the individual acids of a given glyceride tends to be distributed as evenly as possible among all the glyceride molecules. Hence an acid should constitute greater than two-thirds of the total acid content before it can form any appreciable amount of a simple (only one type of fatty acid) triglyceride; in addition, acids comprising more than one-third of the total fatty acids are expected to furnish one mole of acid for each glyceride molecule and a second mole for some; obviously the fatty acids appearing in minor amounts should not occur more than one time in any glyceride. While this rule holds quite closely for the seed lipides, many decided deviations (probably due to the higher amount of saturated fatty acids) have been observed in animal lipides.

However, as Hilditch has emphasized, he always stated and intended only to classify the general pattern of glyceride structure according to observed findings. Thus, no attempt was made to find any numerical formula that would fit all instances and, in fact, such a formula by nature would appear improbable.

Rule of random distribution. Longenecker [51] proposed that the fatty acids of animal glycerides tend to follow a random distribution among the glyceride molecules. Later, Norris and Mattil [59] also considered this a valid proposal. Thus, apparently no set pattern should be observed, but only a random distribution. At present, though, this particular theory appears not to be consistent with experimental findings and is not thought to be generally applicable.

Rule of partial random distribution. The inadequacies in certain instances of the two aforementioned rules prompted the development of the partial random distribution rule by Doerschuk and Daubert.[24] Essentially it involves a compromise between the above rules. It simply states that monoacid or simple triglycerides occur more often than Hilditch's even distribution theory and less often than the Longenecker random distribution proposal. However, while apparently applicable to corn oil, sufficient information on different source material has not been secured in support of the proposition.

Rule of restricted random distribution. This relatively new proposal is credited to Kartha,[42] who has accumulated a certain amount of data in support of this theory. In essence this proposition considers that the types of glycerides existing in nature are: trisaturated, disaturated-monounsaturated, diunsaturated-monosaturated, and triunsaturated and that the fatty acids are distributed at random among these four glyceride types. However, these occur only if the trisaturated type is in the liquid state *in vivo*. Thus, the fully saturated glycerides can be present only to the extent that they can remain liquid. Hence the chances for fatty acids to be distributed among all the glycerides will depend on the amount of fully saturated glycerides present.

A detailed discussion of these four theories is presented in a review by Van der Wal.[75] As he emphasizes, Kartha's proposal represents the best to date, no doubt due to the attention to details of the analytical procedures used in structure proof. A critique of this theory is offered by Hilditch,[36] who feels, in essence, that this theory is constructed on rather scanty experimental evidence.

Although these proposals have been argued pro and con in a rather extensive manner, it has become convincingly clear that no one rule suffices for all glycerides. There is the distinct possibility, particularly in the animal glycerides, that the distribution may vary not only from one species to another but from one tissue to another and one organ to another. A non-random type distribution of the fatty acids among the glycerides was noted in lard, beef tallow, and mutton tallow.[63] On the basis of thermal cooling curves and X-ray diffraction techniques applied to various forms of these lipides, the conclusion was reached that lard was composed largely of 2-palmityl glycerides whereas the tallows were composed largely of 1-palmityl glycerides. However, the critical use of this type of approach should be made with considerable care. It would appear that a more specific method, i.e., the lipolytic degradation of the glycerides, would be desirable and effective as a measure of the positions of the fatty acids. Recent studies show that in swine glycerides the 1 and 3 positions have preferential affinities for unsaturated fatty acids resulting in 1,3 diunsaturated, 2 saturated triglycerides as the major type present. Both the even and random theories are untenable in this particular case. However, this may be a good example of asymmetric or specific configuration of the glyceride fatty acids. A high proportion of 2-palmitoyl oleoyl stearin and 2-palmitoyl diolein has been observed in lard, but not in rat, cow, sheep, and human adipose tissue. These observations lend support to the above comments on possible "tissue" variability in distribution of fatty acids in glycerides.

Thus, the same reasoning, as applied previously to the lecithins, may well apply to the glycerides. At present, the asymmetric arrangement of fatty acids of the glycerides of liver has not been determined, and if the results obtained by Savary et al.[68] hold for all tissue triglycerides, the liver triglycerides are not comparable to the lecithins in fatty acid arrangement. However, this does not negate the point that there are several species of glycerides, each one of which may well behave or participate in a different metabolic reaction or pathway.

It is well to emphasize that the above rules are useful in a preliminary classification of the fatty acids in a glyceride, but of little aid, at present, in metabolic studies. As will be outlined below, the use of a specific type of enzyme, i.e., the lipases, should be of considerable aid in the study of the distribution of fatty acids on the glycerides and also in metabolic studies on the interrelationship of long-chain fatty acid derivatives.

Isolation, Fractionation, and Purification Procedures. Although the details of the most commonly encountered isolation and fractionation schemes proposed for the neutral lipides were discussed in Chapter 2, it appears in order at this time to review briefly certain facets of these procedures.

In most cases, the initial extraction of the neutral lipides has involved the use of chloroform-methanol (2:1, v/v) or ethanol-diethyl ether (3:1, v/v), or possibly pure acetone, at room temperature for two to three short-time (3 hours) extraction periods. While these procedures will usually remove all the neutral lipides and phospholipides from a tissue or organ, it is always well to check for the presence of long-chain fatty acids in the extracted residue. As a normal procedure, any exposure to air, light, and elevated temperatures (above 25° to 30°) should be maintained at an absolute minimum. It is also highly advisable that preparations be as freshly prepared as possible, since storage for long periods of time appears to cause some degradative changes in lipide samples. In general, lipide samples should be stored at a temperature of −25° or lower in the dark and in a neutral solvent which does not develop peroxides or free acids on standing.

While enzyme catalyzed degradations of phospholipides can be activated by solvents used in the extraction procedure, no comparable activation of lipolytic enzymes by solvents was noted by Desnuelle and Constantin.[17] However, the presence of contaminant pigments can cause a decided increase in the susceptibility of glycerides to oxidative alterations. Tappel [73] has noted a powerful catalysis at 0° of oxidation of unsaturated fatty acids by hematin. This reaction can be inhibited by tocopherol and similar compounds. In many cases, a preliminary fractionation of the mixed lipides on silicic acid with chloroform as the eluting solvent (see Chapter 2) can remove the major portion of the pigments from the remainder of the lipides. Consequently, a relatively color-free neutral lipide fraction can be isolated and by further refractionation on silicic acid (see Chapter 2) the entire triglyceride component can be obtained in high yield. While the amounts of diglycerides and monoglycerides are usually small in most tissues, it is well to run a complete quantitative chromatogram and check for their presence.

The use of acetone as the sole agent for fractionation of the neutral lipides from the phospholipides, although of considerable value, may not be as effective as desired. For example, whereas beef liver lipides may be separated to the extent of 95% by acetone treatment, the fractionation of the lipides of the erythrocyte or DPNH oxidase by a similar procedure may extract as much as 50% of the phospholipides in the acetone.[30] Conversely, the use of a low temperature in this acetone fractionation may cause the more saturated glycerides to precipitate with the phospholipides and hence distort the distribution picture. As outlined above, a chromatographic separation on silicic acid has provided an excellent general fractionation procedure. A brief summary of the more effective procedures for fractionation or isolation of glycerides from naturally occurring mixtures is presented here.

Low temperature crystallization. The separation of glycerides by low temperature crystallization has been applied to a relatively large number of naturally occurring lipide mixtures. Generally the most useful separation can be effected by crystallization of the glyceride from an acetone solution at temperatures ranging from +10° to −70°. Through the use of this technique, glycerides varying in composition from completely saturated to completely unsaturated (and intermediate) types may be isolated. While applicable in general to rather large quantities of starting material, the usefulness of this procedure on the more moderate levels of glycerides encountered in biochemical studies has been somewhat limited. Brown and Kolb [11] have outlined in a review the application of the low temperature technique to fatty acids, glycerides, and other similar compounds.

Chromatographic separation. As illustrated in Chapter 2, a convenient and reproducible means for the fractionation of the glycerides of a tissue in high yield involves chromatography on silicic acid.[5, 25] This procedure, although not as effective in defining individual classes of glycerides as low temperature crystallization is, nevertheless permits the glycerides to be separated free from practically all contaminants, except free fatty acids, by use of the proper solvent system. The contaminating free fatty acids can be removed by washing the preparation with ethanolic alkali. While not extensively documented as yet, evidence is accumulating that a partial fractionation of glycerides, as regards unsaturation, can occur on a silicic acid column. In a manner similar to that experienced with the lecithins (see Chapter 2), the more unsaturated components are eluted at a more rapid rate than the saturated components. At present the particular value of the chromatographic procedure for the triglycerides is that these lipides can be isolated on a small scale, i.e., 50 to 100 mg., and free of sterols, sterol glycosides, and other comparable compounds. Moreover, there is the definitive possibility, as suggested above, that particular species of glycerides can be obtained by this type of fractionation procedure.

The technique of displacement chromatography was applied by Hamilton and Holman to the separation of model mixtures of glycerides.[29] The adsorbabilities of a series of glycerides from ethanol or benzene solvents onto charcoal was determined. It was shown that the single displacement technique was dependent on the nature of the solvent. In general, it appeared with the model substances that saturated glycerides are more easily accommodated than the unsaturated glycerides (triunsaturated glycerides are poorly adsorbed). In a preliminary run, this procedure was used on the glycerides of beef tallow from which several different fractions, which varied in melting point, were obtained. No further report has appeared on the applicability of this method to the separation and identification of the naturally occurring glycerides and insofar as can be ascertained it has not been applied in any large degree to the fractionation of lipides.

As regards detection by paper chromatographic techniques, Dieckert and Reiser have reported a separation of various glycerides, cholesterol, and cholesterol esters by chromatography on a fine glass fiber filter paper impregnated with silicic acid.[20, 21] The spots were visualized by spraying the chromatograms with $18N$ H_2SO_4. No differences, due to variations in unsaturation of the glycerides, were observed.

Structure Proof

The obvious major problem here is that of the proper procedures to be used for the assay and establishment of the fatty acid "structure" of the glycerides. Hence a primary consideration is general composition of a fraction, especially as regards its fatty acid and glycerol content. These assays, together with the iodine uptake determinations, saponification equivalent, ester value (hydroxamate), and titratable acidity (for free fatty acids), should provide a reasonable index of the nature of the glyceride fraction. As indicated above, an additional study of the chromatographic behavior of the fraction on a silicic acid column should prove informative on the possible presence of diglycerides or monoglycerides (and their relative amounts).

General Routes. Prior to an assay for glycerol and fatty acids, it is necessary to effect a complete hydrolysis of the glycerides. In general, an acid hydrolysis in aqueous solution is not particularly effective, with only a small portion of the glyceride attacked. Even at reflux temperatures and with thorough mixing the degree of hydrolytic cleavage is small. This can be illustrated by the fact that a diglyceride isolated from yeast phosphoinositide was degraded to only 0.3% of theory on refluxing for 2 hours in $2N$ HCl. Thus the water insolubility and physical form of the glycerides obviously must be a primary reason for its resistance to acidic attack. In most instances hydrolysis of the glycerides can be accomplished in the most effective manner by reflux in an alcoholic alkali medium for 2 to 4 hours; usually $0.5N$ KOH in 95% ethanol provides an adequate mixture for a complete hydrolysis. Consequently, at the termination of the reflux the solution is cooled, the alcohol removed, and the resultant mixture acidified. The free fatty acids are extracted with petroleum or diethyl ether and this extract is washed several times with water until free of mineral acid, then the washings are combined with the original water soluble fraction. These fractions can then be analyzed for glycerol, and the fatty acids by techniques outlined in the following discussion.

Glycerol assay. The detection and estimation of glycerol is one of the more difficult and less rewarding analytical problems in lipide chemistry. In recent years considerable progress has been made toward a more specific means of assay for glycerol. Recently it has been established that glycerol can decompose or be volatilized under conditions frequently employed in the hydrolysis of glycerides. In particular, it has been noted that refluxing in $6N$ HCl will destroy a significant amount of glycerol whereas $2N$ HCl under similar conditions causes no alteration.[29] Furthermore, glycerol is very volatile when aqueous extracts are evaporated to dryness for removal of acid, either at low or high temperatures in the usual procedure. Similar losses of glycerol by volatilization have been noted by Harvey and Higby,[33] Ramsay and Stewart,[64] Lovern,[52] and LeBaron et al.[49]

PAPER CHROMATOGRAPHIC DETECTION. Glycerol may be determined by the paper chromatographic technique of Olley.[60] In some cases multiple spotting of glycerol has been observed, in which case the chromatographic separation can be effected on borax impregnated paper.[31] In this system, Whatman No. 3 paper is impregnated with $0.08M$ borax solution. Glycerol samples, in a range from 10 to 100 μg., are spotted on the paper and the chromatogram is run in an ascending system with a mixture of 150 parts n-propanol, 70 parts water, and 90 parts $0.08M$ borax (any less water will cause precipitation of the borax). As much as 200 μl. of $2N$ HCl can be tolerated in a sample run by this technique. Due to the presence of borax, glycerol spots cannot be detected by the spray reagent of Trevalyan et al.[74] In fact, this spray apparently works well only in neutral solvent systems. Therefore, guide strips of glycerol were used and the glycerol detected by use of 1% lead tetraacetate in benzene, and the corresponding areas in the other parts of the paper were cut out, eluted with water, and assayed by the above chromotropic acid method. As much as 60 μg. of glycerol were recovered quantitatively in the presence of 60 μg. each of serine, ethanolamine, glucose, arabinose, ribose, mannose, fructose, inositol, and galactose. The glycerol had an R_f in this system of 0.60, and all the above compounds had R_f values of at least 0.1 unit less. The solvent system was not effective in separating glycerol and glycerophosphate, and any glycerophosphate must be removed by resin or some other technique before chromatography or a better solvent can be used.

DIRECT ESTIMATION. The quantitative estimation of glycerol on total hydrolysates can be accomplished by a combination of the methods of Frisell et al.[27] and of Lambert and Neish.[48] This technique is described by Hanahan and Olley.[31] The contaminants most likely to be encountered in these fractions gave the following yields of "apparent" glycerol from 1 mg. material: ethanolamine, 2.4 μg., glucose, 19 μg., whereas serine and inositol phosphate gave no reaction. A suitable and reliable standard for the glycerol assay system is monomethyl-dimethylhydantoin (18.98% available formaldehyde). Solutions of this compound may be stored indefinitely with no evidence of decomposition.

Glycerophosphate interferes in the glycerol assay and must be quantitatively removed. An aliquot of the lipide hydrolysate is passed through sufficient Dowex 1, 50 to 100 mesh (placed on OH cycle), to remove both HCl and glycerophosphate and the glycerol in the effluent is determined by the periodate-chromotropic acid method. The Dowex resins can release formaldehyde and must be thoroughly washed before being used in the glycerol assay. If the resin is allowed to stand for several days before reuse, formaldehyde is reformed and must be removed. It was found that Amberlite IRA-410 was completely unsatisfactory for the removal of phosphate esters. Although it removed glycerophosphate, at the same time it fortuitously released a sufficient amount of base yielding formaldehyde on periodate oxidation to compensate for the glycerophosphate removed.

An interesting approach to the estimation of glyceride-glycerol was reported by Van Handel and Zilversmit.[76] This technique depended on the selective quantitative "extraction" of triglycerides from plasma by Doucil (a zeolite) and chloroform. In essence, the triglycerides (also cholesterol and cholesterol esters) were not adsorbed, and after alkaline hydrolysis the glycerol could be estimated by the Lambert-Neish peroxidative technique. These investigators found that without proper precautions losses of glycerol could occur even under the conditions normally employed for removing ethanol. The above extraction procedure compared favorably with a chloroform-methanol extraction and subsequent fractionation on silicic acid.

As illustrated by Doerschuk,[23] glycerol may be isolated as its tribenzoate derivative from lipide hydrolysates. In brief, the water soluble fraction from a lipide hydrolysate is treated first with lead and barium salts to remove any phosphate or phosphate esters, followed by a typical Schotten-Baummann reaction with benzoyl chloride in an alkaline medium. The glycerol tribenzoate is recrystallized from ligroin (m.p. 72°). No yields or analyses on this compound were cited but there is little doubt that it provides one of the best derivatives of glycerol. In some instances, investigators have submitted the water soluble fraction from a hydrolysate to oxidation with periodic acid followed by the isolation of formaldehyde as the dimedon derivative. However, this should not be interpreted as final evidence for the presence of glycerol since various substances could yield formaldehyde under similar conditions.

Through the use of celite as the adsorbent and a solvent system of ethyl acetate and also benzene-butanol, Neish[58] reported a separation of glycerol from other polyols. The five and six carbon sugars and sugar alcohols remain on the column, while the glycerol and other similar short-chain polyols can be eluted in a fractional manner.

Fatty acids.   The fatty acids obtained by hydrolytic cleavage can be subjected to the usual characterization procedures, such as neutral equivalent determination, iodine and hydrogen uptake values, paper chromatographic behavior, etc.   Subsequently, more detailed information on the specific types of fatty acids present can be gained from an examination by procedures such as reverse phase and/or gas phase chromatography, low temperature fractionation, and infrared spectrum.   These techniques are described in more detail in Chapter 3. Any highly purified fraction can be submitted to the usual criteria employed for proof of structure of a compound; in this case, molecular weight determination, derivative preparation, melting point, hydrogen uptake, nature of products from specific degradation techniques (such as $KMnO_4$ or ozone action on unsaturated fatty acids), and X-ray diffraction pattern.

The details of the types of fatty acids usually found in the glycerides from a variety of sources are documented in Hilditch's book [37] as well as in Deuel's treatise.[19]   A comparison of the fatty acids of the glycerides and the phosphatidyl choline (lecithin) fractions of rat liver is given in Table 7.1.   It serves to illustrate the multiplicity of the types of fatty acid esters present in these two fractions and the rather directed inclusion of the more highly unsaturated forms in the lecithin component.

Table 7.1

Comparison of Fatty Acid Composition of Triglyceride and
Phosphatidyl Choline Fraction of Rat Liver *

Fatty Acid, in Mole Per Cent

	Unsaturated		Saturated	
	Oleic Acid	Linoleic Acid	Palmitic Acid	Stearic Acid
Triglyceride	41	27	23	7.0
Phosphatidyl choline	15	35	30	20

* Taken from Dittmer.[22]

SPECIES OF GLYCERIDES. Pursuant to the observation of the diverse types of fatty acids and hence glycerides possible from these units, it is well to emphasize the concept of species of glycerides as was proposed for the phosphoglycerides (see Chapter 3). According to the most recent reports, an asymmetric positioning of fatty acids on the glycerides has only limited possibilities; there are indications, however, that specific positioning may result in certain instances and may be comparable, in part, to that found for the phosphoglycerides. Nonetheless, this does not detract from the possibility that there are several species of glycerides, i.e., I, II, III, each of which may well behave quite differently and/or participate in separate metabolic reactions or pathways. The inclusion of these possibilities in the outlining of experimental studies on glycerides would seem highly desirable.

Specific Routes.

Enzymatic degradation. The use of lipases appears to afford a mild, selective means of degradation of triglycerides and hence should prove most helpful in assigning the position of attachment of constitu-

ent fatty acids. The lipases may be classified as hydrolyases, catalyzing the hydrolytic cleavage of the fatty acids from the triglycerides. This type of attack may be illustrated by the following equation:

$$RCOOR_1 + HOH \rightleftarrows RCOOH + R_1OH$$

which shows the hydrolytic as well as the synthetic action of these enzymes. The chemical nature of the R and R_1 groups causes special types of specificity among the esterases. If the ester is of low molecular weight and a simple type, i.e., ethyl butyrate, then this is an example of an esterase activity. If the ester is a glyceryl derivative and contains long-chain fatty acids, then these enzymes are called the lipases.

The recognition of the formation of "partial" glycerides in the *in vitro* hydrolysis of glycerides by pancreatic lipase was first indicated by Artom and Reale.[2] Later, Desnuelle et al.[18] established that the pancreatic lipases hydrolyzed only glycerol esters of long-chain fatty acids but not of short-chain fatty acids. Since that time, mainly through the efforts of Borgstrom,[7,9] Desnuelle,[66–68] and Mattson,[55,56] considerable information has accrued on the characteristics of the lipases.

SPECIFICITY OF ATTACK. Desnuelle et al.[18] noted that the action of lipases gave rise to a series of reactions from triglycerides to diglycerides to monoglycerides. Ultimately, if calcium ion was present, glycerol and fatty acid were formed. However, the quantitative aspects of this study were diminished by the assumption that the attack was random. Subsequently, contributions from the laboratories of Borgstrom, Mattson, and Desnuelle have established that the attack by lipase is not random but appears to be directed almost exclusively towards the 1 and 3 positions of the glyceride.

In his proof of the site of action of pancreatic lipase, Borgstrom[7] studied the hydrolysis products of the reaction of this enzyme with olive oil. The glycerides were separated on silicic acid, hydrogenated, and the diglyceride, in particular, subjected to oxidation with chromium oxide under relatively mild conditions, i.e., 97.5% acetic acid at 37° for 3 to 6 hours. According to theory, a 1,3 diglyceride should consume 1 atom of oxygen per mole, while a 1,2 diglyceride should consume 2 atoms of oxygen per mole. On the experimental sample, 2 atoms of oxygen per mole were consumed and a 1,2 diglyceride structure was indicated. In addition, Borgstrom noted that during *in vitro* hydrolysis of the triglycerides by lipases an exchange of glyceride fatty acids and free fatty acids in the medium did occur, as was shown by incorporation of carbon 14 labeled fatty acids into the glycerides.[8, 9] The results also showed a high incorporation of label into triglycerides, with smaller amounts into diglycerides and very low levels into the monoglycerides. Thus, Borgstrom reasoned that the 1 and 3 positions of glyceride were easily exchangeable or hydrolyzable groups. This can be represented as follows:

1 ⎡—OFA ↔ exchangeable with free fatty acid
2 ⎢—OFA ← not easily exchangeable
3 ⎣—OFA ↔ exchangeable with free fatty acid

Hence, these results indicated a decided difference in the reactivity of the 2 primary esters groups as compared to the secondary ester group.

Mattson and Beck[55, 56] have supplied convincing evidence that in the *in vivo* hydrolysis of triglycerides, 1,2 diglycerides and 2-monoglycerides are the predominant products. An apparent conversion of the 2-monoglyceride to the 1-isomer occurred but it was not evident

Table 7.2

Nature of Digestion Products from Pancreatic
Lipase Action on 2-Oleoyl-Dipalmitin *

Fraction	Iodine Value
Free fatty acid	
Observed	8.7
Palmitic (theory)	0
Oleic (theory)	90
Monoglyceride	
Observed	61
Monolein	71
Monopalmitin	0
Diglyceride	
Observed	44
Oleoyl palmitin	43
Dipalmitin	0

* Taken from Mattson and Beck.[56]

whether this was enzyme or non-enzyme catalyzed reaction. Additional evidence was supplied by Mattson and Beck on the specificity of pancreatic lipase for the primary hydroxyl groups of the glycerides. A synthetic glyceride, 2-oleoyl dipalmitin, was subjected to the action of pancreatic lipase and the various fractions, diglycerides and monoglycerides, were isolated by countercurrent extraction and examined for their iodine absorption values. Their results, shown in Table 7.2, support the specificity of the site of attack of lipase on the primary ester group as follows:

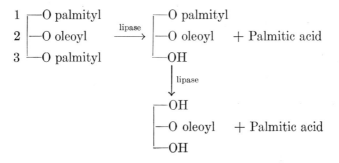

In a comparable study, Savary and Desnuelle [65,66] investigated the specificity of pancreatic lipase towards 1- and 2-oleoyl dipalmitin, 1-palmito diolein, and mixtures of glycerides with randomly distributed chains. Their results showed that the 1 and 3 acyl groups were attacked more rapidly than the 2 acyl, with the production of a high proportion of 2-monoglyceride. However, some 10 to 30% of the monoglyceride fraction was the 1-isomer. These authors argued that the latter occurrence was due to enzymatic attack at the 2 position rather than chemical isomerization of the 1,2 diglyceride or the 2-monoglyceride.

While it is evident that certain facets of the mode of attack and exact specificity of lipase activity must be clarified, it is apparent that the use of this enzyme system can be of considerable value in the assay of fatty acid distribution in naturally occurring glycerides.

ASSAY SYSTEMS. Two methods, in particular, appear to be the ones of choice in the estimation of lipolytic action. The first procedure, essentially that of Grossberg et al.[28] as modified by Borgstrom,[9] is based on the observed optical density changes (a decrease due to clearing) noted in emulsions of glycerides subjected to lipase action. Its value is in its rapidity, ease of operation, and the requirement of small amounts of substrates. The second technique involves a titrimetric assay for the fatty acids released in the process of lipolytic attack. While this latter procedure involves larger quantities than the turbidimetric method above, it does allow at the same time the possibility of subsequent fractionation of the glyceride fragments for further assay. This approach would be a necessity in studies on glyceride structure. Subsequent to the titrimetric assay for the degree of hydrolysis, the products can be isolated by countercurrent distribution technique or by silicic acid chromatography. In the latter instance, it has been noted that 2-monoglycerides can isomerize on silicic acid columns to the 1-isomer; hence the possibility of acyl migrations is always a consideration in the isolation and purification of these compounds. A brief summary of some observations on this subject appears worthwhile and is described in the following section.

ACYL MIGRATION. This phenomenon, commonly termed transesterification, is an intramolecular rearrangement wherein ester transfer is effected without production of a mole of water. It may be acid, base, or enzyme catalyzed.

Under acidic or basic conditions, a β (or 2-) mono acyl glyceride or an α,β (1,2-) di acyl glyceride (I) rearrange (non-enzymatically) to the respective α (or 1-) mono acyl glyceride or α,α' (1,3) diacyl glyceride (III):

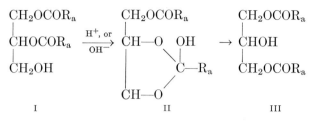

where R_a = a long-chain alkyl group.

Many instances of such migrations have been reported and can operate possibly through the ortho acid intermediate (II). Fischer observed a migration of the β-acyl groups in the deiodination of α-iodo-α',β-di-(p-nitro benzoyl) glycerol and proposed that an ortho acid intermediate would best explain this type of migration.[26] Thus, as proposed by Winstein and Buckles,[79] this latter reaction could be described as follows:

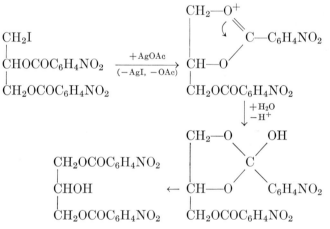

A similar mechanism probably is operative in the observed non-enzymatic and enzymatic conversion of β-lysolecithin to α'-lysolecithin.

Stimmel and King [71] found that β-monopalmitin was converted in a quantitative manner to the α-isomer in 24 hours at room temperature in an alcoholic solution of $0.05N$ HCl or $0.1N$ NH$_4$OH. This was true of aromatic derivatives as well, but in more dilute solutions the migration of the aliphatic esters proceeded more rapidly than with the corresponding aromatic esters. Jackson and King [39] observed a complete β- to α-shift of the palmityl group at temperatures as low as $-30°$ when removing (HBr in acetic acid) the triphenyl group from the α-trityl ether of 1,2 dipalmitin (IV). In agreement with Helferich and Sieber,[34] however, no shift was observed when the ether

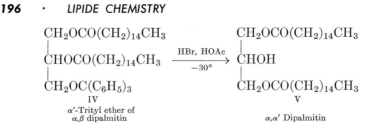

$$CH_2OCO(CH_2)_{14}CH_3$$
$$CHOCO(CH_2)_{14}CH_3 \xrightarrow[-30°]{HBr, HOAc} CHOH$$
$$CH_2OC(C_6H_5)_3 \qquad CH_2OCO(CH_2)_{14}CH_3$$
$$\text{IV} \qquad\qquad\qquad \text{V}$$
$$\alpha'\text{-Trityl ether of} \qquad\qquad \alpha,\alpha' \text{ Dipalmitin}$$
$$\alpha,\beta \text{ dipalmitin}$$

group was hydrolyzed from the analogous aromatic esters by the use of cold HBr-acetic acid solution.

While the above results indicated that a quantitative conversion of the β (2) to α (1) forms had occurred, the methods employed for assay were not as critical as desired. Martin [54] has provided substantial evidence for the occurrence of an equilibrium mixture of the two forms in this type of reaction. He observed that perchloric acid was particularly effective as a catalyst in isomerizing 2-monoglycerides, with the resultant formation of an equilibrium mixture containing approximately 90% 1-monoglyceride and 10% 2-monoglyceride. Thus, 2-monoglycerides could be determined by treatment first with $HClO_4$, then assayed for vicinal hydroxyls by the well-known periodate reaction. As an example of the rapidity of the transesterification process, Martin found that 2-monopalmitin, in pure chloroform containing 0.5% ethanol, was isomerized within 10 minutes at room temperature with catalytic amounts of 56% $HClO_4$, to a mixture of 90 to 92% 1-monopalmitin and 10 to 8% 2-monopalmitin. This procedure represents a convenient and reliable route to assay for 2-monoglycerides.

In many instances, the preparation of glycerides, as illustrated in procedures A and B, may fail to yield the expected product.

Procedure A (no migration):

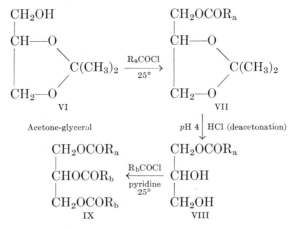

$$CH_2OH \qquad\qquad CH_2OCOR_a$$
$$CH—O \qquad\qquad CH—O$$
$$\qquad\quad C(CH_3)_2 \xrightarrow[25°]{R_aCOCl} \qquad\quad C(CH_3)_2$$
$$CH_2—O \qquad\qquad CH_2—O$$
$$\text{VI} \qquad\qquad\qquad \text{VII}$$

Acetone-glycerol $pH 4$ | HCl (deacetonation)

$$CH_2OCOR_a \qquad\qquad CH_2OCOR_a$$
$$CHOCOR_b \xleftarrow[\substack{pyridine \\ 25°}]{R_bCOCl} CHOH$$
$$CH_2OCOR_b \qquad\qquad CH_2OH$$
$$\text{IX} \qquad\qquad\qquad \text{VIII}$$

Procedure B (migration):

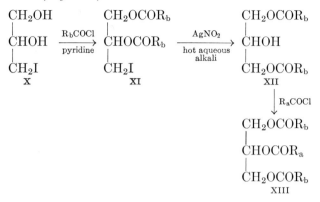

Compound XIII should have been identical with IX, but was not because proper precautions were not taken to block any acyl migration.

Thus, from the few observations cited above, it is amply evident that in studies with glycerides suitable precautions must be taken to minimize conditions favorable for the migration of acyl groups. This consideration covers not only the direct chemical investigation on the glycerides but the isolation and fractionation procedures as well.

CHEMICAL DEGRADATION. The most frequently employed procedure for a strictly chemical degradation of the glycerides is that devised by Hilditch.[35, 37] This technique involved the oxidation of the unsaturated fatty acids of the glycerides by anhydrous potassium permanganate in an organic solvent, usually acetone, and subsequent isolation of the products. While Kartha[42] has applied this oxidative technique to several naturally occurring glycerides, the low yields render it of somewhat limited usefulness on the small scale required in the case of lipides from certain mammalian sources. The various facets of this technique, as practiced by Kartha, have been subjected to careful scrutiny by Van der Wal.[75] Currently a more commonly used degradative technique embodies the principles outlined in the method of Lemieux and Von Rudloff[50] and Von Rudloff.[77] In this procedure the monounsaturated and diunsaturated fatty acid esters can be oxidatively cleaved at room temperature by a mixture of permanganate-sodium periodate. (Under the alkaline conditions of this reaction there is a continuous regeneration of expended permanganate by periodate action.) Subsequently the products of the reaction can be separated by chromatographic procedures. Recently, Jones and Stolp[40] reported a modification of this technique for a more accurate determination of the position of unsaturation in monounsaturated fatty acids. However, as illustrated by the results of Coleman and Swern,[15] the products of the reaction of permanganate on compounds with olefinic linkages depend on the conditions, with oxidant to olefin ratio (and pH) of considerable importance.

GLYCERYL ETHERS

In contrast to the lipide ester and amide linkages normally encountered in nature, the occurrence of a lipide ether grouping is limited; nonetheless it warrants due attention.* Not only are these compounds of interest by virtue of their rather close similarity to the glyceride esters, but also by their possibly close relationship to the plasmalogens (Chapter 3). In the latter case, the glyceryl ethers may well be precursors or possible metabolic products of these phosphorylated glyceryl ethers. As normally isolated through procedures involving

---

* The occurrence of other derivatives of glycerol in nature has not gone unrecognized. In the benzene extractable lipides of bleached wheat flour, at least two galactosyl glycerides have been demonstrated [H. E. Carter, R. H. McClure, and E. D. Lifer, *J. Am. Chem. Soc.*, **78**, 3735 (1956)]. One of these is apparently a β-D-galactopyranosyl-1-glycerol (I) and the other is an α-D-galactopyranosyl-1,6-β-D-galactopyranosyl-1-glycerol (II):

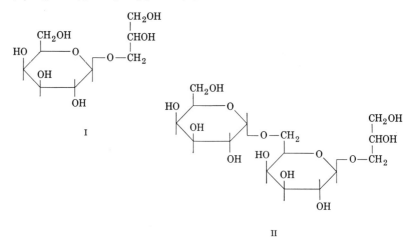

It is of interest to note that α-D-galactopyranosyl-2-glycerol has been isolated from red marine algae [E. W. Putman, and W. Z. Hassid, *J. Am. Chem. Soc.*, **76**, 2221 (1954)].

alkaline hydrolysis (in the non-saponifiable fraction), the naturally occurring lipide ethers can be represented by this formula:

The R group apparently is restricted almost entirely to three fatty alcohols, palmityl, stearyl, and oleyl, which in the combined form are known as chimyl, batyl, and selachyl alcohol, respectively. In the best documented studies to date, this R group is found exclusively on the α'(C-1) carbon of the glycerol. The proof of structure of batyl alcohol was correctly deduced by Davies et al.[16] in the following manner:

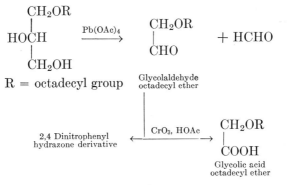

A similar mode of attack on the naturally occurring glyceryl ethers by periodic acid was reported by Karnovsky and Brumm,[41] who also isolated the glycolaldehyde octadecyl ether as the 2,4 dinitrophenyl hydrazone and substantiated the above proof of structure of the glyceryl ethers.

Sources

The glyceryl ethers have a widespread distribution in marine animals, but are found to a limited extent in land animals. However, it is of interest to note that these compounds have been detected in the bone marrow of the cow,[38] the spleen of the pig,[32] and the arteriosclerotic aortas of humans.[62]

As noted above, the glyceryl ethers are usually isolated in the non-saponifiable fraction of a lipide preparation and may be assayed by a selective periodic acid oxidation procedure wherein the formaldehyde released is estimated by the chromotropic acid procedures. In addition, as reported by Karnovsky and Brumm,[41] these compounds can be isolated as a urea adduct or also by crystallization of the free ether.

Through the use of a solvent fractionation scheme with methanol-acetone mixture (3:1, v/v), Andre and Bloch [1] were able to isolate a fully esterified glyceryl ether from a fish liver oil. This compound was apparently free of any hydrocarbons and triglycerides, and also possessed a definite optical activity. Since these reports, very little evidence has been forthcoming on the identification of glyceryl ether esters.

Synthesis and Stereochemical Configuration

Since the results of Davies et al.[16] showed the naturally occurring ethers to be α-glyceryl ethers, a center of asymmetry is present and hence D and L forms are possible. The synthesis of D-α- and L-α-selachyl alcohol by Baer and Fischer [4] was of considerable value in establishing the correct configuration. In brief, this synthesis was accomplished in the following manner:

α-(p-toluene sulfonyl)-acetone glycerol

$+$

Na salt of oleyl alcohol

$\longrightarrow$ Condensation product $\rightarrow$ α-oleyl glyceryl ether
(selachyl alcohol)

Thus, depending on the use of either the D or L acetone derivative as starting material, the corresponding optical form could be synthesized. In a comparison of the optical activities of the synthetic compound with the naturally occurring ethers, it was apparent that the D form was the predominant one.

CHOLESTEROL ESTERS

At the present writing, the cholesterol esters are the subject of intense interest to the biochemists and clinicians. This is true since many persons, scientist and non-scientist, are concerned with the level of cholesterol in the plasma and the influence that the various types of fatty acids in the diet may have upon this level. This level is considered in many circles to be directly related to atherosclerosis. Notwithstanding the current tremendous interest in this area, more information must be obtained on the exact nature of the plasma (and other) cholesterol esters as regards their fatty acid levels and the influence of other lipides and other factors (thyroid, adrenals, etc.) on the over-all picture. Such information is becoming available and will aid considerably in our understanding of sterol and fatty acid metabolism. However, the main attention here will be devoted to the chemistry of these interesting esters.

Sources

In the mammal there are three main sites of location of the cholesterol esters: the adrenals, liver, and plasma. In the adrenals, the esters represent nearly 90% of the total cholesterol stores. However, in the plasma the cholesterol esters comprise 65 to 70% of the total cholesterol. No other fatty acid esters of any other sterol are normally found in any of these tissues.

Isolation

The amount of total and free cholesterol can be conveniently obtained from the total cholesterol, as revealed by a quantitative Liebermann-Burchard reaction, and the free cholesterol, by the digitonin precipitable material. The latter component can also be determined by the Liebermann-Burchard reaction. Hence the difference between these two values was regarded as the esterified sterol. However, until recently, the actual fractionation of the free and esterified cholesterol posed a more difficult task. As described in Chapter 2, this was largely overcome by the findings of Borgstrom,[8] Fillerup and Mead,[25] and Barron and Hanahan,[5] which showed that chromatographic separation of the cholesterol esters and the free sterol could be effected on silicic acid. Thus, through the use of suitable solvents, i.e., hexane-benzene and hexane-diethyl ether mixtures, the cholesterol esters could be eluted quite rapidly from silicic acid, while the free cholesterol was eluted more slowly and always subsequent to any triglyceride present. Hence a very good separation of these components can be achieved. Also, there is the distinct possibility that the more saturated and unsaturated esters can be fractionated on these columns. However, this is yet to be worked out in a completely satisfactory and reproducible manner. In fact, in this fractionation procedure, no preliminary separation of the phospholipides from the neutral lipides is necessary as the above chromatographic scheme will allow an adequate separation.

Schon and Gey [70] have shown that free and esterified cholesterol of the lipides of organs and serum could be separated by chromatography of the petroleum ether soluble lipides on aluminum oxide (Woelm, alkali free, activity I); the esterified and free cholesterol could be eluted with petroleum ether-diethyl ether (4%) and (40%), respectively. While the latter fraction contained the triglycerides as well, this was of little consequence if only cholesterol was of consideration. However, if a more complete separation was desired, these compounds could be separated as follows: petroleum ether-diethyl ether (2%), cholesterol esters; petroleum ether-diethyl ether (8%), triglycerides; and petroleum ether-diethyl ether (40%), free cholesterol. Hence these separations on aluminum oxide required solvent combinations similar to those used on silicic acid fractionation of the neutral lipides. This technique with aluminum oxide was developed for amounts of serum as low as 0.1 to 0.5 ml. Detailed analyses on the composition of the various fractions were not reported; thus an exact evaluation of this approach is not possible. Apparently the cholesterol esters were not hydrolyzed by passage through this absorbent. Moreover, in a similar study, Clement et al.[14] found aluminum oxide, together with benzene as a solvent, was of value in separating the cholesterol esters of a tissue. These investigators reported failure in attempts to effect a preferential hydrolysis of glycerides in the presence of cholesterol esters with *Ricinus* or pancreatic lipase. Previously Kelsey and Longenecker [44, 45] had reported that such a procedure was of value in preferential cleavage of glycerides in the presence of cholesterol esters. However, a part of this difficulty may be attributed to differences in source material and treatment. Also, even if enzymatic cleavage did proceed well, it is virtually certain that the monoglycerides would contaminate the cholesterol ester fraction.

In an interesting report, Keegan and Gould [43] noted the isolation of nearly pure cholesterol oleate from the plasma of dogs and humans. The yields of this material represented at least 50% of the total cholesterol ester fraction in human plasma. In the isolation of this component two procedures were used: (1) solvent fractionation in which acetone-ether washes of a cholesterol digitonide precipitation gave, on standing, long needles (m.p. 42–44°); (2) chromatographic separation of the petroleum ether soluble lipide of the plasma on aluminum oxide. When diethyl ether-petroleum ether (1:9) was used as the eluting agent, the crystalline residue obtained from this fraction was nearly pure cholesterol oleate (98% of the calculated cholesterol and 87% of the calculated fatty acids). The slightly higher iodine absorption value indicated a possible contamination with polyunsaturated acids.

Identification

After isolation via chromatographic fractionation, a suitable characterization of these esters must be obtained. On the intact ester, iodine absorption values, saponification equivalent, ester to cholesterol values (from hydroxamate reaction and also total fatty acids by hydrolysis), infrared examination (where possible), and glycerol content (for presence of any glyceride contaminant) are of value. Subsequently the preparation can be submitted to hydrolysis and the cholesterol and fatty acids can be examined in detail.

The hydrolytic cleavage of cholesterol esters can be effected by an alcoholic alkali reagent or an enzymatic attack.

Alcoholic Alkali Hydrolysis. Apparently the effectiveness of this hydrolysis is dependent on the source of material. Barron and Hanahan [5] reported that the cholesterol esters of beef liver were hydrolyzed completely in 6 hours under nitrogen in 0.5N alcoholic KOH, whereas the sterol esters of rat liver required a longer reflux of 24 hours in 1.0N alcoholic KOH for complete cleavage. Subsequently the hydrolysate was diluted with water to 40% ethanol and extracted four times with fresh charges of diethyl ether. After washing well with water, the ether soluble fraction was analyzed for cholesterol. The original water soluble fraction from this hydrolysate, now sterol free, was acidified and the fatty acids extracted with diethyl ether, washed well with water and analyzed.

Enzymatic Attack. While the potential of this procedure has not been sufficiently explored, it does possess very good possibilities for a mild and quite selective process. A characterization of the cholesterol esterase is given in a report by Swell and Treadwell.[72]

Consequently, depending on the amounts, the examination of the cholesterol fraction could include melting point, optical activity, elemental analysis, derivative preparation (i.e., the benzoate), digitonide formation, and assay by quantitative Liebermann-Burchard reaction. The fatty acids may be characterized by neutral equivalent, iodine and hydrogen absorption values, infrared analysis, derivative preparation (where applicable), and the techniques illustrated in the glyceride section above and in the fatty acid section of Chapter 3. Finally, the cholesterol to fatty acid value should obviously prove of value in fully describing the ester fraction.

Synthesis

The preparation of cholesterol esters of known composition is of obvious value in enzyme specificity studies, metabolic experiments, and for comparative purposes. While several reports on the synthesis of particular esters have been made, only two reports, which effectively describe the entire area, will be discussed here. Essentially, the preparation of fatty acid esters of cholesterol can be accomplished in a manner similar to that used for most ester syntheses with the fatty acids.

Kritchevsky and Anderson,[47] in a study of the possible isomorphic modifications of cholesterol esters, reported on three different synthetic routes to cholesterol laurate. In brief, these procedures involved: (1) reaction of cholesterol and lauric acid in CO_2 atmosphere at 200° for 3 hours,[61] (2) combination of cholesterol and lauric acid in benzene at reflux in the presence of p-toluenesulfonic acid,[12] and (3) reaction of cholesterol and lauroyl chloride in pyridine at reflux temperatures for 1 minute. A comparison of the properties of the products of these preparations showed the existence of isomorphic forms. The yield of ester (reaction 3) was 80%, while no indication of yields on other reactions was reported.

In a more detailed investigation, Swell and Treadwell[72] synthesized a series of cholesterol esters containing saturated fatty acids of chain length from 2 to 18 carbons and also cholesterol oleate. These syntheses, which resulted in yields of 75 to 90%, were accomplished by treating cholesterol in anhydrous pyridine with the appropriate acid chlorides at 80° for 20 minutes. The melting point characteristics, molecular weights (from saponification equivalent), and the optical rotation values were supplied for such fatty acid esters. As noted by Swell and Treadwell, certain of these constants differed from those previously reported, but in view of the high purity of the starting materials used, these authors reasoned that their observations were more representative of the true values. Subsequently, these esters were used in studies on the synthetic and hydrolytic action of cholesterol esterase. The increasing availability of pure linoleic and linolenic and arachidonic acid should make the synthesis of comparable cholesterol esters more convenient.

Fatty Acid Composition

While early investigations indicated a probable high content of unsaturated fatty acids in the cholesterol esters,[6, 13, 69] the nature of certain of the fractionation procedures employed was such as to cast some doubt on the general validity of this idea. Within the past few years improved separation techniques have allowed a re-evaluation of this general observation.

Mukherjee et al.[57] have presented data on the chemical nature of the various lipide fractions present in the blood of rats on a normal diet. After removal of the blood (apparently no separation of the erythrocytes and plasma was made), the lipides were isolated by an ethanol-diethyl ether extraction at room temperature and subsequently this fraction was subjected to chromatography on silicic acid. Through the use of pentane-diethyl ether mixtures, a separation of the cholesterol esters, triglycerides, and phospholipides was realized. There was a preponderance of saturated fatty acids in all these fractions and the dienoic acids appeared to be the main polyunsaturated fatty acids in the cholesterol ester and neutral lipide fraction. Of considerable interest was the finding that no oleic acid was present in any of these lipides. This is rather puzzling when these observations are compared with the findings of Keegan and Gould[43] that at least 50% of the cholesterol ester of human plasma is the oleate. Perhaps this is a typical case of species specificity.

Recently, Klein[46] presented a preliminary report on the polyunsaturated fatty acid composition of the cholesterol esters of rat liver and plasma. In the esters of the liver, linoleic acid was the major polyunsaturated component, with almost negligible amounts of trienoic, tetraenoic, and pentaenoic acids present. Even in dietary states where linoleic acid was fed in amounts equivalent to 30% corn oil, the content of these polyunsaturated fatty acids never exceeded 36%. However, with the plasma cholesterol esters, the distribution pattern was entirely different. On the lowest linoleic acid intake, the amount of polyunsaturated fatty acids in the ester was nearly 39%, whereas on the highest linoleic acid diet (equivalent to 30% corn oil) the value rose to 102%. At the same time, a very significant rise in the tetraenoic acid content (to 36%) occurred. Not only does this indicate a probable difference in any equilibrium pattern between the liver and plasma compounds, but it also illustrates possible differences, due to dietary considerations, in reports on the composition of the cholesterol esters of mammalian tissue. No evidence of the nature of the other fatty acids present in the rat plasma was cited by Klein.

REFERENCES

1. Andre, E., and A. Bloch, *Bull. soc. chim.,* **5,** 789 (1935)
2. Artom, C., and G. Reale, *Bull. soc. ital. biol. sper.,* **10,** 877 (1935).
3. Baer, E., and D. Buchnea, *J. Biol. Chem.,* **230,** 447 (1958)
4. Baer, E., and H. O. L. Fischer, *J. Biol. Chem.,* **170,** 337 (1947)
5. Barron, E. G., and D. J. Hanahan, *J. Biol. Chem.,* **231,** 493 (1958)
6. Bloor, W. C., *J. Biol. Chem.,* **56,** 711 (1923).
7. Borgstrom, B., *Acta Chem. Scand.,* **7,** 557 (1953).
8. Borgstrom, B., *Acta Physiol. Scand.,* **30,** 231 (1954).
9. Borgstrom, B., *Biochim. et Biophys. Acta,* **13,** 491 (1954).
10. Bourne, E. S., M. Stacey, J. C. Tatlow, and J. M. Tedder, *J. Chem. Soc.,* **1949,** 2976.
11. Brown, J. B., and D. K. Kolb, *Prog. in Chem. Fats Lipids,* **3,** 57 (1955).
12. Cataline, E. L., L. Worrell, S. F. Jeffries, and S. A. Aronson, *J. Am. Pharm Assoc.,* **33,** 107 (1944).
13. Channon, H. J., and G. A. Collison, *Biochem. J.,* **23,** 1212 (1929).
14. Clement, G., J. Glement-Champougny, and A. Louedec, *Arch. sci. physiol.,* **8,** 233 (1954).
15. Coleman, J. E., and D. Swern, *J. Am. Oil Chem. Soc.,* **35,** 675 (1958).
16. Davies, W. H., I. M. Heilbron, and W. E. Jones, *J. Chem. Soc.,* **1933,** 136, 165.
17. Desnuelle, P., and M. J. Constantin, *Bull. soc. chim. biol.,* **35,** 382 (1953).
18. Desnuelle, P., M. Naudet, and M. J. Constantin, *Biochim. et Biophys. Acta,* **13,** 491 (1954).
19. Deuel, H. J., Jr., *The Lipids,* Vol. I, Interscience (1951).
20. Dieckert, J. W., and R. Reiser, *Science,* **120,** 678 (1954).
21. Dieckert, J. W., and R. Reiser, *J. Am. Oil Chem. Soc.,* **33,** 123 (1956).
22. Dittmer, J. C., Ph.D. Thesis, University of Washington (1958).
23. Doerschuk, A. P., *J. Biol. Chem.,* **193,** 39 (1951).
24. Doerschuk, A. P., and B. F. Daubert, *J. Am. Oil Chem. Soc.,* **25,** 425 (1948).
25. Fillerup, D. L., and J. F. Mead, *Proc. Soc. Exptl. Biol. Med.,* **83,** 574 (1953).
26. Fischer, E., *Ber. chem. Ges.,* **53B,** 1612 (1920).
27. Frisell, W. R., L. A. Meech, and C. G. Mackenzie, *J. Biol. Chem.,* **207,** 709 (1954).
28. Grossberg, A. L., S. A. Komarow, and H. Shay, *Am. J. Physiol.,* **168,** 269 (1952).
29. Hamilton, J. G., and R. T. Holman, *J. Am. Chem. Soc.,* **76,** 4107 (1954).
30. Hanahan, D. J., unpublished observations.
31. Hanahan, D. J., and J. N. Olley, *J. Biol. Chem.,* **231,** 813 (1958).
32. Hardegger, E., L. Ruzicka, and E. Tagman, *Helv. Chim. Acta,* **26,** 2205 (1943).
33. Harvey, S. C., and V. Higby, *Arch. Biochem.,* **30,** 14 (1951).
34. Helferich, B., and H. Sieber, *Z. physiol. Chem.,* **170,** 311 (1927).
35. Hilditch, T. P., *J. Soc. Chem. Ind. (London),* **52,** 101 (1933)

36. Hilditch, T. P., *Ann. Rev. Biochem.,* **22,** 123 (1953).
37. Hilditch, T. P., *The Chemical Constitution of Natural Fats,* 3rd edition revised, Wiley (1956).
38. Holmes, H. N., R. E. Corbet, W. B. Berger, N. Kornblum, and W. Alexander, *J. Am. Chem. Soc.,* **63,** 2607 (1941).
39. Jackson, D. T., and C. G. King, *J. Am. Chem. Soc.,* **55,** 678 (1933).
40. Jones, E. P., and J. A. Stolp, *J. Am. Oil Chem. Soc.,* **35,** 71 (1958).
41. Karnovsky, M. L., and A. F. Brumm, *J. Biol. Chem.,* **216,** 689 (1955).
42. Kartha, A. R. S., *J. Am. Oil Chem. Soc.,* **30,** 280 (1953).
43. Keegan, P., and R. G. Gould, *Federation Proc.,* **12,** 228 (1953).
44. Kelsey, F. E., *J. Biol. Chem.,* **130,** 195 (1939).
45. Kelsey, F. E., and H. E. Longenecker, *J. Biol. Chem.,* **139,** 727 (1941).
46. Klein, P. D., *Arch. Biochem. Biophys.,* **72,** 238 (1957).
47. Kritchevsky, D., and M. E. Anderson, *J. Am. Chem. Soc.,* **74,** 1857 (1952).
48. Lambert, M., and A. C. Neish, *Can. J. Research, Sect. B,* **28,** 83 (1950).
49. LeBaron, F. N., J. Folch, and E. Rothleder, *Federation Proc.,* **16,** 209 (1957).
50. Lemieux, R. V., and E. Von Rudloff, *Can. J. Chem.,* **33,** 1701, 1710 (1955).
51. Longenecker, H. E., *J. Soc. Chem. Ind.,* **56,** 199T (1937).
52. Lovern, J. A., *Biochem. J.,* **63,** 373 (1956).
53. Malkin, T., and T. H. Bevan, *Prog. in Chem. Fats Lipids,* **4,** 97 (1957).
54. Martin, J. B., *J. Am. Chem. Soc.,* **75,** 5483 (1953).
55. Mattson, F. H., and L. W. Beck, *J. Biol. Chem.,* **214,** 115 (1955).
56. Mattson, F. H., and L. W. Beck, *J. Biol. Chem.,* **219,** 735 (1956).
57. Mukherjee, S., K. T. Achaya, H. J. Deuel, Jr., and R. B. Alfin-Slater, *J. Biol. Chem.,* **226,** 845 (1957).
58. Neish, A. C., *Can. J. Research, Sect. B,* **28,** 535 (1950).
59. Norris, F. O., and K. F. Mattil, *J. Am. Oil Chem. Soc.,* **24,** 274 (1947).
60. Olley, J., in *Biochemical Problems of Lipids,* edited by Popjak and LeBreton, p. 49, Interscience (1956).
61. Page, I. H., and H. Rudy, *Biochem. Z.,* **220,** 304 (1930).
62. Prelog, V., L. Ruzicka, and P. Stern, *Helv. Chim. Acta,* **26,** 2222 (1943).
63. Quimby, O. T., R. L. Wille, and E. S. Lutton, *J. Am. Oil Chem. Soc.,* **30,** 186 (1953).
64. Ramsay, W. N. M., and C. P. Stewart, *Biochem. J.,* **35,** 39 (1941).
65. Savary, P., and P. Desnuelle, *Bull. soc. chim. France,* **21,** 936 (1954).
66. Savary, P., and P. Desnuelle, *Biochim. et Biophys. Acta,* **21,** 349 (1954).
67. Savary, P., and P. Desnuelle, *Compt. rend.,* **240,** 2571 (1955).
68. Savary, P., J. Flanzy, and P. Desnuelle, *Biochim. et Biophys. Acta,* **24,** 414 (1957).
69. Schaible, P. J., *J. Biol. Chem.,* **95,** 79 (1932).
70. Schon, H., and F. Gey, *Z. physiol. Chem.,* **303,** 31 (1956).
71. Stimmel, B. E., and E. G. King, *J. Am. Chem. Soc.,* **56,** 1724 (1934).
72. Swell, L., and C. R. Treadwell, *J. Biol. Chem.,* **212,** 141 (1955).
73. Tappel, A. L., *Arch. Biochem. Biophys.,* **47,** 223 (1953); **44,** 378 (1953).
74. Trevalyan, W. E., D. P. Proctor, and J. S. Harrison, *Nature,* **166,** 444 (1950)
75. Van der Wal, R. J., *Prog. in Chem. Fats Lipids,* **3,** 327 (1955).
76. Van Handel, E., and D. B. Zilversmit, *J. Lab. Clin. Med.,* **50,** 152 (1957).
77. Von Rudloff, E., *Can. J. Chem.,* **33,** 1714 (1955).
78. Von Rudloff, E., *J. Am. Oil Chem. Soc.,* **33,** 126 (1956).
79. Winstein, S., and R. E. Buckles, *J. Am. Chem. Soc.,* **64,** 2787 (1942).

8

by Frank R. N. Gurd *

Association of lipides
with proteins

A prime objective of biochemistry at the present time is to bring together and reconcile the understanding of the structure and function of the cell as pictured by the morphologist and by the chemist. The relation between lipides and proteins is of central interest from both points of view. The morphologist recognizes that lipides appear to share with proteins a role in maintaining the integrity of the cell, and that both are found in many structures that present large surfaces. He recognizes also that most of the lipides in healthy cells, with the ex-

* The preparation of Chapters 8 and 9 has benefited greatly from the patient help and critical skill of Dr. J. L. Oncley. Valuable comments, suggestions, and encouragement were contributed by Drs. R. E. Basford, R. E. Clark, D. E. Cornwell, J. T. Edsall, D. S. Goodman, D. E. Green, M. L. Karnovsky, and V. du Vigneaud. Unpublished material was kindly made available by Drs. R. E. Basford, D. E. Cornwell, D. M. Gibson, D. S. Goodman, and E. Stotz. Many colleagues have kindly granted permission to reproduce illustrations and tables.

The permission of the following sources to use certain tabular and illustrative material is gratefully acknowledged: Academic Press, Acta Chemica Scandinavica, American Chemical Society, American Physiological Society, American Society of Biological Chemists, British Council, Faraday Society, Macmillan and Co., New York Academy of Sciences, Swiss Academy of Medicine. Special thanks are due to Dr. J. J. Wolken of the University of Pittsburgh School of Medicine for permission to reproduce Figure 12 from his article, "Studies of Photoreceptor Structures," which appeared in Annals of the New York Academy of Sciences, Volume 74, Article 2.

ception of those specialized for the storage of triglyceride, are highly dispersed. Furthermore, much of the lipide in tissues is not readily extracted by treatment with such good fat solvents as diethyl ether, unless the tissues are hydrolyzed or treated drastically with more polar organic solvents.[105,155]

In recent years the chemist for his part has observed that procedures designed to isolate individual proteins from mixtures such as blood plasma lead to isolation of lipide-protein complexes containing rather regular proportions of various lipides and proteins.[111,126] Grossly considered from the point of view of solubility, these complexes have the characteristics of proteins, and therefore are called "lipoproteins." Other tissues, such as brain, have yielded complexes containing lipides and proteins which have the solubility characteristics of lipides, and so have been called "proteolipides." [65] Perhaps most challenging of all have been the observations that intracellular particulate fractions such as mitochondria and microsomes contain large quantities of lipides, notably phospholipides. The separation of individual enzymes or sets of enzymes from these structures has been accomplished by treatments directed particularly at disrupting or removing the lipide moieties.[15,94,156] Some general aspects of the association of lipides with proteins will be considered before the isolation and properties of some specific lipoprotein systems are taken up. There is little evidence that lipides and proteins ordinarily combine with each other through primary covalent linkages, such as ester bonds. The combination seems to be due more to interactions between similar types of functional groups in the two classes of compounds, such as between non-polar, hydrophobic residues of the fatty acid moieties of lipides and the similar residues of certain of the side-chain groups of proteins. Other interactions may involve polar or charged groups.

To borrow from current knowledge of the binding of small molecules by proteins [84,98,145] and of the action of enzymes,[110,124] it may be expected that the tightness and specificity of the binding of lipides to proteins may depend to a great extent on steric arrangement. Indeed, vague as these interactions may seem compared to the familiar covalent bond, it must be borne in mind that such interactions are believed to determine at least in part the mode of combination of enzymes with substrates and coenzymes. It is quite possible, therefore, that strong binding of lipides to proteins may depend on the same factors of closeness of fit, multiple attachment, and matching of polarity that are recognized to determine the combination of substrates, inhibitors, and coenzymes with enzymatically active proteins.

The methods of measuring and interpreting the binding of small molecules and ions by proteins may be applied directly to the study of the simplest lipoproteins, such as the serum albumin-fatty acid complexes.[79] It is customary to interpret such binding in terms of the combination of the small molecules (here fatty acid anions) with individual sites on the surface of the protein, each composed of appropriate arrangements of several side-chain groups of the amino acid residues.

The simple assumption of individual sites, in which the bound lipide molecule allies itself only with appropriate functional groups in the protein, cannot be extended in a straightforward way to those lipoproteins that are richest in lipide. For example, the beta-lipoproteins of human blood plasma contain roughly 75% lipide, composed of a complex mixture of phospholipides, cholesterol esters, cholesterol, triglyceride, and small quantities of other lipides.[126] An individual lipoprotein particle may contain 1000–2000 lipide molecules. So much lipide is present that only certain of the lipide molecules may be pictured as making separate direct contact with the protein * at any one time. Most of the lipide molecules find themselves in contact with other lipide molecules. In order to develop an understanding of such structures it is necessary to consider both the relations of lipide molecules to protein structures and of lipide molecules to each other. Accordingly, the following discussion will deal first with the types of forces that are characteristic of the interactions of the component parts of lipides and proteins with their environment, and second with the ways in which these forces may direct the association of the lipide molecules with each other and with protein structures.

NON-POLAR AND POLAR GROUPS OF LIPIDES AND PROTEINS †

Non-Polar Structures

In the tetrahedral arrangement of bonds about carbon atoms in hydrocarbons, in the related chains of fatty acids, or in the side chains of certain of the amino acid residues in proteins the shared pairs of electrons forming the —C—C— or —C—H bonds are rather

---

* For certain purposes it is desirable to stress the fact that the protein contained in a given lipoprotein complex has not been isolated directly from a natural source as an entity in itself, free of lipide; for this reason the expressions lipide moiety and peptide moiety will be used frequently in what follows.

† As a general reference see Edsall and Wyman.[50]

symmetrically distributed. Regions of marked localization of positive or negative charge are not found, and these molecules or atomic groupings are termed *non-polar*. Such molecules or parts of molecules exert only the weak attractive forces on each other that are generally found between all molecules. These so-called van der Waals forces operate effectively over very short distances and are important only when the contours of the interacting groups allow the apposition of large fractions of their surfaces.

Polar Structures

In bonds between atoms of widely different electronegativity the shared pairs of electrons tend to be distorted from a symmetrical distribution. For example, the O—H bond is polarized by the greater attraction of O for the electron pair, so that the region of the O atom contains a net negative charge and that of the H atom a net positive charge. Such a grouping is said to be *polar*.

Polar molecules tend to attract each other, which accounts, for example, for much of the considerable difference in cohesiveness between chloromethane and the hydrocarbon butane. The effects are particularly marked in water in which the oxygen atom tends to attract a hydrogen atom from each of two neighboring water molecules at the same time as its own pair of hydrogen atoms is attracted to two other oxygen atoms. The tetrahedral ice-like arrangement is propagated over small volumes and is constantly being disrupted and reformed. This aspect of the structure of water will be considered in more detail later.

The individual water molecules may be thought of as linked together by nearly linear O—H . . . O bridges in which the weaker intermolecular linkage is denoted by the dotted line. Such bridges between the strongly electronegative O atoms are called *hydrogen bonds*. It is common to refer to the —OH group on the left as a donor of the hydrogen atom in the formation of the bridge and to the O on the right as an acceptor.

An oxygen atom bearing a hydrogen atom can act either as donor or acceptor of a hydrogen atom in the formation of hydrogen bonds; in the case of water it plays both roles at once. The oxygen atom of a hydroxyl group in a lipide or protein may behave likewise. On the other hand, ethereal and carbonyl oxygen atoms act only as acceptors of hydrogen atoms borne by other electronegative atoms. Other types of hydrogen bonds to be considered in lipides and proteins involve nitrogen as an electronegative atom which may bear an unshared pair

Table 8.1

Examples of Classes of Groups in Lipides

Polarity	Group	Example of Compound in Which Found
Non-polar	Saturated straight hydro-carbon chain	Saturated fatty acids and derivatives
	Saturated branched hydro-carbon chain	Cholesterol Cholesterol esters
	Fused hydrocarbon rings	Cholesterol Cholesterol esters
Polarizable (no permanent dipole)	Unsaturated hydrocarbon chain	Unsaturated fatty acids and derivatives Sphingolipides
Polar (permanent dipole)	Ester	Triglycerides Phosphoglycerides Inositides Cholesterol esters
	Ether	Lipide ethers
	Vinyl ether	Plasmalogens
	Carbinol	Sphingomyelins Monoglycerides and diglycerides Lysophosphoglycerides Hydroxy fatty acids Cytolipin H Cerebrosides Inositides Cholesterol and other steroids
	Phenol	Steroid estrogens
Charged	Primary phosphate	Phosphatidic acid
	Primary sulfate	Sulfatides
	Secondary phosphate	Phosphoglycerides Sphingomyelins
	Carboxyl	Fatty acids
	Carboxyl (in amino acid grouping)	Phosphatidyl serine
	Quaternary ammonium	Lecithins Sphingomyelins
	Primary amino	Phosphatidyl ethanolamine
	Primary amino (α to carboxyl group)	Phosphatidyl serine

of electrons. Such bonds may link two nitrogen atoms or one nitrogen atom with an oxygen atom.

Charged Structures

Many of the polar groups in proteins and lipides act as proton donors or acceptors and are present in the physiological pH range as *charged*

Table 8.2

Examples of Classes of Groups in Protein Side Chains

Polarity	Side-Chain Group	Example of Compound in Which Found
Non-polar	Aliphatic branched hydrocarbons	Glycine Alanine Valine Leucine Isoleucine
Polarizable (no permanent dipole)	Aromatic hydrocarbons	Phenylalanine
Polar	Aromatic (only slightly polar)	Tryptophan
	Hydroxyl-containing	Serine Threonine Tyrosine
	Sulfur-containing	Cysteine Methionine
	Imino acids	Proline Hydroxyproline
	Amides	Asparagine Glutamine
Charged	Carboxyl	Aspartic acid Glutamic acid
	Imidazole	Histidine
	Ammonium	Lysine Hydroxylysine
	Guanidinium	Arginine

groups. The very strong forces exerted by the charged structures decrease with increasing distance much more slowly than the forces between non-polar molecules or the molecules of intermediate polarity discussed above. Ions attract and repel each other over appreciable distances, and also attract and orient polar molecules or groups.

Examples of Groups in Lipides and Proteins

The progression in molecular electrical asymmetry that we have classified roughly according to the sequence of non-polar, polar, and

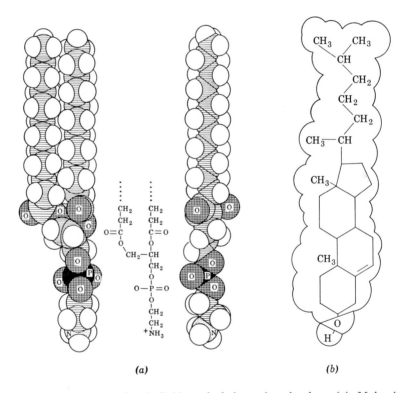

(a) (b)

Fig. 8.1. Drawings of phospholipide and cholesterol molecules. (a) Molecular model of a phospholipide molecule, phosphatidyl ethanolamine; views in two mutually perpendicular directions. (b) Structural formula of cholesterol together with the approximate outline of the corresponding molecular model. Taken from J. B. Finean and J. D. Robertson, *Brit. Med. Bull.*, **14,** 267 (1958).

NONPOLAR ALIPHATIC R GROUPS HYDROXYL-CONTAINING R GROUPS ACIDIC R GROUPS

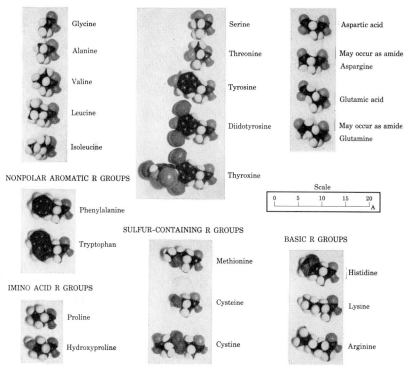

NONPOLAR ALIPHATIC R GROUPS

Glycine

Alanine

Valine

Leucine

Isoleucine

NONPOLAR AROMATIC R GROUPS

Phenylalanine

Tryptophan

IMINO ACID R GROUPS

Proline

Hydroxyproline

HYDROXYL-CONTAINING R GROUPS

Serine

Threonine

Tyrosine

Diidotyrosine

Thyroxine

SULFUR-CONTAINING R GROUPS

Methionine

Cysteine

Cystine

ACIDIC R GROUPS

Aspartic acid

May occur as amide
Aspargine

Glutamic acid

May occur as amide
Glutamine

Scale

0   5   10   15   20
L____|____|____|____|A

BASIC R GROUPS

Histidine

Lysine

Arginine

Fig. 8.2. Packing models of naturally occurring amino acids as dipolar ions. The carboxyl oxygen directed downward in each model is made with a concavity which allows it to lie in the plane of the ammonium group in the orientation found in the crystal structures studied so far. Taken from B. W. Low, in *The Proteins,* Vol. IA, edited by H. Neurath and K. Bailey, Academic Press (1953).

charged properties is shown in its full range by the groups contained in lipides and proteins. Examples of these classes of groups in lipides are collected in Table 8.1. A similar listing is made in Table 8.2 in the form of the side-chain R groups of the amino acid residues in proteins. The three-dimensional arrangements of the groups in some lipide molecules are illustrated by drawings of molecular models in Fig. 8.1. The three-dimensional appearance of the amino acid side-chain groups is shown in Fig. 8.2, and a short length of peptide chain is illustrated in Fig. 8.3.

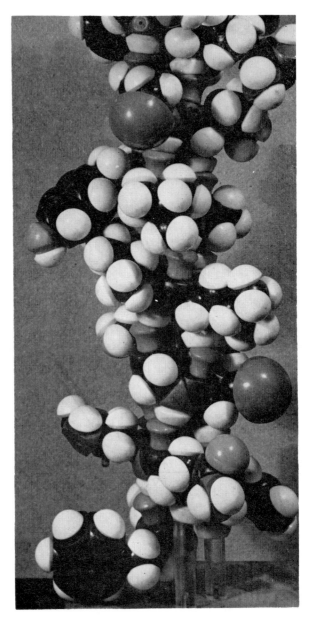

Fig. 8.3. Model of a polypeptide chain coiled in a helical configuration. The polypeptide helix proper rises vertically above the supports seen at the bottom of the figure. The first residue at the bottom is phenylalanine. One-third of the way up the figure on the right is a large S atom (with no H shown on it) and projecting immediately above it a leucine side-chain. Taken from B. W. Low, in *The Proteins,* Vol. IA, edited by H. Neurath and K. Bailey, Academic Press (1953).

ASSOCIATION OF LIPIDES

Polar Lipides

Phospholipides, cerebrosides, and fatty acids are examples of what may be classed as polar lipides. They possess strongly polar or charged groups arranged in such a way in the molecule that they may be oriented towards water or other polar molecules or groups at the same time as their non-polar portions are oriented away from the polar environment. The polar lipides may be defined further as those lipides in which the tendency to anchor one part of the molecule in water is sufficiently pronounced that they must either show detectable solubility in water or else show a strong tendency to occupy the interface between a non-polar region and a polar or aqueous region.

Non-Polar Lipides

A hydrocarbon such as beta-carotene is an example of a non-polar lipide. More plentiful in nature are the higher triglycerides, whose non-polar portions are generally so predominant that they do not mix with water. When dispersed mechanically in water, triglycerides normally form spherical droplets whose surface area of contact with water is minimal. These droplets tend to coalesce to larger droplets having a smaller total interfacial area. The droplets may be stabilized to some extent by the presence of polar lipides or proteins which tend to occupy the interface. Such materials are called *surface active agents*. Stabilized dispersions of non-polar lipides in aqueous solutions are classed as *emulsions,* and will be discussed later.

The steroids hold an intermediate position between polar and non-polar lipides. Some, such as the bile salts, contain several polar groups and show measurable solubility in water. Most of these compounds tend to orient themselves at aqueous interfaces. Cholesterol is the most plentiful of the animal steroids, and among the most non-polar of them. It is extremely insoluble in water and requires the admixture of surface active agents to stabilize its dispersion in aqueous solutions.

Formation of Micelles

Most polar lipides disperse molecularly in water to only a small extent, and if larger quantities are introduced into the aqueous medium, aggregates are formed. In general these aggregates are called *micelles*. The formation of micelles has been studied in great detail by those interested in soaps and synthetic anionic, cationic, or non-ionic detergents. Much of the following discussion will draw heavily on such studies; it will apply directly to the soaps, but will be shown later to extend in certain respects to the consideration of the phospholipides and even of proteins.

If a crystalline soap or synthetic detergent is introduced into water, a sharp change in the properties of the solution will be observed in the neighborhood of a characteristic concentration known as the *critical micellar concentration* (C.M.C.).[64, 74, 90, 117, 180] Among the properties affected are the surface tension of the solution and the ability to take up or "solubilize" water-insoluble compounds such as higher fatty alcohols and water-insoluble dyes. In the latter instance the change in environment of the dye as it passes into the micelle may be reflected in a spectral shift. These and other observations have been interpreted in terms of the formation of micelles in which the molecules of detergent are aggregated so that their hydrocarbon chains are directed inward with the probable exclusion of water from the inside of the micelle. The polar groups are pictured as extending into the aqueous environment. The shape of the micelles may be spherical, spherocylindrical, or cylindrical. It probably varies somewhat with the nature of the compound and the total concentration. The shapes that have been postulated are consonant both with experimental measurements and with the idea that the thickness of the micelles is limited by the length of the hydrocarbon chains since the polar ends resist incorporation into the central, non-polar region.

The micelles are in equilibrium with the single molecules of which they are constituted. Above the C.M.C. the addition of more detergent enriches the number and perhaps the size of the micelles, but causes a relatively small increase in the concentration of the free, single molecules.

Goddard, Hoeve, and Benson have suggested recently that the process of aggregation into micelles involves a gain of entropy.[74, 90] They have concluded that the driving force is derived from the tendency of non-polar molecules to stabilize the "ice-like" structure of water around them,[30, 68, 69] an effect which is limited to the free molecules because the non-polar chains in the micelles have a non-aqueous environment. Estimates of heats of micelle formation are in agreement with the idea that the hydrocarbon interior of the micelles is liquid. The mutual repulsions between charged polar groups in the surface of the micelle, e.g., carboxylate groups of fatty acids, should work against the stability of the micelles.[43] Goddard et al. estimate this effect to be small. This effect may be manifest, however, in the well-known ability of neutral salts to lower the C.M.C. Presumably the added salts act to shield the repulsive forces between the ions in the micellar surface. The picture developed by Benson and co-workers gains general support from recent work by Matijevic and Pethica, who claim, however, more accurate measurements of heats of micelle formation.[117]

Solubilization of substances in a detergent micelle may involve alignment of the added molecules in parallel with the palisade of detergent molecules.[148] In such an arrangement a long-chain alcohol, for example, may be interspersed between fatty acid anions, with the hydrocarbon portions intertwined and the carbinol and carboxylate groups sharing the surface. Such an arrangement may stabilize somewhat larger micelles than those of the detergent alone.

Less polar additives may be incorporated into the body of the hydrocarbon portion of the micelles, and swelling is often believed to result. This accommodation of a new layer in the middle of a micelle involves some separation of the hydrocarbon chains of the original micelle.[96] With most geometric arrangements the fully altered micelle and the original micelle are likely to be more stable than a micelle that has incorporated only part of its potential charge of additive. In other words, the process of solubilization is cooperative.[28]

Association of Lipides at Interfaces

The discussion of micelle formation has brought out the tendency of molecules containing polar and non-polar "heads" and "tails" to associate, with the heads projecting into the aqueous environment and the tails packing into the interior. Much more detailed information about the forces between polar moieties and between non-polar moieties, and about the nature of the packing and adlineation, may be gained from studies of the properties of films of such molecules at interfaces. The information that has been obtained not only throws light on the properties of lipides but also may be carried over to the consideration of the structure of proteins and to the nature of lipide-protein interactions, as discussed in the following two sections.

Most studies on interfacial films have dealt with the air/water interface. Very small quantities of the substance under study are spread on water and various parameters such as spreading pressure

(π), surface tension (γ), and surface potential (ΔV) are measured.[2] From knowledge of the surface area and the amount of material in the interface, the area occupied per molecule can be calculated and related to the other parameters. Depending on how cohesive the film is, it may be classified broadly as gaseous or condensed. Condensed films may be further subclassified as liquid or solid. A variety of terms has been used to express the gradation in cohesiveness of the films. Recently, measurements of surface viscosity [25] and surface entropy [24] have permitted more detailed descriptions of the films than are available for most of the systems that will be discussed.

The attenuated gaseous films conform to the simple equation of state

$$\pi A = kT$$

where A is the area per molecule expressed in square angstroms, π the surface pressure in dynes per centimeter, k the gas constant in appropriate units, and T the temperature in degrees Kelvin. For liquid films in which molecular interaction is appreciable, the following two-dimensional analogue of the van der Waals equation was introduced by Langmuir:

$$(\pi + B)(A - A_0) = kT$$

where B is a measure of cohesion between the molecules and A_0 corrects for the co-area actually occupied by the molecules.[106, 142] Other equations of state have been found useful under appropriate conditions.[6, 7, 86]

Films at the air/water interface composed of saturated long-chain alcohols or fatty acids are condensed at low pressures.[5] The hydrocarbon chains tend to pack in an elongate form very similar to the packing in the crystalline substances near the melting points, and oriented nearly normal to the interface. The bond angles are about 112° and the repeating zigzag is close to 2.54 A. Translational freedom in the interface is restricted but even in close-packed arrays there is probably considerable freedom of rotation about the long axes of the molecules.[24] In keeping with the expected increased attractive forces, cohesion increases with chain length. It is striking that these cohesive forces between hydrocarbon chains are largely disrupted if the same molecules are studied at the benzene-water interface, where the benzene can penetrate between the paraffinic chains. Under such conditions the area occupied by the molecules at a given pressure tends to increase sharply, reflecting the greatly reduced value of B.[8, 32]

It should be stressed that continuous films are formed by many substances which have appreciable solubility in water and that films form and exert surface pressure even when the C.M.C. is not reached. On the other hand, applying pressure to lessen the surface occupied by a film may either drive part of the substance into the bulk of the solution, or buckle the film on itself, depending on its cohesive properties. Of course, solutions containing micelles will usually bear interfacial films as well.

Films in which the head groups are charged, e.g., long-chain quaternary ammonium salts, reflect the repulsive effects of the like charges. The alignment of the charged groups in the surface carries with it a strong electrostatic field whose behavior is extremely difficult to predict on a theoretical basis.[89] Davies' adaptation [41] of the Gouy theory has been extended successfully in some cases of low average charge.[118] The effect of mutual repulsion is illustrated by the fact that for films spread at large areas per molecule at interfaces between oil and aqueous solutions of low ionic strength, the theory reduces to the form [41, 142]

$$\pi A = 3kT$$

The repulsion is very materially reduced as the ionic strength approaches the physiological range. Oppositely charged ions crowd into the interface and compensate much of the repulsion.[118–120, 133]

The diffuse layer of solution immediately under the surface film contains an excess of ions of opposite charge. Thus a film of a soap such as laurate spread on water is subjected to a considerable potential, tending to pull the soap ions out of the interface; no such force operates on the uncharged lauric acid.[142]

The magnitude of the electrostatic effects in the diffuse double layer is made tangible by the observation that the apparent *"pK"* of long-chain fatty acids in interfacial films is of the order of as much as 4 *p*H units higher than in the bulk phase. Almost as large discrepancies in the opposite direction have been observed for long-chain amines. In these studies the quantities of material in the interface are very minute, and the course of the titration is followed by measuring interfacial tension, pressure, or potential as a function of the *p*H of buffers used in the aqueous medium. Early and very incomplete theoretical treatments led to the conclusion that a "surface *p*H" could be defined in these systems, differing by about 2 units from that in the bulk of the solution.[38] More refined treatment by Matijevic and Pethica [21, 118] has reconciled the surface measurements with *pK* values within 0.7 unit of the corresponding bulk value, although only for measurements made on films at low compression and with low charge density. The effect of the potential field within the diffuse double layer should not be confused with the numerically similar effect of a mixed solvent medium of low dielectric constant.

If repulsive effects of charges borne by the polar heads of the film-forming substance are weak or absent, net cohesive forces between these groups may be apparent. The cohesive effects of the polar heads enter the balance between the dissipating effect of thermal agitation and the cohesive tendencies of the hydrocarbon moieties. Detailed interpretations of the role of the polar heads in cohesion and packing of various films have been made in terms of hydrogen bonding. Alexander has discussed in some detail the evidence for hydrogen bonds between polar heads in films of long-chain acetamides, ureas, amides, acetanilides, aldoximes, carboxylic acids, and α-amino acids.[4] These studies will be discussed further in connection with association phenomena in proteins.

The cohesiveness and packing of fatty acid films is affected by the nature of the non-polar chain. For example, saturated acids such as stearic pack closely together and form solid films readily, as does the *trans*-unsaturated acid, elaidic. The crimping introduced by a *cis* configuration as in oleic acid hinders close packing and its films remain liquid under pressures where stearic and elaidic acids are solid. The same tendencies are shown by the triglycerides of saturated and unsaturated fatty acids, e.g., tristearin and triolein.[19] The triglycerides generally form somewhat less cohesive and more liquid films than their corresponding fatty acids. The difference is probably attributable at least in part to the lack of tendency of the esters to form hydrogen bonds with neighboring molecules.[5] Such differences in cohesiveness and packing have been correlated with the ability of surface films to retard evaporation of water.[87, 149, 175]

Cholesterol and cholesterol esters form solid films in which the hydrocarbon moieties presumably interact strongly. Their large bulk seems to preclude strong hydrogen bonding between the hydroxyl groups. This is in marked contrast to the behavior of the long-chain alcohols whose films seem to be stabilized by such hydrogen bonding.[5]

The difficulties of preparing pure samples of natural phospholipides have been stressed in Chapter 2. Almost certainly all studies, up to the present, on the surface properties of such materials have been marred by effects due to impurities. One study on pure synthetic (distearoyl) phosphatidyl choline has been reported by Anderson and Pethica.[11] Over the *p*H range 2.5–7 the curve of ΔV versus A did not vary when the underlying solution contained $0.1M$ NaCl. At lower pH values the potential at a given area per molecule rose, as was to be expected from the suppression of the dissociation of the secondary phosphate group. A drop in potential was observed at pH above 8.5, and was very marked at pH 10. This range of pH is far too low to correspond to decomposition of the quaternary ammonium group in the choline moiety. Unfortunately, no back titrations were reported whereby the possibility of decomposition of other parts of the lecithin could be ruled out. The changes in potential at pH values near 7 were accompanied by expansion of the film. At pH values above 10 (unspecified) the monolayer tended to dissolve. In the presence of $5M$ NaCl, the film was much expanded. Such high concentrations of NaCl also caused a considerable rise in potential at a given area per molecule. Penetration of the plane of the hydrophilic head groups by ions at high concentrations is well known,[119, 120] as are salting-out effects. The area of closest stable packing was found to be about 40 square Angstrom units per molecule.

Mixed Films

The behavior of films containing two different film-forming substances may give considerable information about the types of interactions that may occur between their respective polar or non-polar moieties. The titration of a film of a pure fatty acid with alkaline solutions makes it possible to study the simple case of interaction between fatty acid and soap in which only the polar groups differ. The relations between area, surface potential, and pressure in films of fatty acids on solutions of dilute acids have been interpreted in terms of hydrogen bonds having bond lengths similar to those measured in crystalline dimeric carboxylic acids. As the pH is increased, however, striking changes occur. The film becomes stiffer and occupies less area at a given pressure. The ionized and un-ionized carboxyl groups probably combine together through hydrogen bonds that are stronger than the bonds between the un-ionized carboxyl groups alone. The effect of this sharing of a hydrogen ion between two carboxyl groups should be similar to, but may be weaker than, the effect of the sharing in the biphthalate ion. It should be noticed that the charge built up in the film would be expected, in itself, to work against the increased cohesion.

The difficulties of interpreting electrostatic effects in the diffuse double layer hinder the detection of any effect of hydrogen bonding in mixed films of fatty acid and soap by a distortion of the titration behavior. Pethica and co-workers have found that the behavior of mono-layers of octanoic acid and stearic acid deviated from theory in the direction that would be expected if such hydrogen bonding inter-vened.[21, 120] They found agreement with the theoretical electrostatic treatment only at low degrees of compression of the film and at very low degrees of conversion of fatty acid to soap.

The hypothesis of sharing of a hydrogen ion between carboxyl groups is much more strongly supported by the findings of Dervichian and Kepes, who titrated $0.2M$ potassium laurate with HCl.[46] At this con-centration the soap is largely associated in micelles. One mole of acid is taken up in two clearly defined steps which are separated by a region of very slight buffering near 0.5 mole between pH 9 and 6.5. The stabilization of the acid soap form in the micelles may parallel the postulated behavior of the surface films. In these measurements the ionic environment varied continuously and no study of gross changes in aggregation was made. It is possible that the mode of packing of the molecules of soap and fatty acid in the micelles allows much more efficient cooperative changes than the planar arrangement in surface films. The question deserves searching study.

The most generally used method of studying mixed films has been to spread a film of one substance and then to inject a solution of a second substance into the aqueous solution beneath.[151, 153] Penetration occurs if both polar and non-polar moieties of the injected substance can interact strongly and simultaneously with the corresponding parts of the material in the original film. This penetration is similar to the previously discussed infiltration of the palisade layer in micelles. It may be detected by a tendency of the film to expand which is meas-urable as an actual expansion if the surface is maintained at constant pressure, or as an increase in pressure if the area is not allowed to change.[134] Strong interaction may also be reflected in non-additive changes in surface potential, indicating interaction of the dipoles in the head groups. A strong interaction leads to a definite stoichio-metric ratio of the molecules in the films such as 1:1, 1:2, or 1:3. In some cases the interaction may be strong enough that the association between the two substances persists even up to applied surface pres-sures at which the film as a whole buckles.[150] In certain instances, one component can be forced out of the film by compression, but can penetrate again on lowering the pressure. In other cases no penetration occurs, but interaction of the injected substance with the polar heads of the molecules in the film can be detected by solidification of the film, small changes in area per molecule, or changes in surface potential.

Very stable films are formed by cholesterol and digitonin in equimolecular proportions.[151,153] That the interaction involves the C-3 OH of the cholesterol, as it does in the bulk interaction, is shown by the much weaker interaction between digitonin and cholesterol acetate. It would be interesting to test the behavior of the alpha—OH isomer of cholesterol which is not precipitated from solution by digitonin. Schulman and Rideal have drawn a number of parallels between the formation of stable mixed films and the formation of complexes in bulk.[151]

Films of cholesterol are condensed and quite stable but are penetrated by long-chain compounds containing many different polar head groups, such as sulfate, sulfonate, ammonium, carboxylate, and trimethylammonium.[134,142,151] Roughly speaking, penetration commences with a C_9 chain when attached to a very reactive head group such as sulfate, and with a C_{12} chain when attached to a weakly reacting group. The maximum effect is observed with C_{18}. Part of the penetrating ability of the long-chain sulfates may be ascribed to a balance between cross-sectional dimensions of the hydrocarbon tail and the polar head, which makes for suitable packing in the film without involving particularly strong cohesive forces between the two molecular species. Weakly interacting components in films have been shown on several occasions to prefer certain mole ratios that probably allow close and ordered packing.[42,76,116] The range of the degrees of interaction in monolayers is too broad to be discussed adequately here, and the reader is referred elsewhere.[2,5,7,10,75,142,151,153]

Special mention should be made of interaction between a monolayer and substance which combines with the polar head groups without penetrating the film.[35] Relatively simple organic acids such as p-cresol, resorcinol, and benzoic acid react weakly with films of octadecylamine. The spreading properties and the surface potential are affected but not the rigidity. A long-chain omega-dicarboxylic acid such as thapsic acid (C_{18}) is strongly adsorbed. The acid tends to lie flat in the interface and the area occupied by the film per molecule of octadecylamine may be more than three times as large at low pressures as in the absence of the acid. Gallic acid at pH 8 offers multiple attachment to the octadecylamine and a fragile skin is formed. The same tendency is carried farther by tannic acid.

Effect of Metal Ions on Films

Un-ionized monolayers are little affected by univalent or polyvalent metal ions. As mentioned earlier, charged films such as those of long-chain sulfates or carboxylates are somewhat sensitive to the ionic strength of the underlying solution. When the film is maintained at low areas per long-chain ion and the ionic strength is high, counter ions tend to penetrate into the plane of the film ions, resulting in a net attractive energy for the ionic system.[41,167] Polyvalent ions have very marked effects on the properties of films of carboxylic acids.[38,159,166,168] As the pH is increased in a solution containing calcium chloride, a film of stearic acid becomes more condensed and more rigid. The films of calcium soap are formed at very low bulk concentrations of calcium ion. Their presence may be suspected whenever a surface property is markedly affected by the addition of a substance such as fluoride ion. When a metal ion such as Cu(II) is used, which tends to combine with hydroxyl ions, it is found that the contracted films undergo some expansion and solidification as the pH reaches the neighborhood of the onset of hydrolysis. This pH is characteristic of the metal ion. It has been suggested that basic soaps are formed, of the type of Cu(OH) stearate.[159] The behavior of systems containing uranyl, ferric, and aluminum salts is very complicated. Suggestions have been made concerning the possible role of hydrogen bonding between adjacent molecules of basic soap. The possible involvement of other ions available immediately below the surface film is difficult to evaluate.

The behavior of synthetic detergents is somewhat similar to that of the soaps.[167] Studies with synthetic detergents also have established a parallel in the behavior of divalent metal ions in binding to surface films and to micelles in the body of the solution.[172]

Anderson and Pethica have studied the effect of various salts on films of synthetic (distearoyl) phosphatidyl choline.[11] The dipolar ion was rather insensitive to changes in ionic strength due to NaCl in the range 0.001–0.1. At concentrations below $1M$ there was no binding of K, Na or Li ions as judged by measurements of surface potential. Higher potentials were observed with polyvalent ions, and ascribed to binding to phosphate groups. A rough estimate of order of binding efficiency was made: $UO_2 \gg Al \gg Cs > Cu \geq Mg, Ca > Na$. The uranyl ion was also observed to stabilize a monolayer of the corresponding synthetic phosphatidic acid at pH 5, in contrast to the tendency of such films to dissolve above pH 1 in the absence of this ion. It is to be hoped that such studies will be followed by measurements on well-defined preparations of phosphatidyl ethanolamine and phosphatidyl serine. These molecules contain the primary amino and amino acid groupings, whose interactions with metal ions have been studied in some detail.[84] Their combination with ions such as cupric ions may be studied under conditions of competition with hydrogen ion, which may allow internal checks of the adequacy of the electrostatic interpretation of effects due to the diffuse double layer. Appropriate positively and negatively charged analogues could constitute useful controls.

Without such studies, the idea of defining reactive groups in cell surfaces by their "charge-reversal spectrum" may not bear much fruit.[16,44] An interesting beginning has been made in the difficult task of correlating the pioneering ideas of the Dutch school of colloid chemists with recent efforts of those interested in the interactions between ions and proteins.[160]

Films and Micelles of Bile Salts

The association behavior of the bile acids and their derivatives is of special interest because these compounds represent some of the most polar steroids and because they have been used as reagents to disrupt lipoprotein structures (see Chapter 9). The principal bile acids may be looked upon as derivatives of cholanic acid, shown in Fig. 8.4(a). The most common bile acids are lithocholic acid (3-hydroxycholanic acid), deoxycholic acid (3,12-dihydroxycholanic acid), and cholic acid (3,7,12-trihydroxycholanic acid).[163] All these compounds have rings A and B fused in a *cis* conformation and the 3—OH group in the α (polar) position. In both these respects they differ from cholesterol [Fig. 8.4(c)] which has the *trans* conformation and the 3—OH in the β (equatorial) position. These differences give the bile acids a somewhat more angular shape than cholesterol.[169]

Conjugates of bile acids with taurine or glycine are more abundant in nature than the free bile acids. The structure of glycocholanic acid is shown in Fig. 8.4(b).

The properties of surface films of cholanic acid, glycocholanic acid, and cholesterol have been compared by Ekwall, Ekholm, and Norman.[53] The bile acids were studied on water or $3M$ sodium chloride adjusted to pH 2 with hydrochloric acid. It was concluded that the three molecules were oriented on water as shown in Fig. 8.4. The bile acids occupied slightly more area per molecule than the cholesterol, in keeping with their more angular shape. In a later paper the same authors showed that the addition of a hydroxyl group at the 3 position to form lithocholic acid or glycolithocholic acid caused a large change in the properties of the surface films.[54] Instead of the closely packed films characteristic of cholanic acid, lithocholic acid appeared to assume an orientation lying flat on the surface of the aqueous phase. The same sort of behavior has also been observed by Adam, Askew,

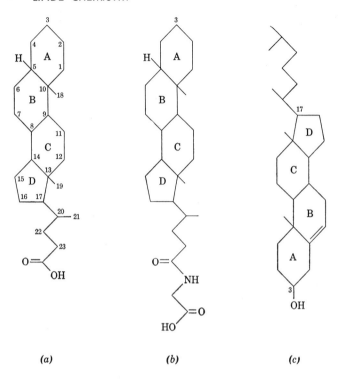

(a)   *(b)*   *(c)*

Fig. 8.4. Structures of cholanic acid (*a*), glycocholanic acid (*b*), and cholesterol (*c*) arranged to show the approximate orientations in monolayers spread on aqueous solutions. Taken from P. Ekwall, R. Ekholm, and A. Norman, *Acta Chem. Scand.,* **11,** 693 (1957).

and Danielli[3] for the dihydroxycholenic acids, apocholic acid, and β-apocholic acid. The tendency of both ends of the hydroxyl-bearing bile acids to maintain contact with the aqueous layer beneath is similar to the behavior of thapsic acid, mentioned previously. When films of lithocholic or glycocholic acid are compressed the molecules appear to slide over each other so that as many as three molecules may be stacked horizontally above one another on the surface.[54]

Bile salts and conjugated bile salts form micelles, as judged by small-angle X-ray scattering[55,56] and solubilization of hydrocarbons.[54,57] The acids formed on partial titration of cholate or deoxycholate with hydrochloric acid are themselves incorporated into the micelles.[57,58] The ability of the micelles of bile salts to solubilize hydrocarbons, long-chain alcohols, or fatty acids appears to alter stepwise as the concentration of bile salt is increased.[52] This observation suggests that more than one type of micellar structure may be stable. Ekwall and coworkers have stressed that the micelles of bile salt do not appear to incorporate long-chain alcohols into a palisade layer as do soaps or long-chain alkyl sulfates.[59]

Gelation of bile salt solutions appears to be a somewhat less general phenomenon than simple micelle formation. Sobotka and Czeczowiczka observed gelation with deoxycholate and lithocholate, but not with cholate or several conjugated bile salts.[158] The presence of a small proportion of the acid form may promote gel formation.

Even more specific is a type of aggregation phenomenon in solutions of deoxycholate described recently by Rich and Blow.[140] Ultracentrifugation showed that large aggregates were formed. The aggregates appeared to be elongate. X-ray diffraction studies of drawn-out air-dried fibers showed that the deoxycholate molecules were arranged in a helical form. The type of packing appeared to be influenced by the presence of an amino acid or of the peptide glycylglycine. At least part of the glycylglycine appeared to become attached to the outside of the helical framework. Helical complexes could not be prepared with sodium cholate, sodium glycocholate, sodium taurocholate, sodium lithocholate, or sodium apocholate.

As Rich and Blow point out, it is interesting that almost as high specificity has been encountered in the formation of the choleic acids, in which only deoxycholic acid or the closely related apocholic and β-apocholic acids can take part.[23, 179] In the choleic acid complexes, fatty acids, esters, alcohols, ethers, phenols, hydrocarbons, and alkaloids crystallize with deoxycholic acid in reproducible proportions.[139] The straight chain molecules probably occupy channels formed by the arches of the A/B ring systems of contiguous pairs of the bile acid molecules.[31, 73, 104] The existence of more than one type of structure is implied by the accommodation of such bulky substances as aromatic hydrocarbons.[169] The stereochemistry of these complexes has been summarized by Turner.[169]

Imbibition of Water by Lipides

Lipides such as lecithins may be considered to occupy a place between the water-insoluble triglycerides and the water-soluble lysolecithins. In the higher triglycerides the adhesion between non-polar chains completely overweighs any tendency of the glycerol moiety to enter an aqueous environment. In the lysolecithins, the attraction of the charged groups for water predominates over adhesion between the single non-polar chains. In the lecithins, the two opposing tendencies are well developed and both are satisfied when a particle of lecithin is brought into contact with water: water is imbibed but the lecithin does not go into true solution. The lecithin particle takes up water by swelling on the periphery and cylindrical excrescences appear. These grow in smooth or twisted forms and the cylinders are birefringent. They do not coalesce when they come into contact with each other. The forms are similar in appearance to the myelin sheath of nerve fibres, and they are generally called myelinic figures. Some very elaborate and beautiful forms have been photographed.[123,138]

Bear, Palmer, and Schmitt studied X-ray diffraction spacings of lipide preparations before and after stirring with two volumes of water.[18] The spacings of the cerebrosides changed very little with wetting. The long spacings of sphingomyelin increased about 23%, those of the lecithin about 60%. The "cephalin" preparation, which probably contained acidic phospholipides such as phosphatidyl serine, showed a much greater increase of about 270%. Dervichian has pointed out that the wet lecithin preparation probably consisted of fragments of myelinic figures.[45]

Myelinic figures may be obtained with mixtures of components which do not themselves form the figures. For example, equimolecular mixtures of lysolecithin and cholesterol swell and form figures. The lysolecithin does not pass into solution but remains associated with the cholesterol. Acid soaps, formed from equimolecular mixtures of fatty acids and soap, behave likewise and may swell to contain 30–40% of water. Other comparable mixtures that form myelinic figures are composed of sodium cetylsulfate with cholesterol, stearylcholine hydrochloride with cholesterol, and cetyl alcohol with digitonin.[45]

The cylindrical protrusions appear to be composed of macroscopic cylindrical sheets consisting of a great number of molecular double layers separated by a fixed number of layers of water. The individual sheets are rolled inside each other.

Dervichian has stressed that the components of mixed myelinic figures must be mixed together in the same molecular proportions as are required for fluid films of mixed monolayers. Indeed, the fluid two-dimensional lattice is very similar in the two systems. One important difference exists, however, in that the minimum repeating unit normal to the axis of the cylinder takes in two double layers of lipides; presumably the hydrocarbon tails intermesh to some extent in each double layer. A layer of head groups on one side of a double layer faces another layer of head groups separated from it by a few layers of water molecules. Dervichian summarizes evidence for the intercalation of one to four layers of water molecules between double layers of soaps. He believes that the structure of the first layer of water next to the polar carboxylate heads is conditioned by the structure of the soap layer. The effect is probably reciprocal. Dervichian also borrows from the ideas of Hendricks to suggest that the intercalated water has a hexagonal structure.[88, 121] He points out that the number of layers of water that may be taken up is probably limited by the ability of water to propagate a non-tetrahedral structure, for which four layers is a reasonable estimate in the present instance.[45]

It is worth recalling that sodium oleate micelles, whose structure is probably very similar to that of the myelinic figures, can take up other molecules either in the palisade layer (e.g., long-chain alcohols) or in layers between the hydrocarbon tails.[96, 148] Kiessig and Philippoff concluded that benzene takes up the latter position, possibly in an intercalated layer about three molecules thick.[96] It is important to recognize that the layering tends to propagate in any one micelle, so that it is unlikely that a single micelle would be found with an intercalated benzene layer in one part of it and no such layer in the region immediately adjacent. In other words, the taking up of foreign molecules in a given layer tends to be an "all-or-none" process in any one micelle; the same appears true for the most part in the myelinic forms.

A remarkable effect was observed by Bear, Palmer, and Schmitt.[18, 130] A mixture of lipides containing "cephalin" or a total extract of beef spinal cord (containing mixed phospholipides and cholesterol) showed only a single long spacing when studied in the presence of water. The individual components showed distinct and non-identical spacings under these conditions. Apparently a structure compatible with the properties of all the lipides in the mixture could be obtained in the presence of water. The authors pointed out that four molecules of cholesterol could find their place in a double layer of the longer phospholipides. The width of the aqueous layer was reduced in the presence of KCl or NaCl, but the mixture remained uniform in appearance and did not resemble a coagulum. Calcium chloride appeared to bring the polar heads of the lipides together, thereby expelling almost all the intercalated water. The effect of calcium chloride in expelling intercalated water is reminiscent of the effect of ions in flocculating aqueous dispersions of phospholipides "sensitized" by the admixture of cholesterol or triolein.[44]

An important characteristic of the lipide systems that form myelinic figures is their fluidity. This property implies the ability of the molecules to diffuse within the structure. A soap will show the required behavior only above a certain characteristic temperature known as the Krafft point. Myelinic figures containing mixtures of lipides normally will bend smoothly when deformed by pressure. Nageotte has published pictures showing a change in appearance on cooling. The bends in the cold myelinic figures were more angular, so that the cylinders were composed of short rounded segments between straight sections instead of the smooth, gradual bending seen at higher temperatures.[123] It is possible that the degree of flexion of the cylinder determines which molecules collect at certain locations and that with time a process akin to zone melting might occur. It remains to be seen how strictly pure materials would behave. All the phenomena discussed in this section deserve to be re-examined with materials of known structure and composition.

Imbibition of water has been observed in solutions of long-chain salts in non-polar solvents.[97, 128, 157] For example, water is taken up by solutions of dodecylamine butyrate and octadecylamine propionate in xylene. The water uptake reaches as many as 29 molecules per mole of soap. The addition of the water promotes micelle formation.[128] Dodecylammonium butyrate in cyclohexane takes up as many as 24 moles of water per mole of detergent. In benzene and carbon tetrachloride, the caprylate salt takes up 3 or 4 moles of water. In a system such as this, the critical micelle concentration is higher the longer the hydrocarbon chain of the fatty acid.[97]

Emulsions

Mechanical agitation of two insoluble phases such as water and an oil composed of triglyceride or hydrocarbon will cause the dispersion of one phase as droplets in the other. The resulting emulsion is most easily formed if film-forming materials are present to occupy the interface. The interfacial film lowers the surface tension and retards coalescence of the droplets. Some emulsions are formed so easily that convection and turbulence caused by local inequalities in density and surface tension are sufficient to provide the required mechanical agitation.[154]

Emulsification is promoted by the presence of two film-forming materials which interact in the interface to form stable mixed films.[154] For example, mixtures of sodium dodecyl sulfate with cholesterol promote the emulsification of mineral oil in water more effectively than the sulfate alone.[115] Similar results have been obtained with mixtures of potassium laurate and cholesterol.[34]

Addition of electrolyte usually promotes flocculation of emulsions. The oil globules in a flocculated emulsion may still resist the coalescence which leads to separation of the bulk phases. Van den Tempel has shown that coalescence is prevented by the presence of a film of water on paraffin globules stabilized with sodium dodecyl sulfate. Rupture of the water film precedes coalescence.[171] The film of water separating the globules was at least 100 A thick, and decreased in thickness as the concentration of NaCl in the aqueous medium increased. Van den Tempel concluded that some unknown repulsive force took effect as the distance of separation of the globules became less than about 125 A. It is tempting to speculate that some of the effects may involve structuring of the water near the interface.

Most investigations of the properties of emulsions have dealt with dispersions of hydrocarbons. Recently, however, the preparation of fat emulsions for intravenous alimentation has received considerable attention. Several satisfactory emulsions have been prepared in a reproducible manner. One of these contains 10% triolein, 1.2% of a soybean phosphatide preparation, and 0.2% of a non-ionic detergent, Pluronic-F 68. The fat globules are less than 1 μ in diameter. The emulsions are prepared under nitrogen and are sterilized by autoclaving.[72]

ASSOCIATION PHENOMENA IN PROTEINS

General Structure and Stability

Associated lipides consist of groups of individual molecules. The individual units usually are held together by interactions between both their non-polar and their polar parts. Because these units are themselves molecular they can be dissociated from each other completely by changes of environment or by displacement with more strongly interacting substances.

Proteins are made up of individual units, the amino acid residues, whose side-chains have in common many of the attributes of polarity and non-polarity that are characteristic of the lipides. These side-chains interact with each other and their association probably plays a prime part in stabilizing the rigid, compact structure characteristic of corpuscular proteins. The amino acid residues are free to interact with each other through their side-chains, but this freedom is sharply limited by the peptide linkages between each residue and its two neighbors in the peptide chain. The protein molecule can respond to changes in environment or to strongly interacting substances only by modifying the interactions between amino acid residues, with abandonment of certain inter-residue interactions or formation of others. Instead of separating into fragments, the amino acid residues can only change their relation to each other in space. Very local changes may be limited to small alterations in the relative position of two side-chain groups. More extensive changes may involve the disruption of many interactions at once, coincident with changes in configuration of the peptide chain and marked changes in gross properties such as solubility.

The arrangement of amino acid residues in a peptide chain helps determine the properties of the protein by determining the sequence of the side-chain units. The peptide chain has the potential ability to determine its own configuration by assuming helical arrangements in which the —CO—NH— groups act as acceptors and donors of hydrogen bonds, with similar groups at some repeat stage along the peptide chain. The stability of such peptide chain ("backbone") structures probably depends on their ability to form cooperatively numerous linkages of this kind.[109, 132, 146] Somewhat similar repeating structures have been observed in bile salt preparations[140] and have been postulated as explaining the stability of films of long-chain amides.[5] Such helical structures appear to exist in certain polypeptides dissolved in solvents that are able to form hydrogen bonds to a limited extent.[146] The helical hydrogen-bonded structure is abandoned in the highly polar aqueous medium where water can form hydrogen bonds with the —CO— and —NH— groups, and where the side-chain groups may well find the helical arrangement of the chain a condition of higher free energy than other configurations which the experimenter describes as a "random coil".

In a protein, therefore, both the peptide chain backbone and the side-chain groups may contribute to the stability of the native structure. With the exception of the covalently bonded —S—S— bridges of the cystine residues, all potential interactions between side-chains share with the peptide bond interactions a degree of stability comparable to the interactions that we have already described as stabilizing the associations between lipide molecules. In order to be effective, such interactions require fairly closely defined spatial orientations and the mutual stabilization due to a number of them working in consort. The sensitivity of proteins to heat and denaturing agents reflects the weakness of the individual stabilizing interactions and the large number of energetically similar alternative structures that can be derived from the native structure. Sometimes the native configuration is regained spontaneously on removal of the disturbing agent. More often the process of randomization of the structure continues until many alternative cross-linkages are established; if some of these are intermolecular, insoluble polymers usually form, resulting in a very low probability of spontaneous regeneration of the native configuration.[135]

Configuration in Interfaces

That the stabilizing forces in native corpuscular protein molecules are of the same order as those that we have examined in the association of lipide molecules is illustrated by the tendency of many proteins to unfold and denature in air/water or oil/water interfaces.[9, 33, 71, 125] The spread protein at the interface generally has been found to occupy an area corresponding to a thickness of the protein film no greater than that of a single polypeptide chain instead of the thickness corresponding to at least three or four chains characteristic of even fairly small proteins in their native coiled, interlaced, or folded configuration (see Fig. 8.5).[95]

In the interface we may expect non-polar side-chains to project out of the aqueous phase and polar side-chains to project into the aqueous phase. The initiation of the unfolding may involve no more than a tendency for non-polar and polar groups to sort themselves out on each side of the interface, a process which directly or indirectly disrupts the stabilizing interactions. Few has presented evidence that in gramicidin SA the decapeptide ring, shown in Fig. 8.6, orients itself in an air/water interface with the peptide chain approximately in the plane of the interface.[63] The residues marked with a dashed line are believed to point into the aqueous phase and the others into the air. Side-chains belonging to valyl, leucyl, and prolyl residues are seen to be constrained to point into the aqueous phase, an arrangement that is inappropriate for them. Furthermore, the arrangement of the peptide chain ring in the plane of the interface restricts the peptide bonds so that only half as many hydrogen bonds can be formed between them as could be formed theoretically in a long helical arrangement. The arrangement in the surface film is thus the result of several different compromises between balancing tendencies. In larger structures, such as spread collagen, possibly half of the non-polar residues find themselves forced to accept the (for them) poorer choice of being directed into the aqueous phase.[62] If this distribution is generally typical of spontaneously spreading proteins, it implies a sizable compensatory loss of free energy, perhaps due in part to hydra-

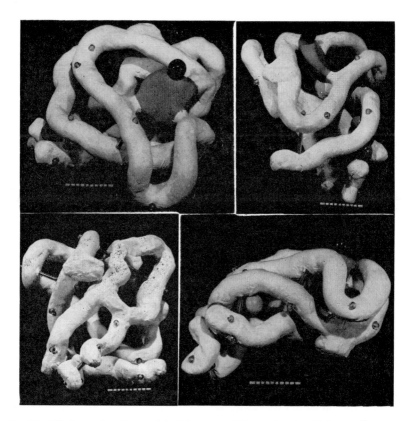

Fig. 8.5. Photographs of a model of the myoglobin molecule. Polypeptide chains are white; the gray disk is the heme group. The three spheres show positions at which heavy atoms were attached to the molecule (black: Hg of *p*-chloromercuri-benzenesulfonate; dark gray: Hg of mercury diamine; light gray: Au of auri-chloride). The marks on the scale are 1 A apart. The resolution of the X-ray diffraction studies has not been carried to the point where side-chains can be differentiated—so that the polypeptide rods in the model must be imagined as clothed in an invisible integument of side-chains, so thick that neighboring chains in reality touch. Taken from J. C. Kendrew, G. Bodo, H. M. Dintzis, R. G. Parrish, H. Wyckoff, and D. C. Phillips, *Nature,* **181,** 662 (1958).

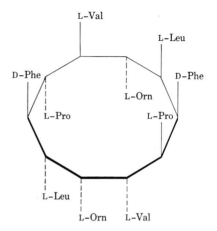

Fig. 8.6. Schematic diagram of orientation of side-chain groups in gramicidin SA spread on an aqueous solution. Solid lines represent side-chains projecting out of the water and dashed lines those projecting into the water. The decagonal ring represents the approximate plane of the cyclic peptide chain and the amino acid residues are labeled according to the usual convention.

tion of the peptide bonds which may well be buried in the native molecule.

Role of Non-Polar Groups

From considerations of the orientation of side-chain groups in protein monolayers and of the general availability of polar side-chain groups for reaction, it is reasonable to suppose that in the corpuscular water-soluble proteins the polar side-chains are directed outward and the non-polar side-chains inward. The picture is analogous to that in detergent micelles, in which the packing together of non-polar chains helps cement the association of the units. The possible role of non-polar side-chain interactions in stabilizing a compact configuration in long-chain compounds is illustrated by the resourceful work of Strauss and his collaborators on synthetic polysoaps.[164] One such polysoap was prepared by partial quarternization of poly-2-vinyl pyridine with n-dodecyl bromides. Addition of heptane, benzene, or 1-octanol to the linear polymer caused a decrease in the viscosity of the solutions. This change in viscosity was interpreted in terms of a more compact configuration made possible by the association of the solubilized molecules with the non-polar parts of the polysoap. Indications of stoichiometry in the process have been obtained. For example, it has been found with several polysoaps that solubilization of one long-chain alcohol molecule per dodecyl group corresponds to a minimal value of the viscosity of the solution, and that the limit of saturation corresponds to the attachment of two long-chain alcohols per dodecyl group.

Role of Polar Groups

The actual structure assumed by a corpuscular protein probably makes a compromise between the tendency of non-polar groups to clump together in small bundles or islands of hydrocarbon chains, and the tendency of charged and polar side-chains and probably the peptide chain backbone as well, to orient into the aqueous surroundings. The polar and charged side-chain groups in proteins occupy an irregular interface between non-polar regions and the aqueous environment. Stabilizing interactions between polar groups are presumably very much like those between the polar head groups that were shown by the studies with surface films. Only a few such studies of surface films have been made with the express purpose of applying the information to analogous interactions that could occur in proteins.[5]

Near the isoelectric state a protein may acquire stabilization from purely electrostatic interactions between oppositely charged groups.[165] In the presence of appreciable net charges repulsive effects may render the protein unstable, a probable mechanism in the denaturation by strong acids and alkalis. This effect is probably involved as well as in the reversible swelling that is sometimes observed, e.g., with serum albumins.[14, 165] Charged groups that are not shielded by counter ions tend to repulse each other and to render the structure less stable. However, charged groups such as carboxylate ions often interact more strongly than the uncharged carboxyl groups with closely neighboring groups such as phenoxyl or primary alcohol groups. Apparently the balance between long-range disruptive forces and short-range stabilizing forces may be maintained in protein molecules bearing considerable net charges. Thus, the effect of net charge in disrupting the structure of protein molecules is often seen at pH values considerably removed from their isoelectric range.

If triple interactions exist between polar side-chains in proteins, they may be expected to offer crucial opportunities for ordering and stabilization. A triple interaction may be thought of as the stabilization of a two-membered interaction by the close approximation of a suitable third group capable of interacting with the two-membered complex itself. The stabilization is likely to be most effective if packing can be very close and if the electronic configurations of the two-membered interaction product and of the third member are well suited

for charge-transfer interactions.[37, 85, 122] It is interesting that both requirements seem to be met by a triple interaction involving hydrogen
bonding between a carboxylate group and a phenoxyl group [107] to
form a planar system [12, 47] stabilized by interaction with a guanidinium
group. The three amino acid residues represented are aspartyl (or
glutamyl), phenoxyl, and arginyl.

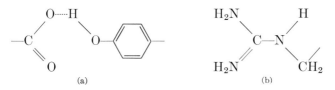

(a)   (b)

In the carboxylate-phenoxyl system (a) there are three centers of
maximum electron density located about the oxygen atoms, over which
the formal negative charge is distributed. In (b), correspondingly, the
three nitrogen atoms are formal centers of the delocalized electron-
paucity. When the two planar structures (a) and (b) are brought
together, it seems reasonable to postulate electronic sharing (charge
transfer) between them with the formation of a new molecular orbital
system embracing the common triangular configuration. The nitrogen
atom substituted with the alkyl chain probably should be assigned the
least partial positive charge; its corresponding phenolic oxygen atom
probably should be assigned the least partial negative charge. The
alkyl chain attached to the guanidinium group can pass over the benzene nucleus of the phenoxyl group. Although model systems of this
type have not yet been studied, the probable steric properties of the
proposed structure may be suitable for the interaction.[47, 93]

Such triple interactions may be vulnerable to disruption by several
different kinds of agents. Obviously, high or low pH values will result
in the disruption of the complex. A guanidinium ion should be able
to disrupt the triple complex if it is able to approach the carboxylate-
phenoxyl planar surface and displace the guanidinium group of the
arginyl residue from its attachment on the opposite side. It is possible that an ion such as lead could attack the complex by displacing
both the guanidinium group and the hydrogen ion that binds together
the carboxylate and phenoxyl groups, with substitution of the lead ion
in place of the hydrogen ion. Both guanidinium and lead salts might
allow some stabilization of the carboxylate-phenoxyl interaction after
the displacement of the guanidinium group of the arginyl residue.
It is well known that certain proteins remain soluble after their structure has been disrupted by guanidinium salts, but precipitate in a de-

natured condition when the concentration of the denaturing agent is reduced. In the case of lead ions, a possible parallel is in their reaction with human oxyhemoglobin at *p*H near 5. Small alterations in the protein structure are indicated by changes in the visible absorption spectrum, but gross evidence of denaturation and loss of solubility is not apparent until immediately after a chelating agent is added to remove the lead ion.[83]

The possibility of stabilizing interactions between peptide linkages and side-chains of other amino acid residues must be considered. Architecturally, such interactions would be comparable to triple side-chain interactions. Peptide linkages are known to have considerable affinity for phenols,[80, 81] represented in proteins by the phenoxyl group of the tyrosine residue. The phenoxyl-peptide system probably prefers a planar conformation and may share some of the properties of the phenoxyl-carboxyl interaction discussed above.

Association Between Molecular Units

Stabilizing interactions between side-chain groups in single polypeptide chains have their counterpart in interactions between polypeptide chains, and indeed between molecular units capable of existing either as separate entities or in association with each other. A number of such associations have been ably reviewed by Waugh.[174] An interesting recent example is the finding by Richards that the inactive fragments formed from the action of subtilisin on ribonuclease are capable of reassociating in a specific manner so as to regain the enzymatic activity of the intact ribonuclease molecule.[141] Many very large protein molecules appear to be made up of smaller units associated together in specific ways but not joined in continuous networks maintained by primary covalent bonds.[82, 113, 114, 174]

Reactivity of Groups in Proteins

The polar and charged side-chain groups in a protein can take part either in associations with other side-chain groups or in reactions with external reagents. It may be postulated that for a given side-chain group to be very strongly involved in one role or the other means that its ability to assume the other role is restricted. For example, some groups in certain proteins have been recognized to be unreactive in the native protein, but fully accessible to reaction in the denatured protein. These masked groups either are buried below the surface of the molecule and take part in associations in the interior, or are involved in such strong interactions with other groups that they are not detectable even in an exposed part of the protein molecule. Classic examples of such groups are sulfhydryl groups in ovalbumin,[13] and some unidentified polar groups in hemoglobin.[161] Failure to detect the reactivity of a given side-chain group is not proof that it is involved in internal linkage. It is always possible that the group in question is sterically hindered from reaction even though not actually buried. The opposite proposition must also be considered, namely, that the ability to demonstrate the reactivity of a side-chain group is not proof that it is not involved in interactions which are responsible for internal stabilization of the configuration of the protein.

Different types of polar side-chain groups in proteins show many similarities in their reactivity, so that a reagent which combines with one particular group in a protein may do so only after it has disrupted the structure of the protein by prior attack on some other type of group. An example of the wide range of reactivity of a single reagent with different types of groups in proteins is afforded by iodine.[92] Not only may different groups be involved but also different mechanisms, ranging in this case from the readily reversible reaction with amino groups through the substitution reactions with phenoxyl and imidazole groups to the oxidation-reduction processes involving the sulfhydryl group. The last-named reaction may pass through a series of steps to the stage of formation of —S—S— bonds and may contribute strong but spurious cross-linkages to the structure of the protein derivative. Under some circumstances the intermediate products of the reaction may be unable to react further to yield the —S—S— bonds and may remain stabilized but potentially highly reactive in the protein derivative.[67] Other reactions that are more restricted in mechanism such as dinitrophenylation or coupling with diazonium salts still tend to involve at least phenoxyl, imidazole, and amino groups concurrently.[100, 136, 162]

In only a few cases has it been possible to decompose stable derivatives in such a way as to regain the original protein apparently unchanged. Unless this is done, it is impossible to establish that no other changes have occurred in the structure of the protein beyond the recognized formation of the derivatives.

Two alternative approaches to the study of the reactivity of side-chain and terminal groups in proteins are measurement of the equilibria with ions and small molecules and measurements of the catalytic properties of the side-chain groups. These two approaches share the advantages that no permanent change in the structure of the protein need result from the measurements and that the protein can be recovered and tested for any irreversible changes that may have occurred.[101]

Complex formation between proteins and cations, such as hydrogen ions and metal ions, often may be measured over wide ranges of equilibrium conditions. Added metal ions usually may be removed without difficulty under mild conditions, so that irreversible changes in structure are more easily detected than when stable derivatives are formed. Here again, overlapping of reactivity is a serious complication and many metal ions tend to combine with several classes of groups at the same time. Depending on the affinities for the cations shown by the groups and on the pH values, complex formation is affected by competition between metal ions and hydrogen ions. An indication of the groups involved in complex formation may be obtained from the study of this competition. Some guidance in the study of such equilibria may be had from studies with model systems. The models that have been studied so far correspond more closely to groups in a protein as they react individually rather than as they may act in close association with other side-chain groups.[84]

Chelate structures formed from clusters of two or more side-chain groups are believed to be responsible for holding the tightly bound metal ions in naturally occurring metalloproteins.[84,170,173] Presumably many of the clusters of side-chain groups which are responsible for maintaining the native configuration or which show specialized reactivity in normally metal-free proteins are potential sites for the chelation of added metal ions. The use of the term "site" draws attention to the fact that the cluster of two or more side-chain groups holding the cation in chelation acts as a unit. The added metal ion may be thought of as a tiny polyfunctional reagent that combines with the members of the cluster in a way that is very sensitive both to the nature of the side-chain groups involved and to their geometrical arrangement. The small size of the metal ion means that the integrity of the cluster may escape serious disruption, a possibility that is much more difficult to visualize if a large polyfunctional organic reagent were used to combine stably with the several members of the cluster.

The study of the equilibrium between metal ions and such sites has great potential value for their detection and characterization, particularly for clusters involving hydrogen bonds between side-chain groups. Since the displacement of the hydrogen ion by the metal ion need not require a large geometrical rearrangement, the metal ion itself may assume the role of the hydrogen ion in stabilizing the local structure.[84,144]

Kinetic measurements have great potential usefulness in assessing the reactivity of side-chain groups in proteins. Preferably the measurements should be made under conditions of pure catalysis or should be designed to measure initial reaction rates. The basic forms of many of the polar side-chain groups in proteins may be expected to show activity in general basic catalysis or to show parallel behavior in reactions that lead to the formation of stable derivatives. A systematic study of model compounds, peptides, and proteins is in progress.[101–103]

Certain interacting pairs or larger clusters of side-chain groups in any protein may be expected to have potential catalytic activity inherently similar to that of recognized enzymes. A cluster of side-chain groups may act as a whole or its component groups may act individually; just as an active center in an enzyme may act as a unit in normal catalysis but can also be disrupted by having one of its components react preferentially. A common example of the latter is the poisoning of some enzymes by reagents that combine with sulfhydryl groups.[124] On the other hand, the reaction of a cluster as a unit may stabilize the configuration of a protein, as judged by the well-known tendency of certain enzymes to be more stable in the presence than in the absence of their substrates.

Kinetic measurements of the reactivity of side-chain groups in proteins appear to be compatible with concurrent equilibrium measurements of binding of ions to the same types of groups. The advantages of combining the kinetic and equilibrium approaches have been outlined in studies on model systems.[101–103]

Hydration of Proteins

Proteins retain moisture very tenaciously on drying, and in solution their hydrodynamic properties are believed to reflect the binding of 0.1 to 0.2 g. of water per gram of protein.[48] Presumably all polar groups that are accessible to the aqueous environment bind water in some degree.

The tetrahedral arrangement of water molecules in ice is shown diagrammatically in Fig. 8.7.[50] Pure water is believed to contain temporary aggregates of water molecules arranged tetrahedrally in about this form.[20, 68, 69] These ice-like aggregates are in very mobile equilibrium with more disordered arrangements of the same general type.

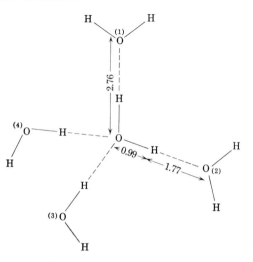

Fig. 8.7. Tetrahedral coordination of water molecules in ice. Molecules (1) and (2), as well as the central H_2O molecule, lie entirely in the plane of the paper. Molecule (3) lies above this plane, molecule (4) below it, so that oxygens (1), (2, (3), and (4) lie at the corners of a regular tetrahedron. Distances are in Angstroms. Taken from J. T. Edsall and J. Wyman, *Biophysical Chemistry*, Vol. I, Academic Press, 1958.

When solutes are introduced into water they tend to affect the equilibrium of the water structure, either by stabilizing the more ordered arrangement or by disrupting it. The reason for the stabilization by solutes, which at first sight seems surprising, is that the more ordered structure is also rather open and gains stability by having spaces within it occupied by some other molecule. Sometimes very elaborate crystalline structures are built up if the guest molecule is non-polar and does not exert strong enough forces on the surrounding water to perturb the lattice.[17] As has been pointed out in the discussion of micelle formation, non-polar portions of dissolved molecules also tend to promote the more highly ordered water structure in their vicinity.[68, 69, 74]

The strong electrostatic field exerted by an ion orients and probably immobilizes the first layer or two of water molecules around it. Beyond the inner oriented shell, the water surrounding an ion goes through a region of transition leading back to the usual equilibrium structure. The nature of this transition depends on the size and charge of the ion. Much of the uncertainty in interpreting the properties of electrolyte solutions centers on the difficulty of describing the region of transition. In this region any given water molecule finds itself under two opposing influences that are more or less in balance. One is the orienting influence upon the water dipole of the spherically symmetrical ionic field. The other is the orienting influence that water molecules normally exert on each other. The transition in water structure surrounding a small ion is sketched in Fig. 8.8 taken from Frank and Wen.[69] Ions of larger radius not only can promote the normal water structure better because of their size but also subject the water structure around them to a less intense disruptive electrostatic field.[69]

The spherically symmetrical field about a cationic group will tend to set up a repeating arrangement in the water in which the oxygen atoms orient towards the ion and the hydrogen atoms away. The disturbance will die away with distance as described above (Fig. 8.8). An anionic group will behave likewise, with the exception that the orientation of the water molecules will tend to be reverse. Ackermann has described these opposing orientations graphically for the special cases of hydrogen and hydroxyl ions.[1] In speculating about such structuring of water near charged groups, it seems wise to bear in mind the importance of the shape of the charged groups; the planar

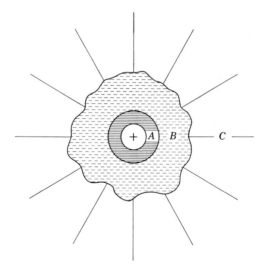

Fig. 8.8. A simple model for the structural modifications in water produced by a small ion. *A*—region of immobilization of water molecules; *B*—region of structure breaking; *C*—structurally "normal" water. Taken from H. S. Frank and W.-Y. Wen, *Disc. Faraday Soc.*, **24**, 133 (1957).

guanidinium and imidazolium groups should be contrasted with the tetrahedral ammonium groups.

The effect of a protruding side-chain of a protein on the water in its vicinity need not differ markedly from the effect of a corresponding structure in free solution unless cooperative effects are present. For example, under certain conditions a cation and an anion may be expected to orient the water molecules in between them in a more or less regular pattern. In general, the water molecules in the vicinity of the individual side-chain groups on the surface of a protein will be subjected to specific influences according to the type and orientation of the group nearest them. In some cases a local pattern of water structure will conform to a neighboring pattern and the two may merge and reinforce each other; in other cases the contiguous patterns will be incompatible and may tend to disrupt each other.

Such local cooperative effects may have some influence on the retention of water on the surfaces of protein molecules brought close together, as in the incipient stages of precipitation. Disruption of the water structure patterns may allow precipitation to proceed. It is interesting that there is a parallel between the effects of a series of ions on the structure of water about them and their effects on the solubility of human γ-globulins.[83] The solubility effects have been observed in alcohol-water mixtures near pH 5.5 where the γ-globulin molecules bear net positive charges. The addition of as little as 0.01M concentrations of the salts tested reduced the solubility of the protein. Among the cations, lithium is particularly suited to breaking the normal structure of water;[68, 69] its efficiency as a precipitating agent for the γ-globulins is astonishing. Ions such as barium which have much less tendency to disrupt the normal structure of water have much less marked precipitating action. Among anions, acetate, propionate, and other short-chain soaps have structure-promoting properties and are least active precipitants. Divalent anions lacking hydrocarbon moieties are recognized as having structure-breaking properties and are highly effective precipitants of γ-globulins under these conditions.

That the observed effects depend intimately on a property associated with the protein and not on a general modification of the solvent as a whole (cf. salting-out[50]) is suggested by the very low concentrations of salts required, and the fact that the precipitating effects are no longer apparent if the pH is raised to about 7. At pH 7 the usual salting-in effects are apparent, except in the case of those ions such as zinc which are rather general protein precipitants under such conditions.[83, 84]

The possibility that extensive cooperative effects on the structure of water surrounding a protein might occur has led to a suggestion that the layer of water near the surface of the protein should be considered as "frozen".[99] A peculiar requirement of such a rigid, cooperative arrangement is that the different tendencies of cationic, anionic, and uncharged groups would have to work together to maintain the ice-like shell. It is clear from the preceding discussion that each of these different types of groups tends to promote a different type of water structure.

Klotz has proposed a rather far-reaching application of the idea of structuring of water to the behavior alike of individual groups and of the protein molecule as a whole.[99] Much of Klotz's argument depends on the interpretation of studies of hydrogen ion binding by the azo mercurial substituent:

$$\text{Protein—S—Hg—}\langle\bigcirc\rangle\text{—N=N—}\langle\bigcirc\rangle\text{—N(CH}_3)_2$$

This substituent is believed to combine with sulfhydryl groups in several proteins. Peculiarities of the hydration shell are taken to be responsible for stabilizing the basic form of the dimethylamino group. An alternative explanation could be made in terms of the ability of this large substituent to take part in charge-transfer interactions such as have been discussed on p. 238. The basic structure is probably planar, whereas the protonated form would be unlikely to remain so. Charge-transfer interactions with planar structures in the protein would be favored by the basic form of the azo mercurial. At the moment there is insufficient evidence to support either hypothesis.

ASSOCIATION OF LIPIDES WITH PROTEINS

Broadly speaking, the association of lipides with proteins may be considered in two categories. In the first the lipide molecules are bound to distinct sites on the protein molecule in much the same way as substrates, coenzymes, or competitive inhibitors are bound to enzyme molecules. Interactions of this type have been ably discussed by Scatchard, Klotz, and others.[98, 110, 124, 145] In the second category are complexes in which proteins combine with lipide molecules which are themselves associated in some way, for example, in interfacial films, micelles, or emulsions.

Binding of Fatty Acid Anions

Most lipides are sufficiently insoluble in water that it is very difficult to study their interaction with proteins in a way that can be interpreted thermodynamically in terms of binding sites and intrinsic association constants. Goodman has published recently a careful study of the interaction of human serum albumin with six long-chain fatty acid anions.[79] Varying quantities of the fatty acids were equilibrated between two phases, *n*-heptane, and an aqueous solution of serum albumin in phosphate buffer, pH 7.45, ionic strength 0.16, at 23°C. From identical experiments in the absence of serum albumin,[78] it was possible to determine the concentration of unbound fatty acid in each aqueous phase by measuring the equilibrium concentration in the heptane.[79] The fatty acids studied were lauric, myristic, palmitic, stearic, oleic, and linoleic acids. The results for each anion were interpreted in terms of three classes of binding sites: two sites of highest affinity, five of somewhat lower affinity, and about twenty of distinctly lower affinity. Apparent association constants for each class of sites are denoted by k_1', k_2', and k_3' and are listed in Table 8.3 for each fatty acid anion. The value of k_1' is greatest for oleate, and among the saturated fatty acids there is a rise from laurate through stearate.

Table 8.3

The Apparent Association Constants for the Interaction of Human Serum Albumin with Fatty Acid Anions

pH 7.45; ionic strength 0.16, 23°C

Three classes of binding sites, with $n_1 = 2$, $n_2 = 5$, and $n_3 = 20$ *

Fatty Acid Anion	k_1'	k_2'	k_3'
Laurate	1.6×10^6	2.4×10^5	6×10^2
Myristate	4.0×10^6	1.4×10^6	2×10^2
Palmitate	6.0×10^7	3.0×10^6	1×10^3
Stearate	8.0×10^7	8.0×10^5	1×10^3
Oleate	1.1×10^8	4.0×10^6	1×10^3
Linoleate	1.3×10^7	2.5×10^6	2.5×10^3

* Taken from D. S. Goodman, *J. Am. Chem. Soc.*, **80**, 3892 (1958).

Palmitate and stearate are nearly identical, and the author points out that a simple Traube's rule type of increase in affinity with chain length seems to break down. Linoleate binds less strongly than either oleate or stearate. The second and third classes of sites seem to distinguish less closely between one long-chain fatty acid and another. Goodman points out that these latter classes of sites are probably capable of binding many other types of anions. On the other hand, the first class of sites shows greater structural specificity and is unavailable for the binding of relatively bulky anions, such as methyl orange. Nevertheless, this first class of sites might well be available for the binding of small, simple ions, such as chloride, iodide, or thiocyanate, and of ions of structure similar to that of long-chain fatty acids, such as dodecyl sulfate ions. It is interesting to speculate whether the carboxyl group of the fatty acid anion could take part in a triple interaction of the sort described in a previous section.

The serum albumin used in Goodman's studies was specially treated to remove impurities, including traces of fatty acids that are normally present after the usual purification.[77] Serum albumin has a remarkable tendency to take up molecules such as decanol, chloroform, benzene, and even short-chain fatty acid anions, all of which influence the behavior of the protein in some way.[91,98] Such molecules may act competitively with other molecules for binding sites; for example, fatty acids and benzene compete with L-tryptophan for a site on human serum albumin.[112] Decanol, chloroform, and fatty acids promote the crystallization of serum albumin under certain conditions.[36] Fatty acids have been observed to affect the rate of formation of mercuric dimers of serum albumin.[49] In each of these cases only a few moles of fatty acid need be added. A number of anions such as caprylate and acetyl-L-tryptophanate are effective stabilizers of human serum albumin against heat and urea denaturation.[26,27]

Binding of Detergents

Long-chain anionic detergents, such as dodecyl sulfate [129] or dodecylbenzenesulfonate,[181] react strongly with about ten or twelve sites in bovine serum albumin with what appears to be the usual random-statistical binding behavior. As more detergent is added to the system and saturation of these sites is approached, some cooperative structural change takes place in the protein and additional binding sites are exposed. Putnam and Neurath showed that in the interaction of horse serum albumin with sodium dodecyl sulfate two discrete protein complexes are formed, PD_n and PD_{2n}, where n is approximately 55.[137] Foster and Aoki have adduced evidence [66] that the binding of sodium dodecyl sulfate to bovine serum albumin affects the "isomerization" equilibrium of the protein observed in the pH range 3.5–4.5.[14] They conclude that the equilibrium between the compact native configuration and an expanded one may be shifted in either direction by appropriate anions. The binding of the detergent anions seems to be accompanied either by displacement of other bound anions, e.g., chloride, or by binding of hydrogen ions. Similar effects have been found by Brand and Johnson, who studied the interaction of sodium dodecyl sulfate with legumin.[29] This interaction also proceeds by discrete stages in which some molecules appear to undergo cooperative, "all-or-none" changes in structure leading to a form which has a higher binding capacity, for the detergent, than the native protein. From measurements of the electrophoretic mobility of the complexes it was concluded that a large proportion of the long-chain ions was accompanied by simple counter ions, so that the net charges appeared less than expected. It is characteristic of closely packed, oriented ions, such as those present in surface films or in micelles, that they retain counter ions rather more closely than seems to be characteristic of the less crowded charged groups in native proteins.[21, 119, 120] It may be that the heavily laden detergent-protein complexes bear a resemblance to the micellar structures.

The sites of binding of detergent molecules such as sodium dodecyl sulfate are not easily identified. The maximum number of detergent molecules seems to equal or surpass the number of positively charged groups when many detergent molecules are bound.[137] Their hydrocarbon tails may be able to interact with each other as well as with the hydrocarbon side-chains of the protein. Cationic and non-ionic detergents do not seem nearly as effective denaturing agents towards most proteins.[135] A possible explanation for this experience is that the anionic groups in the detergents share some of the stereochemical properties and charge distribution of carboxylate groups and therefore can compete with them. Most of the cationic detergents that have been tried, such as cetyltrimethyl or octadecyltrimethyl ammonium salts or dodecylpyridinium salts, bear no close resemblance to any of the groups that are believed to be present in proteins. (They resemble instead the choline moiety of a phospholipide!) These compounds are distantly related to the ammonium but not to the guanidinium or imidazolium groups in proteins. More attention should be paid to detergent molecules containing the latter types of polar groups. It would be particularly useful to learn whether such detergents would show the same characteristic ability to elicit new binding sites after the first few molecules are bound to the protein. It would be important also to search for cooperative "all-or-none" effects in the interactions with the cationic detergents. Such "all-or-none" reactions of proteins are not limited to complex formation of this kind.[111]

Binding of Water-Soluble Steroids

Interactions between various water-soluble steroids and a number of proteins have been studied. Evidence for interaction has been obtained by solvent partition, solubility, electrophoresis, and spectrophotometry.[22, 40, 51, 147, 176, 178] Among the corticosteroids increasing numbers of polar substituents such as —OH groups depress the binding to serum albumin.[177, 178] Opposite effects are found with other proteins.[178] Daughaday and Kozak have obtained evidence for the presence of a protein in plasma which shows a higher affinity for corticosteroids than albumin.[39, 40] Levedahl and co-workers have presented evidence for a role of phenoxyl groups in serum albumin in the binding of testosterone.[127] They point out that acetylation of the phenoxyl groups depresses testosterone binding whereas acetylation of ϵ-amino groups does not.[108] Iodination of the phenoxyl groups, claimed to occur in the 2 and 6 positions, had no effect on the binding. From this it was inferred that testosterone binds in a configuration continuous with and parallel to the ring structure of the tyrosyl side-chains, and coupled through the phenolic hydroxyl group.[127] Since a supposedly nonenzymic protein such as serum albumin has been shown to catalyze the hydrolysis of certain steroid esters,[143] care must be taken to establish the absence of side reactions in binding studies.

Interactions of Proteins with Associated Lipides

Following their studies on monolayers of proteins and lipides, and on mixed monolayers, Schulman and Rideal investigated the behavior of mixed films of cholesterol and gliadin.[152] Displacement of the protein from the film was obtained on compression, but the protein penetrated the film rapidly again when the pressure was reduced. They inferred that the protein remained attached to the cholesterol monolayer after being displaced. The underlying protein film was apparently responsible for greatly slowing the rate at which saponin penetrated the mixed film. At low compressions the mixed film of cholesterol and gliadin was readily penetrated by saponin.

Eley and Hedge have studied the interaction of bovine plasma albumin, insulin, and fibrinogen with monolayers of cholesterol and stearic acid.[60] The protein molecules were pictured as spreading beneath the lipide layer, often followed by a second layer of unspread, globular adsorbed protein molecules. Eley and Hedge believe that nearly half the side-chains in the proteins penetrate into the monolayer of stearic acid at pH 7.4, but that much fewer side-chains penetrate into the more cohesive monolayer of cholesterol. Their picture is qualitatively plausible. A similar study has been reported by these authors in which α,α'-distearin, α,α'-dipalmitoyl phosphatidyl ethanolamine and α,β-distearoyl phosphatidyl choline were compared.[61] Unfortunately, the use of different positional isomers leaves the interpretation open.

A number of studies has been made of the adsorption of proteins at interfaces in emulsions stabilized by detergent molecules. Cockbain showed that serum albumin in a system containing an emulsion of n-decane in water stabilized with sodium dodecyl sulfate formed complexes of the composition PD_{2n} at the interface.[33] The formation of such a complex in bulk solution has already been discussed.[137] Cockbain also showed that this complex could be formed at the benzene/water interface. In the decane-water emulsion the addition of excess sodium dodecyl sulfate caused the displacement of the protein complex from the interface into the aqueous phase. In the absence of detergents the emulsion acquired a film of irreversibly denatured albumin whose spreading area was independent of the bulk concentration of the albumin, of the pH, and of the ionic strength.[33]

Fraser, Kaplan, and Schulman studied the activity of catalase exposed to hydrocarbon-water emulsions stabilized with various agents.[70] In the absence of any stabilizing agent the enzyme was extensively and irreversibly denatured. In the presence of lecithin the enzyme did not adsorb on the droplets of emulsion, in keeping with its failure to penetrate a surface monolayer of lecithin. In the presence of phosphatidyl ethanolamine (probably contaminated with phosphatidyl serine) the enzyme adsorbed to a considerable extent on the droplets of emulsion, in that case paralleling its tendency to penetrate a surface monolayer of a similar phospholipide mixture. The adsorption was accompanied by partial denaturation, as was adsorption at interfaces stabilized with a mixture of cholesterol and octadecyltrimethyl ammonium bromide. When the latter system contained lauryl alcohol in place of the cholesterol, the catalase did not lose activity on adsorption. When the stabilizing agent was a long-chain (C 21) anthracene sulfonate, the enzyme adsorbed in a number of layers, some of which retained enzymic activity.

Fraser and Schulman concluded that the polar groups in the detergent molecules, as the occupants of the surface of the emulsion droplets, constituted the loci of interaction with the catalase molecules.[70, 71] They pointed out the implication that polar groups in the protein would be involved in the interaction, in contrast with the situation at the clean oil/water emulsion surface or at the air/water interface. They postulated, but could not prove definitely, that partial unfolding could occur at interfaces without complete loss of enzymic activity. Fraser and Schulman found that trypsin showed as wide a variety of behavior as catalase when it was exposed to various hydrocarbon-water-detergent emulsions.[71]

In collaboration with Chargaff, Palmer and Schmitt extended their X-ray diffraction studies on lipides [18, 130] to measurements of spacings in mixtures of histone or globin with preparations of phosphatidyl ethanolamine probably contaminated with phosphatidyl serine.[131] When studied in the absence of added protein or water, the phospholipide was found to be oriented in biomolecular leaflets with an identity period of 43.8 A in the direction perpendicular to the planes of the leaflets. In the presence of histone this identity period was increased by 13–15 A, and in the presence of globin by 7–9 A. The phospholipide-histone complexes took up water very sparingly, and the identity period increased on wetting by only 5–10 A. The components therefore appeared to be fixed to each other, since great increases in the spacings were observed on the addition of water to the phospholipide mixture in the absence of protein. Rather similar results were obtained with a thromboplastin preparation isolated from lung. The attractive forces were taken to be due to the electrostatic interaction between the net negative charges in the polar heads of the phospholipides and the net positive charges borne by the basic proteins. The phospholipide and protein in the synthetic and natural complexes were taken to be arranged according to the pattern shown schematically in Fig. 8.9. The thickness of the protein layer corresponds approximately to that of a spread unimolecular layer. This layer is sandwiched be-

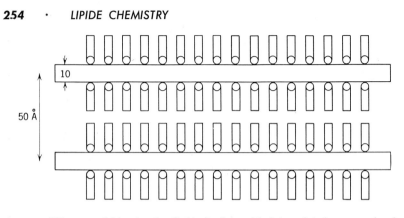

Fig. 8.9. Diagram of bimolecular lipide leaflets with intercalated monomolecular layers of protein.

tween biomolecular leaflets of lipides. The importance of this type of molecular arrangement in membranous structures in the cell will be considered in Chapter 9.

REFERENCES

1. Ackermann, T., *Disc. Faraday Soc.,* **24,** 180 (1957).
2. Adam, N. K., *The Physics and Chemistry of Surfaces,* 2nd edition, Oxford (1938).
3. Adam, N. K., F. A. Askew, and J. F. Danielli, *Biochem. J.,* **29,** 1786 (1935).
4. Alexander, A. E., *Proc. Roy. Soc. (London),* **A179,** 470 (1941–1942).
5. Alexander, A. E., *Proc. Roy. Soc. (London),* **A179,** 486 (1941–1942).
6. Alexander, A. E., *Surface Chemistry,* Longmans, Green (1951).
7. Alexander, A. E., and P. Johnson, *Colloid Science,* Clarendon Press (1949).
8. Alexander, A. E., and T. Teorell, *Trans. Faraday Soc.,* **35,** 727 (1939).
9. Allan, A. J. G., and A. E. Alexander, *Trans. Faraday Soc.,* **50,** 863 (1954).
10. Anderson, P. J., and B. A. Pethica, *Trans. Faraday Soc.,* **52,** 1080 (1956).
11. Anderson, P. J., and B. A. Pethica, *Biochemical Problems of Lipids,* edited by Popjak and LeBreton, p. 24, Interscience (1956).
12. Angell, C. L., N. Sheppard, A. Yamaguchi, T. Shimanouchi, T. Miyazawa, and S. Mizushima, *Trans. Faraday Soc.,* **53,** 589 (1951).
13. Anson, M. L., *Advances in Protein Chem.,* **2,** 361 (1945).
14. Aoki, K., and J. F. Foster, *J. Am. Chem. Soc.,* **78,** 3538 (1956).
15. Ball, E. G., and O. Cooper, *J. Biol. Chem.,* **180,** 113 (1949).
16. Bangham, A. D., B. A. Pethica, and G. V. F. Seaman, *Biochem. J.,* **69,** 12 (1958).
17. Barrer, R. M., *Experentia, Suppl.,* **7,** 113 (1957).
18. Bear, R. S., K. J. Palmer, and F. O. Schmitt, *J. Cellular Comp. Physiol.,* **17,** 355 (1941).

19. Benerito, R. R., W. S. Singleton, and R. O. Feuge, *J. Phys. Chem.,* **58,** 831 (1954).
20. Bernal, J. D., and R. H. Fowler, *J. Chem. Phys.,* **1,** 515 (1933).
21. Betts, J. J., and B. A. Pethica, *Trans. Faraday Soc.,* **52,** 1581 (1956).
22. Bischoff, F., and H. R. Pilhorn, *J. Biol. Chem.,* **174,** 663 (1948).
23. Boedecker, F., *Ber.,* **53,** 1852 (1920).
24. Boyd, G. E., *J. Phys. Chem.,* **62,** 538 (1958).
25. Boyd, G. E., and F. Vaslow, *J. Colloid Sci.,* **13,** 275 (1958).
26. Boyer, P. D., G. A. Ballou, and J. M. Luck, *J. Biol. Chem.,* **162,** 199 (1946).
27. Boyer, P. D., F. G. Lum, G. A. Ballou, J. M. Luck, and R. G. Rice, *J. Biol. Chem.,* **162,** 181 (1946).
28. Brady, A. P., and H. Huff, *J. Phys. Chem.,* **62,** 644 (1958).
29. Brand, B. P., and P. Johnson, *Trans. Faraday Soc.,* **52,** 438 (1956).
30. Butler, J. A. V., and W. S. Reid, *J. Chem. Soc.,* 1171 (1936).
31. Caglioti, V., and G. Giacomello, *Gazz. chim. ital.,* **69,** 245 (1939).
32. Cockbain, E. G., *Trans. Faraday Soc.,* **50,** 874 (1954).
33. Cockbain, E. G., *J. Colloid Sci.,* **11,** 575 (1956).
34. Cockbain, E. G., and T. S. McRoberts, *J. Colloid Sci.,* **8,** 440 (1953).
35. Cockbain, E. G., and J. H. Schulman, *Trans. Faraday Soc.,* **35,** 716 (1939).
36. Cohn, E. J., W. L. Hughes, and J. H. Weare, *J. Am. Chem. Soc.,* **69,** 1753 (1947).
37. Coulson, C. A., *Valence,* Oxford (1952).
38. Danielli, J. F., *Proc. Roy. Soc. (London),* **B122,** 155 (1937).
39. Daughaday, W. H., and I. Kozak, *J. Clin. Invest.,* **37,** 511 (1958).
40. Daughaday, W. H., and I. Kozak, *J. Clin. Invest.,* **37,** 519 (1958).
41. Davies, J. T., *Proc. Roy. Soc. (London),* **A208,** 224 (1951).
42. de Bernard, L., *Bull. soc. chim. biol.,* **40,** 161 (1958).
43. Debye, P., *Ann. N. Y. Acad. Sci.,* **51,** 575 (1949).
44. de Jong, H. G. Bungenberg, in *Colloid Science,* Vol. II, H. R. Kruyt, p. 276, Elsevier (1949).
45. Dervichian, D. G., *Trans. Faraday Soc.,* **42B,** 180 (1946).
46. Dervichian, D. G., in *Biochemical Problems of Lipids,* edited by Popjak and LeBreton, p. 3, Interscience (1956).
47. Drenth, J., W. Drenth, A. Vos, and E. H. Wiebenga, *Acta Cryst.,* **6,** 424 (1953)
48. Edsall, J. T., in *The Proteins,* Vol. IB, edited by Neurath and Bailey, Chap. 7, p. 549, Academic Press (1953).
49. Edsall, J. T., in *Ion Transport Across Membranes,* edited by Clarke, p. 221, Academic Press (1954).
50. Edsall, J. T., and J. Wyman, *Biophysical Chemistry,* Vol. I, Academic Press (1958).
51. Eik-Nes, K., J. A. Schellman, R. Lumry, and L. T. Samuels, *J. Biol. Chem.* **206,** 411 (1954).
52. Ekwall, P., *Conference on Biochemical Problems of Lipids,* Konin. Vlaam. Acad. Weten, Belg. (1953).
53. Ekwall, P., R. Ekholm, and A. Norman, *Acta Chem. Scand.,* **11,** 693 (1957)
54. Ekwall, P., R. Ekholm, and A. Norman, *Acta Chem. Scand.,* **11,** 703 (1957)
55. Ekwall, P., and K. Fontell, *Acta Chem. Scand.,* **10,** 327 (1956).
56. Ekwall, P., K. Fontell, and A. Norman, *Acta Chem. Scand.,* **11,** 190 (1957).
57. Ekwall, P., T. Rosendahl, and N. Lofman, *Acta Chem. Scand.,* **11,** 590 (1957).

58. Ekwall, P., T. Rosendahl, and A. Sten, *Acta Chem. Scand.,* **12,** 1622 (1958).
59. Ekwall, P., A. Sten, and A. Norman, *Acta Chem. Scand.,* **10,** 681 (1956).
60. Eley, D. D., and D. G. Hedge, *Disc. Faraday Soc.,* **21,** 221 (1956).
61. Eley, D. D., and D. G. Hedge, *J. Colloid Sci.,* **11,** 445 (1956).
62. Ellis, S. C., and K. G. A. Pankhurst, *Trans. Faraday Soc.,* **50,** 82 (1954).
63. Few, A. V., *Trans. Faraday Soc.,* **53,** 848 (1957).
64. Flockhart, B. D., *J. Colloid Sci.,* **12,** 557 (1957).
65. Folch. J., and M. Lees, *J. Biol. Chem.,* **191,** 807 (1951).
66. Foster, J. F., and K. Aoki, *J. Am. Chem. Soc.,* **80,** 5215 (1958).
67. Fraenkel-Conrat, H., *J. Biol. Chem.,* **217,** 373 (1955).
68. Frank, H. S., and M. G. Evans, *J. Chem. Physics,* **13,** 507 (1945).
69. Frank, H. S., and Wen-Yang Wen, *Disc. Faraday Soc.,* **24,** 133 (1957).
70. Fraser, M. J., J. G. Kaplan, and J. H. Schulman, *Disc. Faraday Soc.,* **20,** 44 (1955).
71. Fraser, M. J., and J. H. Schulman, *J. Colloid Sci.,* **11,** 451 (1956).
72. Geyer, R. P., F. R. Olsen, S. B. Andrus, W. R. Waddell, and F. J. Stare, *J. Am. Oil Chem. Soc.,* **32,** 365 (1955).
73. Go, Y., and O. Kratky, *Z. physik. Chem.,* **B26,** 439 (1934).
74. Goddard, E. D., C. A. J. Hoeve, and G. C. Benson, *J. Phys. Chem.,* **61,** 593 (1957).
75. Goddard, E. D., and J. H. Schulman, *J. Colloid Sci.,* **8,** 309 (1953).
76. Goddard, E. D., and J. H. Schulman, *J. Colloid Sci.,* **8,** 329 (1953).
77. Goodman, D. S., *Science,* **125,** 1296 (1957).
78. Goodman, D. S., *J. Am. Chem. Soc.,* **80,** 3887 (1958).
79. Goodman, D. S., *J. Am. Chem. Soc.,* **80,** 3892 (1958).
80. Grassmann, W., and G. Deffner, *Z. physiol. Chem.,* **293,** 89 (1953).
81. Grassmann, W., H. Hormann, and A. Hartle, *Makromol. Chem.,* **21,** 37 (1956).
82. Gross, J., *J. Biophys. Biochem. Cytol., Suppl.,* **2,** 261 (1956).
83. Gurd, F. R. N., in *Ion Transport Across Membranes,* edited by Clarke, p. 246, Academic Press (1954).
84. Gurd, F. R. N., and P. E. Wilcox, *Advances in Protein Chem.,* **11,** 311 (1956).
85. Harbury, H. A., and K. A. Foley, *Proc. Natl. Acad. Sci. U. S.,* **44,** 662 (1958).
86. Hedge, D. G., *J. Colloid Sci.,* **12,** 417 (1957).
87. Heller, S., A-M. Fretzdorff, and G. Weitzel, *Z. physiol. Chem.,* **301,** 17 (1955).
88. Hendricks, S. B., and M. E. Jefferson, *Amer. Mineralogist,* **23,** 863 (1938).
89. Hill, T. L., *J. Phys. Chem.,* **61,** 548 (1957).
90. Hoeve, C. A. J., and G. C. Benson, *J. Phys. Chem.,* **61,** 1149 (1957).
91. Hughes, W. L., in *The Proteins,* Vol. IIB, edited by Neurath and Bailey, p. 663, Academic Press (1954).
92. Hughes, W. L., *Ann. N. Y. Acad. Sci.,* **70,** 3 (1957).
93. Hunter, L., *Prog. in Stereochemistry,* **1,** 223 (1954).
94. Järnefelt, J., R. E. Basford, H. D. Tisdale, and D. E. Green, *Biochem. et Biophys. Acta,* **29,** 123 (1958).
95. Kendrew, J. C., G. Bodo, H. M. Dintzis, R. G. Parrish, H. Wyckoff, and D. C. Phillips, *Nature,* **181,** 662 (1958).
96. Kiessig, H., and W. Philippoff, *Naturwissenschaften,* **35,** 593 (1939).
97. Kitahara, A., *J. Colloid Sci.,* **12,** 342 (1957).

98. Klotz, I. M., in *The Proteins,* Vol. IB, edited by Neurath and Bailey, p. 727, Academic Press (1953).
99. Klotz, I. M., *Science,* **128,** 815 (1958).
100. Koltun, W. L., *J. Am. Chem. Soc.,* **79,** 5681 (1957).
101. Koltun, W. L., R. E. Clark, R. N. Dexter, and F. R. N. Gurd, *J. Am. Chem. Soc.,* **80,** 4188 (1958).
102. Koltun, W. L., R. N. Dexter, R. E. Clark, P. Katsoyannis, and F. R. N. Gurd, *J. Am. Chem. Soc.,* **81,** 295 (1959).
103. Koltun, W. L., and F. R. N. Gurd, *J. Am. Chem. Soc.,* **81,** 301 (1959).
104. Kratky, O., and G. Giacomello, *Monatsh.,* **69,** 427 (1936).
105. Kumagawa, M., and K. Suto, *Biochem. Z.,* **8,** 212 (1908).
106. Langmuir, I., *J. Chem. Phys.,* **1,** 756 (1933).
107. Laskowski, M., Jr., and H. A. Scheraga, *J. Am. Chem. Soc.,* **76,** 6305 (1954).
108. Levedahl, B. H., and H. Bernstein, *Arch. Biochem. Biophys.,* **52,** 353 (1954).
109. Low, B. W, in *The Proteins,* Vol IA, edited by Neurath and Bailey, Chap. 4, p. 235, Academic Press (1953).
110. McElroy, W. D., and B. Glass, eds. *The Mechanism of Enzyme Action,* Johns Hopkins Press (1954).
111. Macheboeuf, M. A., *Bull. soc. chim. biol.,* **11,** 268, 485 (1929).
112. McMenamy, R. H., and J. L. Oncley, *J. Biol. Chem,,* **233,** 1436 (1958).
113. Madsen, N. B., and C. F. Cori, *Biochim. et Biophys. Acta,* **18,** 156 (1955).
114. Madsen, N. B., and F. R. N. Gurd, *J. Biol. Chem.,* **223,** 1075 (1956).
115. Matalon, R., *Trans. Faraday Soc.,* **46,** 674 (1950).
116. Matalon, R., *J. Colloid Sci.,* **8,** 53 (1953).
117. Matijevic, E., and B. A. Pethica, *Trans. Faraday Soc.,* **54,** 587 (1958).
118. Matijevic, E., and B. A. Pethica, *Trans. Faraday Soc.,* **54,** 1382 (1958).
119. Matijevic, E., and B. A. Pethica, *Trans. Faraday Soc.,* **54,** 1390 (1958).
120. Matijevic, E., and B. A. Pethica, *Trans. Faraday Soc.,* **54,** 1400 (1958).
121. Mering, J., *Trans. Faraday Soc.,* **42B,** 205 (1946).
122. Mulliken, R. S., *J. Am. Chem. Soc.,* **74,** 811 (1952)
123. Nageotte, J., *Morphologie des Gels Lipoïdes, Actualites sci. et ind.,* Hermann et cie (1936).
124. Neilands, J. B., and P. K. Stumpf, *Outlines of Enzyme Chemistry,* 2nd edition, Wiley (1958).
125. Neurath, H., and H. B. Bull, *Chem. Revs.,* **23,** 391 (1938).
126. Oncley, J. L., F. R. N. Gurd, and M. Melin, *J. Am. Chem. Soc.,* **72,** 458 (1950).
127. Oyakawa, E. K., and B. H. Levedahl, *Arch. Biochem. Biophys.,* **74,** 17 (1958).
128. Palit, S. R., and B. Venkateswarlu, *Proc. Roy. Soc. (London),* **A208,** 542 (1951).
129. Pallansch, M. J., and D. R. Briggs, *J. Am. Chem. Soc.,* **76,** 1396 (1954).
130. Palmer, K. J., and F. O. Schmitt, *J. Cellular Comp. Physiol.,* **17,** 385 (1941).
131. Palmer, K. J., F. O. Schmitt, and E. Chargaff, *J. Cellular Comp. Physiol.,* **18,** 43 (1941).
132. Pauling, L., and R. B. Corey, *Proc. Natl. Acad. Sci. U. S.,* **37,** 251, 282 (1951).
133. Pethica, B. A., *Trans. Faraday Soc.,* **50,** 413 (1954).
134. Pethica, B. A., *Trans. Faraday Soc.,* **51,** 1402 (1955).
135. Putnam, F. W., in *The Proteins,* Vol. IB, edited by Neurath and Bailey, Chap. 9, p. 807, Academic Press (1953).

136. Putnam, F. W., in *The Proteins,* Vol. IB, edited by Neurath and Bailey, Chap. 10, p. 893, Academic Press (1953).
137. Putnam, F. W., and H. Neurath, *J. Biol. Chem.,* **159,** 195 (1945).
138. Revel, J. P., S. Ito, and D. W. Fawcett, *J. Biophysic. Biochem. Cytol.,* **4,** 495 (1958).
139. Rheinboldt, H., P. Braun, E. Flume, O. Konig, and A. Lauber, *J. prakt. Chem.,* **153,** 313 (1939).
140. Rich, A., and D. M. Blow, *Nature,* **182,** 423 (1958).
141. Richards, F. M., *Proc. Natl. Acad. Sci. U. S.,* **44,** 162 (1958).
142. Rideal, E., *Proc. Roy. Soc. (London),* **A209,** 431 (1951).
143. Rongone, E. L., B. C. Bocklage, D. R. Strength, and E. A. Doisy, *J. Biol Chem.,* **225,** 969 (1957).
144. Saroff, H. A., *Arch. Biochem. Biophys.,* **71,** 194 (1957).
145. Scatchard, G., W. L. Hughes, F. R. N. Gurd, and P. E. Wilcox, in *Chemical Specificity in Biological Interactions,* edited by Gurd, p. 193, Academic Press (1954).
146. Schellman, J. A., *Compt. rend. trav. lab. Carlsberg, Sér. Chim.,* **29,** 223, 230 (1955).
147. Schellman, J. A., R. Lumry, and L. T. Samuels, *J. Am. Chem. Soc.,* **76,** 2808 (1954).
148. Schick, M. J., and F. M. Fowkes, *J. Phys. Chem.,* **61,** 1062 (1957).
149. Schulman, J. H., *Disc. Faraday Soc.,* **21,** 284 (1956).
150. Schulman, J. H., and A. H. Hughes, *Biochem. J.,* **29,** 1243 (1935).
151. Schulman, J. H., and E. K. Rideal, *Proc. Roy. Soc. (London),* **B122,** 29 (1937)
152. Schulman, J. H., and E. K. Rideal, *Proc. Roy. Soc. (London),* **B122,** 46 (1937)
153. Schulman, J. H., and E. Stenhagen, *Proc Roy. Soc. (London),* **B126,** 356 (1938–1939).
154. Schwartz, A. M., J. W. Perry, and J. Berch, *Surface Active Agents and Detergents,* Vol. II, Chap. 20, p. 474, Interscience (1958).
155. Serra, J. A., *Science,* **128,** 28 (1958).
156. Siekevitz, P., and M. L. Watson, *J. Biophys. Biochem. Cytol.,* **2,** 653 (1956)
157. Singleterry, C. R., *J. Am. Oil Chem. Soc.,* **32,** 446 (1955).
158. Sobotka, H., and N. Czeczowiczka, *J. Colloid Sci.,* **13,** 188 (1958).
159. Spink, J. A., and J. V. Sanders, *Trans. Faraday Soc.,* **51,** 1154 (1955).
160. Stein, W. D., *Nature,* **181,** 1662 (1958).
161. Steinhardt, J., E. M. Zaiser, and S. Beychok, *J. Am. Chem. Soc.,* **80,** 4634 (1958).
162. Steven, F. S., and G. R. Tristram, *Biochem. J.,* **70,** 179 (1958).
163. Strain, W. H., in *Organic Chemistry,* Vol. II, 2nd edition, edited by Gilman, Chap. 19, p. 1341, Wiley (1943).
164. Strauss, U. P., and S. S. Slowata, *J. Phys. Chem.,* **61,** 411 (1957).
165. Tanford, C., and J. Buzzell, *J Phys. Chem,* **60,** 225 (1956).
166. Thomas, J. G. N., and J. H. Schulman, *Trans. Faraday Soc.,* **50,** 1128 (1954).
167. Thomas, J. G. N., and J. H. Schulman, *Trans. Faraday Soc.,* **50,** 1131 (1954).
168. Thomas, J. G. N., and J. H. Schulman, *Trans. Faraday Soc.,* **50,** 1139 (1954).
169. Turner, R. B., in *Chemical Specificity in Biological Interactions,* edited by Gurd, Chap. III, p. 29, Academic Press (1954).
170. Vallee, B. L., *Advances in Protein Chem.,* **10,** 318 (1955).

171. Van den Tempel, M., *J. Colloid Sci.*, **13**, 125 (1958).
172. Walling, C., E. E. Ruff, and J. L. Thornton, *J. Phys. Chem.*, **61**, 486 (1957).
173. Warner, R. C., *Trans. N. Y. Acad. Sci. Ser. II*, **16**, 182 (1954).
174. Waugh, D. F., *Advances in Protein Chem.*, **9**, 384 (1954).
175. Weitzel, G., A-M. Fretzdorff, and S. Heller, *Z. physiol. Chem.*, **301**, 26 (1955).
176. Westphal, U., *Endocrinology*, **57**, 456 (1955).
177. Westphal, U., *Arch. Biochem. Biophys.*, **66**, 71 (1957).
178. Westphal, U., and B. D. Ashley, *J. Biol. Chem.*, **233**, 57 (1958).
179. Wieland, H., and H. Sorge, *Z. physiol. Chem.*, **97**, 1 (1916).
180. Williams, R. J., J. N. Phillips, and K. J. Mysels, *Trans. Faraday Soc.*, **51**, 728 (1955).
181. Yang, J. T., and J. F. Foster, *J. Am. Chem. Soc.*, **75**, 5560 (1953).

9

by Frank R. N. Gurd

Some naturally
occurring lipoprotein
systems

The description in Chapter 8 of the association phenomena that are observed between lipide molecules and between lipides and proteins gives an indication of the variety of lipide-protein complexes that may be encountered in nature. The least polar lipides, such as higher triglycerides, may be expected to form more or less spherical droplets, possibly covered by a film of more polar lipides or protein or both together. At the other extreme, the most polar lipides, such as fatty acids, lysophosphatides, and certain steroids, may be expected under some circumstances to interact as single and independent molecules with proteins in solution. The molecules of the very plentiful lipides of intermediate properties, such as phospholipides and cholesterol, tend to associate with similar lipide molecules and also to interact with non-polar and polar residues in proteins. Non-polar moieties in these lipides tend to group together, leaving the polar moieties reaching into the aqueous environment. This tendency has expression in the formation of micellar aggregates or of membranous structures, such as myelin forms, either of which may also interact with protein molecules. Possible examples of some of these types of association phenomena in naturally occurring lipoprotein systems are described in this chapter.

The close association between lipides and proteins in tissues and body fluids has been recognized for some time.[42, 176, 177, 183] Primary covalent linkages between lipides and proteins are rare, and the stability of the lipoprotein complexes must be considered in terms of associations of the types discussed in Chapter 8. Besides being sensitive to the usual agents which threaten the integrity of native protein molecules, such as heat and extremes of pH, the lipoproteins show sensitivity to agents that cause deterioration of lipides. For example, the formation of hydroperoxides in isolated plasma lipoprotein preparations has been recognized and may be delayed by the addition of chelating agents to reduce the catalytic activity of contaminating cupric ions. Both lipide and protein moieties are sensitive to other hazards such as exposure to surfaces. As has been pointed out in preceding chapters, lipides occur as complex mixtures whose composition may vary according to the state of nutrition and metabolism of the organism. The fatty acid composition of the lipides in lipoprotein complexes, therefore, is not rigidly fixed. Any preparation of lipoprotein complexes is likely to represent a family of closely related complexes whose fatty acid composition probably varies somewhat from particle to particle. In much of the discussion that follows the composition of lipide mixtures is described only according to class (e.g., phospholipide, triglyceride) without detailed subdivision into different types (e.g., phosphatidyl ethanolamine) or into discrete molecular species according to fatty acid content. Such detailed information is being actively sought in several laboratories with the help of many of the new techniques described in Chapter 2.

In the following discussion, plasma lipoproteins are considered first, with emphasis on methods of isolation, composition, and structure. The association of lipides with various structural elements in the cell is then discussed. Brief mention is made of the highly ordered lipoprotein structures found in specialized tissues, e.g., myelin sheath, visual elements, and chloroplasts. Lastly, a brief description of the proteolipides is given.

LIPOPROTEINS IN BLOOD PLASMA

Isolation According to Solubility

That the lipides in blood plasma are for the most part associated with proteins and are not present in free solution or in a state of simple emulsification has been surmised for some time. Numerous early workers noticed that lipides are precipitated from plasma along with proteins.[16, 43, 99, 128, 129, 266] Others remarked on the clarity of plasma as evidence that the lipides are not present in large aggregates.[252] Still others noticed that the lipides are incompletely extracted from plasma by solvents such as ether.[198, 240, 242, 252]

In 1929, Macheboeuf published an account of the isolation from horse serum of an albumin-like substance which contained reproducible proportions of phospholipides, cholesterol esters, and proteins.[181, 182] The substance was isolated by ammonium sulfate fractionation with repeated precipitation near pH 3.8 followed by resolution at higher pH. Because of the method of preparation, Macheboeuf used the term "cénapses acidoprécipitables" for the complexes,[183] and other workers have used the initials "C.A.M." for "cénapses acidoprécipitables de Macheboeuf". These complexes have been the subject of very interesting studies of stability that are to be discussed later. Some of the lipides in horse serum are associated with protein fractions other than the C.A.M.

The systematic studies of human plasma undertaken in E. J. Cohn's laboratory about 1940 also led to the recognition of more than one lipoprotein component. Two major lipoproteins were described and named for their electrophoretic behavior as α_1-lipoprotein (concentrated in Fraction IV-1) and β_1-lipoprotein (concentrated in Fraction III-0).[49, 124, 204, 207] The observation that the electrophoretic mobility of these substances tended to change with time [8] is considered later in connection with the aging of lipoproteins and their ability to bind small molecules. Subsequent refinements of procedure in Cohn's laboratory and elsewhere have been introduced to allow quite sharp separations of the two gross classes of lipoproteins by fractional precipitation in ethanol-water mixtures.[47, 167, 231] Very laborious attempts to free the separated lipoprotein complexes from contaminating lipide-poor proteins by fractionation in ethanol-water mixtures have been unsuccessful.[121] The use of more specific precipitants for the isolation of plasma lipoproteins is discussed later.

During the studies of plasma fractionation, the separation of different lipoprotein components was followed primarily by analyses for cholesterol and phospholipide and it was recognized that the proportion of phospholipide to cholesterol was higher in the fractions rich in the α_1-lipoprotein than in those rich in the β_1-lipoprotein.[47, 167, 231] The significance of the isolation of fatty acids associated with serum albumins, reported by Kendall [151] in 1941 and discussed further by Hughes [48] in

1947, was not recognized at the time as adding a third major member to the lipoprotein system in fasting plasma.

Isolation According to Density

The most widely used procedure for the separation of lipoproteins is by flotation in the ultracentrifuge. The density of a lipoprotein complex reflects the densities of the components of which it is composed.[204] Oncley has offered some approximate density values as follows: [202] peptide 1.35, triglyceride 0.92, cholesterol 1.06, cholesterol esters 0.99, and phospholipide 0.97. Complexes containing appreciable lipide may be caused to rise in an ultracentrifuge cell or tube in a medium of appropriate density, such as a concentrated salt solution. The early development of the method involved contributions by Pedersen, Oncley, and Gofman's group, and has been reviewed numerous times.[61, 62, 109, 169, 172, 204, 208, 214, 215]

Flotation in Homogenous Media

Two general procedures have emerged for separating different classes of plasma lipoprotein by ultracentrifugation in media of adjusted density. In the procedures developed originally by Gofman's group the serum or serum fraction is mixed with a given quantity of salt solution (sometimes containing D_2O) to yield a small-molecule environment of a predetermined density.[62] During ultracentrifugation the small molecules of the solvent sediment very little so that lipoprotein molecules in all parts of the ultracentrifuge cell are subjected to much the same buoyancy factor. In the analytical ultracentrifuge, the rate of flotation of the lipoprotein boundaries may be observed and the various components characterized according to Svedberg units of flotation. The notation S_f has been employed [62] as a measure of the rate of flotation in a unit centrifugal field when the lipoprotein is suspended in an aqueous sodium chloride solution of density 1.063 at 26°. The rate of flotation is determined by (1) the difference in density between the medium and the lipoprotein complex, (2) the particle weight, and (3) the usual shape factor.[79] Most lipoproteins in plasma do not seem to depart very far from the spherical so that the shape factor is not of such great importance as it may be for simple proteins.

The technique of ultracentrifugal analysis in media of adjusted density has made possible the detection and characterization of lipide-rich proteins in the presence of lipide-poor proteins. The boundaries of the former develop at the bottom of the cell and move inward towards the axis of rotation, whereas the boundaries of the latter move in the usual outward direction.[109] For simplicity, it is usual to separate the lipide-rich proteins to be studied by a preliminary flotation carried on long enough to concentrate the desired material in a small volume at the top of a preparative ultracentrifuge tube.[62] By proper adjustment of the density of the medium in a sequence of preparative ultracentrifugations, it is possible to isolate a series of lipoprotein fractions containing complexes of densities within prescribed limits.[33, 131, 135, 136]

A diagram illustrating the isolation of low-density lipoproteins in a solvent density of 1.063 g./ml. is shown in Fig. 9.1.[170] A general scheme of the ultracentrifugal composition of human sera is shown in Fig. 9.2.[171] Some approximate molecular sizes are shown, as well as average serum concentrations present in 45 year old males. At least three main classes of lipoproteins are illustrated: high-density lipoproteins (HDL's), S_f 0–20, and S_f 20–400. The largest lipide-rich particles, $S_f > 400$, are present in greatest concentration during the period of absorption of fat from the intestine. Electron microscopy lends general support to the picture of nearly spherical shape and the progressive increase in size with increasing S_f value [132] as shown in Fig. 9.2.

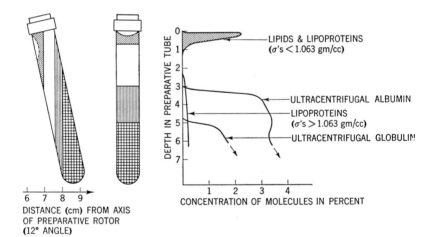

Fig. 9.1. Diagram illustrating the isolation of low-density lipoproteins in a solvent density of 1.063 g./ml. Taken from F. T. Lindgren, H. A. Elliott, and J. W. Gofman, *J. Phys. and Colloid Chem.,* **55,** 80 (1951).

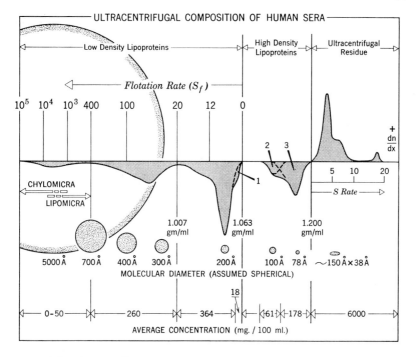

Fig. 9.2. The ultracentrifugal composition of human sera showing relative molecular sizes as well as average serum concentrations present in 45 year old males. The ultracentrifugal residue, plotted on a thirtyfold reduced dn/dx scale, contains the total ultracentrifugal albumin, globulin, and "20" components. Taken from F. T. Lindgren and J. W. Gofman, *Bull. schweiz. Akad. med. Wiss.*, **13**, 152 (1957).

In Fig. 9.2 the density 1.063 g./ml. represents the point of division between the more dense α-lipoproteins and the less dense β-lipoproteins according to the fractionation by solubility developed by Cohn et al.[47,49] Throughout the following discussion the various lipoprotein preparations will be named whenever possible according to the method of preparation or characterization actually used.

Flotation in Density Gradients

The second general procedure for separating different classes of lipoproteins is by establishing a density gradient in an ultracentrifuge tube through variation in the concentration of salt or other small solute. This may be done by simply layering a less dense solution on a more dense one. Reproducible density gradients may be obtained which will remain sufficiently stable to allow clear separations of lipoproteins to occur over periods of 18–24 hours of ultracentrifugation. At the completion of the ultracentrifugation the various lipoprotein fractions may be harvested in discrete horizontal bands. The lipoprotein complexes tend to collect at a point in the centrifuge tube where the density of the medium corresponds closely to their own. This procedure was developed by Oncley and Mannick and applied by Oncley, Walton, and Cornwell to a study of the variations in composition of certain lipoproteins as a function of small variations of their density.[193, 209] The procedure is being actively employed in several laboratories.[51, 123, 156, 209]

Turner and co-workers in 1951 published a method of ultracentrifugation of whole serum without the addition of any substance to adjust the density.[271] Under these conditions a gradient of protein and lipoprotein begins to develop so that the density varies from about 1.006 at the top of the centrifuge tube to about 1.110 at the bottom. The procedure has the advantage of involving the least possible interference with the natural state of the lipoprotein system. Resolution was extremely poor, but certain lipoprotein components could be seen to behave about as anticipated from other studies.

The cesium chloride equilibrium gradient procedure of Meselson et al.[196] has been applied successfully to a study of the plasma lipoproteins of highest density.[201] In this procedure the centrifugal field itself establishes a permanent gradient in concentration of cesium chloride, which in turn determines the distribution of lipoproteins. The procedure has not been applied to lipoproteins of low density.

Composition of Major Lipoprotein Classes

A summary of the gross composition of several major classes of plasma lipoproteins is presented in Table 9.1. The percentage values for peptide, phospholipide, cholesterol alcohol and esters, triglyceride, and non-esterified fatty acid (NEFA) are average values compiled by Oncley from a number of sources.[202] The fractions were isolated either by successive ultracentrifugations in media of various densities or by the use of density gradients. With the possible exception of the separation of the classes of density 1.09 and 1.14, in each case the ultracentrifugation was carried on sufficiently long that the separations were quite sharp.

It is worth noting that a distribution made primarily on the basis of density may not exactly match a distribution described in terms of

Table 9.1

Composition of the Major Human Plasma Lipoproteins

Average per cent values taken from Oncley *

Normal Concentration in Plasma (mg./100 ml.)	Peptide	Phospholipide	Cholesterol		Triglyceride	NEFA	Carotenoid Present †	N-Terminal Amino Acid ‡		Approximate S_f Class
			Alcohol	Ester				Major	Minor	
Chylomicrons										
100–250	2	7	2	6	83	§	Lutein	Ser, Thr	Asp	>400
Lipoproteins, density 0.98										
130–200	9	18	7	15	50	1	Lutein	Ser, Thr	Asp, Glu	~10–400
Lipoproteins, density 1.035										
210–400	21	22	8	38	10	1	β-carotene, lycopene; lutein	Glu	Thr, Ser	~3–9
Lipoproteins, density 1.09										
50–130	33	29	7	23	8	§	Lutein;		Ser, Thr	
Lipoproteins, density 1.14										
290–400	57	21	3	14	5	§	β-carotene, lycopene	Asp		

* J. L. Oncley, in *The Lipoproteins: Methods and Clinical Significance*, edited by F. Homburger and P. Bernfeld, p. 14, S. Karger, New York (1958).

† N. I. Krinsky, D. G. Cornwell, and J. L. Oncley, *Arch. Biochem. Biophys.*, **73**, 233 (1958).

‡ M. Rodbell and D. S. Fredrickson, *J. Biol. Chem.*, **234**, 562 (1959).

§ Not determined.

S_f values. A given density class may contain complexes of a controllable degree of homogeneity with respect to density but of varying size. A given S_f class may contain complexes which differ from one another, both with respect to size and density. In a medium of uniform density the large complex with a small buoyancy factor will rise at the same rate as a smaller complex with a larger buoyancy factor. In practice the range of particle size associated with a given density class does not appear particularly great.[209]

Each class of lipoprotein listed in Table 9.1 is capable of further subdivision. Oncley, Walton, and Cornwell have shown, for example, that the gross class of lipoproteins of average density about 1.035 may be divided in a gradient column into three subfractions, each more homogeneous than the original total class. The average densities of these subfractions were about 1.027, 1.038, and 1.047 g./ml., respectively, and the subfractions represented approximately 15, 60, and 25% of the original total class. The three subfractions showed S_f ranges of 6–10, 4–8, and 3–6, respectively, compared to a range of 3–9 for the whole class. A steady trend in composition was also noted: the per cent peptide in the total class was 22, and that in the three subfractions, 18, 21, and 24, respectively.[209]

Although each class of lipoproteins shows gradations of composition within it, the differentiation between classes is for the most part quite sharp. The lipoproteins of the density class 0.98 contain much more triglyceride than those of the more dense classes, and likewise contain relatively little cholesterol ester. The most dense classes of lipoprotein contain more phospholipide relative to cholesterol. The principal distribution of carotenoids is included in Table 9.1 to show a preferential binding of the hydrocarbons β-carotene and lycopene by the class of density 1.035 contrasted with a more general distribution for the alcohol lutein.

The distribution of the different types of phospholipides among the principal plasma lipoprotein fractions has been reported in some detail by Phillips.[221] The fractions were prepared by centrifugation of two aliquots of serum, one at a solvent density of 1.019 and the other at a solvent density of 1.063. Three fractions were analyzed: (1) the top fraction from the tube of density 1.019 (<1.019); (2) the top fraction from the tube of density 1.063 (<1.063); (3) the bottom fraction from the tube of density 1.063 (>1.063). The general distribution of lipides in the three density fractions corresponded to that found by Bragdon, Havel, and Boyle.[33] Silicic acid chromatography[219]

Table 9.2

Average Concentrations and Molar Ratios of Phospholipides in Plasma
Liproprotein Fractions *

	<1.019	<1.063	>1.063
	mM./l. Serum		
"Cephalin"	0.032	0.056	0.088
Lecithin	0.40	0.91	1.15
Sphingomyelin	0.15	0.35	0.23
Lysolecithin	0.032	0.056	0.18
	Molar Ratios		
$\dfrac{\text{"Cephalin"}}{\text{Sphingomyelin}}$	0.25	0.17	0.39
$\dfrac{\text{Sphingomyelin}}{\text{Lecithin}}$	0.35	0.38	0.19

* Taken from G. B. Phillips, *J. Clin. Invest.*, **38**, 489 (1959).

yielded average values (eight individuals) for the distribution of phospholipides as shown in Table 9.2. The "cephalin" fraction was further analyzed after hydrolysis and found to consist predominantly of phosphatidyl ethanolamine. An uncertain identification of a small amount of phosphatidyl serine was made. A small quantity of inositol appeared to be present. The "cephalin" fraction isolated from each of the density fractions appeared to have approximately the same composition as the "cephalin" fraction of whole serum. The lecithin fractions yielded choline as the only base on hydrolysis. The sphingomyelin and lysolecithin fractions yielded choline and several lesser ninhydrin-reacting components.

In Table 9.2 are shown the average concentrations of the four phospholipide fractions expressed as millimoles per liter of serum. Molar ratios of "cephalin"/sphingomyelin and sphingomyelin/lecithin are listed for the three density fractions. The proportions of the various phospholipides in the <1.019 fraction are close to those in the broader <1.063 fraction, which, of course, includes the material of the <1.019 fraction. These low density fractions differ from the high density fraction, >1.063, in the proportions of the various phospholipides. The low density lipoproteins are relatively rich in sphingomyelin, which accounts for about 25% of their phospholipide. The proportion of "cephalin" in each fraction was about 4 to 5%. The difference between low and high density fractions in sphingomyelin content has been demonstrated in electrophoretically separated β- and α-lipoproteins by Steele and Kayden.[255]

Using a similar ultracentrifugal procedure, Phillips isolated a lipoprotein fraction of density >1.210.[220] At this density, the major high density lipoprotein components are separated by flotation. The very dense lipoprotein was concentrated in the sediment along with the lipide-poor plasma proteins, and the extracted lipides were studied. The fraction contained little, if any, cholesterol but did contain phospholipide and what appeared to be triglyceride. About one-half the phospholipide in the fraction was identified as lysolecithin and the fraction accounted for about one-half the total lysolecithin in serum. The molar proportion of lipide phosphorus to triester (triglyceride) was about 2 or 3 to 1. The properties of the material were consistent with those of some material isolated previously in the same way by Havel, Eder, and Bragdon, who did not make such an elaborate analysis.[131] Phillips summarizes the few previous studies on this fraction.[131, 135, 270] The possibility must not be overlooked that lysolecithin may be produced by some unknown factor in the preparation of any particular fraction. Conversely, it should not be forgotten that the non-esterified fatty acids in plasma were often assumed until recently to be entirely artifactual.

More than one peptide component is usually present in each lipoprotein class, as shown by the listing in Table 9.1 of major and minor N-terminal amino acid components. There is considerable evidence from metabolic studies to indicate that some at least of the lipoproteins may pass from one ultracentrifugal class to another, presumably by alteration in lipide content. Fredrickson and Gordon have recently suggested that the components with serine and threonine end groups may pass down a metabolic series that overlaps with the major series containing glutamic acid as N-terminal residue (Fig. 9.3).[96]

At the moment, no method seems to be available for separating the proteins of, say, the glutamic acid N-terminal series from the minor constituents of the density class 1.035. Detailed studies of the distribution of lipoprotein complexes within this class as a function of density and of particle size have shown no obvious discontinuity. On the other hand, Oncley and Numa have found evidence for the concentration of the main part of the material listed under density class 0.98 into two separate subclasses.[201] It will be of great interest to determine whether these two subclasses correspond to the components identified by N-terminal serine and threonine residues, respectively.

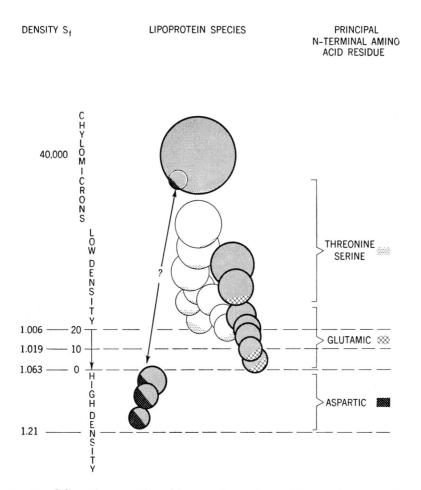

Fig. 9.3. Schematic conception of human plasma lipoprotein groupings according to present information. Polypeptide portions of the molecules are represented by the cross-hatching or stippling shown at the extreme right of the figure for the predominant N-terminal amino acid residue(s) present. No attempt has been made to conform to scale. Taken from D. S. Fredrickson and R. S. Gordon, *Physiol. Rev.*, **38**, 585 (1958).

Electrophoretic Characteristics

The principal lipoprotein fractions of highest density have the mobility of α_1-globulins in free electrophoresis [8,124] and in zone electrophoresis in paper, polyvinyl resin, starch granules,[159] or starch gel.[160] Freshly separated lipoproteins of the density class 1.035 have the mobility of the β_1-globulins and early preparations were called β_1-lipoprotein on the basis of free electrophoresis.[204] The fraction tends to smear from the origin to the β-globulin region in paper electrophoresis but travels as a discrete band in starch granules. The less dense lipoproteins and chylomicron fractions appear to remain close to the point of application in paper electrophoresis, but show a mobility corresponding to the α_2-globulins in the starch granule medium.[159] Both major fractions of low density lipoproteins, those with density of 1.035 and less, show very low mobility in starch gel electrophoresis, a fact which may be ascribed to their relatively large size.[160]

Solubility Characteristics

The plasma lipoproteins have the general solubility characteristics of typical plasma proteins. The addition of ethanol to aqueous solutions decreases their solubility. They are generally more soluble in ethanol-water mixtures when a dipolar ion such as glycine is present.[204]

The human lipoproteins of density classes 1.035 and 0.98 are isolated in Fraction III-0 of Methods 6 and 9 [207] of plasma fractionation, and in the broader Fraction I + III of Method 10.[47] In both methods of fractionation, these lipoproteins probably owe much of their insolubility to interaction with γ-globulins. Studies with isolated materials have shown that lipoproteins of the density class 1.035 form precipitates with γ-globulins over the pH range between about 5.5 and 7.0 where the lipoproteins bear net negative charges and the γ-globulins (for the most part) net positive charges.[203] It has been pointed out [121] that the behavior of this system conforms to the picture advanced by Sørensen [252] of "proteins as reversible dissociating systems". This interaction is greatly reduced by increasing the ionic strength and is not observable at the ionic strength of plasma. Purified preparations of lipoprotein of density class 1.035 have the solubility characteristics of euglobulins, i.e., they are insoluble near their isoelectric point (about pH 5.5) in the absence of salts, but become quite soluble at physiological ionic strength.[204]

The more dense lipoprotein complexes are far more soluble and have much the same solubility characteristics as the serum albumins.[47] They are, however, apparently altered by exposure to low pH as in Method 6, in which they are separated from albumins but concentrated together with various lipide-poor proteins in Fraction IV-1.[47, 124, 207]

All classes of lipoproteins appear to form insoluble complexes in the presence of zinc salts or glycinate complexes.[47] Complete separation from other proteins by this means has not been achieved. It is interesting that zinc salts appear to promote the formation of complexes between the lipoproteins of density class 1.035 and the γ-globulins.[122]

Cationic detergents such as zephiran may be used to precipitate the less dense classes of lipoproteins.[158] Presumably the binding of the cationic detergent neutralizes most of the net negative charge borne by the lipoprotein complexes near pH 7. The precipitation of contaminating lipide-poor proteins may be minimized by dilution of the serum. That a stoichiometric neutralization of charge [118] is involved is indicated by the observation that a concentration of detergent sufficient to precipitate these lipoproteins quantitatively from serum is insufficient to precipitate any material from more concentrated lipoprotein solutions.[119]

Interactions with Polyanions

Apart from the appropriate antibodies, the most specific reagents for precipitation of the lower density (1.035 and less) classes of lipoproteins have proved to be high polymers, especially anionic polysaccharides.[7, 26–28, 36, 39, 209, 234, 235] Sulfated dextran and sulfated amylopectin precipitate these lipoproteins readily from plasma or serum. Dextran sulfate has been used for isolation from plasma fractions.[209] Other polyanions such as heparin, polygalacturonate, and sulfated pectin form complexes which are much more soluble.[26] Among the factors which appear to affect solubility are the degree of polymerization of the polyanion, ionic strength, and the presence of metal ions such as $Ca(II)$, $Mg(II)$, $Ni(II)$, or $Co(II)$.[26, 37, 40, 41, 209] Exhaustive systematic studies have not been reported. It is clear, however, that the formation of insoluble complexes is favored by a higher degree of polymerization of, say, dextran sulfate, by lower ionic strength, and by the addition of the divalent metal ions. Chylomicrons appear to be more readily aggregated by heparin than the other lipoprotein complexes. Various nephelometric procedures based on this aggregation have been developed for estimating the concentration of low density lipoproteins in serum.[7, 26, 32, 39]

The reaction between low density lipoproteins and acidic polysaccharides is a remarkable one. Both reactants bear the same net charge at neutral pH and accordingly might be expected to interact most strongly in a medium of high ionic strength in which repulsive effects could be quenched. On the contrary, not only does the increasing ionic strength render the aggregates soluble but it dissociates them completely so that the components may be separated cleanly by ultracentrifugation in a gradient column containing sodium chloride solution.[209] Such separations happen to have been made in the presence of small quantities of ethylenediaminetetraacetate which may have played a role by sequestering divalent metal ions. On the other hand, an absolute requirement for $Ca(II)$ or $Mg(II)$ is unlikely since some of the studies reported by Oncley, Walton, and Cornwell involved the precipitation by dextran sulfate of lipoproteins in plasma which had been collected over ion exchange resins.[209] Such treatment of plasma usually does not remove every trace of divalent metal ions, however. The abnormal effect of ionic strength may be due to the collapse of an expanded configuration of the polyelectrolyte into a more compact structure, or may involve changes in the lipoproteins.

It is noteworthy that all the specific precipitants for these lipoproteins are polymers and it would be interesting to study the interactions of such compounds with lipide monolayers to see if any inherently weak interactions might be reinforced by multiple attachment. Evidence that the properties of a large polymer have an importance in themselves and apart from charge is provided by the ability of polyvinyl pyrrolidone to precipitate the low density lipoproteins in serum.[35] At very high ionic strength, the effect is largely restricted to the aggregation of chylomicrons in lipemic sera.[38] On the other hand, dextran itself is ineffective unless sulfated.

Stability of Lipoproteins During Isolation

With the exception of some studies on autoxidation of the lipides and some observations on other changes in the lipides during storage, there have been few detailed reports on factors affecting the stability of plasma lipoproteins during isolation. Most workers in the field would probably agree that the lipoproteins are readily damaged by conditions that are usually hazardous to plasma proteins: extremes of pH and, in some cases, of ionic strength, heat, the presence of ethanol except at low temperatures, and exposure to interfaces such as glass/water or air/water. The action of lipide solvents and the effects of freezing and drying will be discussed later.

Although few direct comparisons have been made, it appears that different methods of estimating the quantities of the various major lipoprotein classes in plasma give substantially the same results.[206] Furthermore, methods of purification involving various steps such as ultracentrifugation in very strong salt solutions, the use of ethanol-water mixtures, or the use of metal salts have yielded quite similar preparations. At present, however, all methods for purification of the lipoproteins (except those of lowest density) require the use of agents to increase the density of the medium for ultracentrifugal flotation. Particularly in the case of the lipoproteins of highest density, the addition of substantial concentrations of electrolytes is almost unavoidable. Keltz and Lovelock have made a preliminary report implying that the use of high concentrations of salts may be harmful.[150]

Autoxidation has been held responsible for at least two types of alterations that may be observed during the isolation and storage of the lipoproteins of the density class 1.035.[121, 206, 225] First is a marked change in absorption spectrum illustrated in Fig. 9.4. Above about 410 $m\mu$ the change corresponds to the loss of the spectrum of the carotenoid pigments. Below 410 $m\mu$ there is a general rise in the absorption spectrum with a clear peak near 275 $m\mu$ (Fig. 9.4), and another, particularly apparent in fresh alcohol-ether extracts, near 230–235 $m\mu$.[121] The bleaching of the carotenoids accords with their well-known ease of autoxidation.[149] The changes at shorter wave lengths likewise correspond to changes in the absorption spectrum of fats undergoing autoxidation.[22, 30, 140] For example, during the autoxidation of ethyl linoleate, Holman found enhancement with one maximum at 270–280 $m\mu$ and another stronger maximum at 230–235 $m\mu$. Such changes have been correlated with a sequence of autoxidation steps, which for a fatty acid such as linoleate represent the formation of a hydroperoxide followed by rearrangement and splitting off of water to form a conjugated diene ketone.[22, 23, 30, 140] In keeping with this interpretation, it was found that the ultraviolet absorption was markedly increased when strong alkali was added to an aged lipoprotein preparation or to an alcohol-ether extract of it.[121]

Gurd recognized that the changes in absorption spectrum might involve autoxidation of cholesterol [24, 25] as well as unsaturated fatty acids.[121] This type of change, if it occurred, did not progress to the point where changes in the analyses for total cholesterol or the alcohol

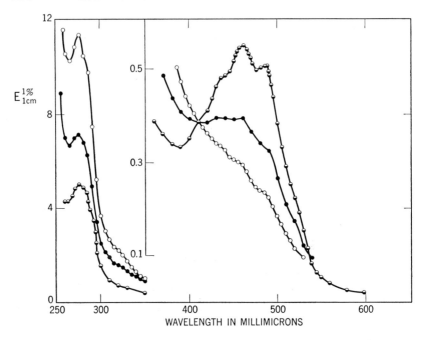

Fig. 9.4. Effect of age on absorption spectrum of β-lipoprotein (density class 1.035). ◐ aged three days in solution; ○ aged thirty-nine days in solution; ● aged sixty-seven days as euglobulin precipitate plus three days in solution. Taken from F. R. N. Gurd, "Studies on Human Serum β-Lipoprotein," Ph.D. Thesis, Harvard University (1948).

were detectable. Likewise, no direct evidence was adduced to rule out the possible formation of non-ketonic products [178] absorbing in the region of 275 mμ, or of products derived from the decomposition of the monohydroperoxide of oleic acid.[142] It was estimated that the spectral changes observed during storage in solution for 1 or 2 months represented the alteration of a considerable proportion of the unsaturated fatty acids probably present. Up to the present time, little attention has been paid to quantitative evaluation of these changes.

The exclusion of air or addition of antioxidants such as tocopherols in the late stages of processing were ineffective in delaying the autoxidation.[121, 206] Presumably, techniques could be developed for handling every stage of isolation under nitrogen.[45]

The second type of change that has been ascribed to autoxidation is observed as a change in the patterns obtained during flotation in the analytical ultracentrifuge.[206, 225] The patterns appear to become more heterogeneous and the rate of flotation is usually decreased. Ray, Davisson, and Crespi showed that the changes are most probably explained by autoxidation catalyzed by cupric ions.[225] The cupric ions are probably introduced as contaminants of the sodium chloride used to adjust the density. The process is furthered by more contamination and exposure to air during dialysis. A number of agents can be used to sequester the cupric ions, of which ethylenediaminetetraacetate is often the most convenient. The lipoproteins are less stable after isolation than in whole plasma, unless precautions are taken. It is almost certain that the observations of Oncley, Gurd, and Melin could not have been made if high concentrations of glycine had not been used in several instances to adjust the density of the isolation media.[204] Glycine has a considerable affinity for cupric ions.[125]

Geyer, Saslaw, and Stare have studied the rate of autoxidation of fat emulsions prepared for use in intravenous alimentation.[101, 102] Soybean phospholipide dispersions rapidly absorbed oxygen. When used in emulsions together with unsaturated oils, they absorbed much less oxygen. The preparations most stable to oxidation contained stabilizers of the sort that would form an oriented film at the oil/water interface (see Chapter 8). Emulsions of oils stabilized with gelatin took up oxygen rapidly.[102]

Tappel has studied the rate of catalysis of linoleate oxidation by cupric ions in the presence of conalbumin, serum albumin, or casein.[260] The main product is conjugated diene hydroperoxide. The cupric ions were found to be more effective catalysts in the presence of the proteins unless the latter were added in great excess. Tappel suggested that the copper proteins probably catalyze the oxidation of linoleate by reacting with linoleate peroxides to promote their decomposition into chain-initiating free radicals. Deborin and co-workers have found likewise that cupric ions catalyze the oxidation of complexes of ovalbumin with ergosterol.[56]

Promotion of the catalytic property of cupric ions is not limited to proteins. Schuler and Meier have shown that cortisone and certain related corticosteroids increase the activity of cupric ions in catalyzing the autoxidation of linoleic acid.[239] The involvement of such important regulatory agents as the corticosteroids in a reaction of this type is most interesting.

Other types of alterations in the serum lipides have been observed. A number of workers have reported the decomposition of phospholipides. In one case, phosphatidic acid appeared to be the principal product.[228] In others, inorganic phosphate was released,[65,120,163,276] and the deposition of calcium stearate observed.[65,93,120,222] Under certain conditions, fatty acids released by hydrolysis of phospholipides may combine with unesterified cholesterol to increase the proportion of total cholesterol in the esterified form.[4,163,164,253,265]

Such extensive changes develop very slowly under refrigeration. On the other hand, the release of small quantities of NEFA during the first few hours after blood is drawn is well known.[96] Usually this phenomenon has been ascribed to the specific action of lipoprotein lipase in splitting triglycerides, but the NEFA may also be derived from phospholipides. The released fatty acids are bound by plasma lipoproteins and by albumins as described below. The bound fatty acid anions contribute to the net negative charge borne by these complexes and, if large quantities are present, will alter their electrophoretic behavior.[8,113]

General Structure of Low Density Lipoproteins

The broadest aspects of the structure of the low density lipoproteins may be surmised from information about their size, composition, and solubility. Because of the heterogeneity of the two main classes of low density lipoproteins, it is difficult to make very accurate determinations of particle weight. Such data could in principle be coupled with information about composition to indicate whether or not the mass of peptide * in each particle of a given class is the same. That some heterogeneity with respect to peptide moiety is found even in the major class of density 1.035 has already been brought out in the discussion of end-groups (Table 9.1). However, immunochemical studies indicate that usually only one major antigen is found in this class,[76,168] so that there is some justification for assuming homogeneity with respect to peptide content for the purpose of forming a picture of the structure of this class of lipoproteins. While the picture will be developed with the 1.035 density class primarily in mind, it may do service for some of the less dense structures as well.

Detailed lipide and amino acid analyses have not yet been reported for lipoprotein preparations that have been carefully characterized at the same time with respect to particle size. A rough picture of the composition of a preparation of material of the density class 1.035 is given in Table 9.3. The percentage composition is taken from Table

* See first footnote on p. 210.

Table 9.3

Molar Composition of Plasma Lipoproteins of Density Class 1.035

Component	Per Cent by Weight	Moles/3,000,000 g.
Phospholipide	22	920
Unesterified cholesterol	8	660
Cholesterol ester	38	1820
Triglyceride	10	380
NEFA	1	110
Peptide	21	5600 *

* As amino acid residues of average weight 120. For other computations see text.

9.1. A molecular weight of 3,200,000 recommended by Bjorklund and Katz [29] has been chosen, with the understanding that it is probably too high for material of the average composition discussed here.[202] Mole ratios of the lipides have been computed using molecular weights for phospholipide, cholesterol, cholesterol ester, triglyceride, and non-esterified fatty acid (NEFA) of 760, 387, 669, 850, and 285, respectively. For comparison a rough estimate of the number of amino acid residues present in the peptide moiety is computed on the assumption of an average residue weight of 120.

Shore has suggested that a lipoprotein preparation characterized by an S_f value of 7.9 contains two peptide chains, each probably containing N-terminal glutamic acid and C-terminal serine with a molecular weight of about 380,000.[243] It may be estimated that about half the positive and negative charges borne by the lipoprotein complex are associated with the peptide moiety at neutral pH.[204]

Because the plasma lipoproteins are soluble in aqueous salt solutions and show the normal solubility characteristics of proteins, it has been postulated that the peptide moieties occupy part at least of their surface.[180, 204] McFarlane first pointed out that the low density lipoproteins of the 1.035 class contain so little peptide that there is not enough to cover even a perfectly spherical complex with a monolayer of peptide.[180] According to an early estimate, about half the surface of the particle could be covered by peptide.[204] A subsequent revision upward in average particle weight for this class has the effect of lowering the estimate. The same consequence would result from accepting a small deviation from spherical shape. The early picture had to take into account a very high estimate of water of hydration, about 0.6 g. of water per gram dry weight of lipoprotein.[208] This estimate has since been revised downward to about 0.1 or 0.2 g., a value in keeping with the usual properties of proteins.[268]

Table 9.3 shows that the number of cholesterol ester molecules, 1820, in the complexes corresponds to twice the number of phospholipide molecules. Most of these latter contain two long hydrocarbon chains. The number 1800 corresponds to about one-third of the total number of amino acid residues in the peptide chains. In terms both of mass and of stoichiometry, lipide-lipide interactions must be of comparable importance in maintaining the structure of the complexes as lipide-peptide or peptide-peptide interactions.

Considering the importance of repeating patterns in maintaining the structure of micelles and films, it is tempting to postulate some form of packing in which the proportion of 2 cholesterol esters to 1 phospholipide molecule lends stability to the complex. A *priori* one would expect that the most hydrophobic lipides such as cholesterol esters and triglycerides would be located deeper within a complex than the more hydrophilic phospholipides and unesterified cholesterol. Since much of the surface of these complexes must be composed of lipide rather than of peptide, it is reasonable that the hydrophilic parts of the phospholipide and possibly cholesterol should be located there. By analogy with the known tendency of lipides to pack together in more or less regular arrays, it is reasonable to postulate that the molecules of phospholipide and cholesterol are oriented quite regularly with respect to the aqueous environment and with respect to the peptide chain in their neighborhood. Perhaps the regularity extends down into the deeper layers that may be assumed to be relatively rich in cholesterol esters and triglycerides. The diameter of the particles is about 200 A, which is the equivalent span of four or five fully extended phospholipide molecules or rather more molecules of any of the lipides oriented in other ways. (Cf. Fig. 8.9.)

The picture developed here is of an aggregate of mixed lipides stabilized and limited by a specific peptide chain. All agents which tend to disrupt the complex—such as heat, shaking, extremes of pH, freezing, solvents, oxidation, proteinases,[119] or phospholipases [216, 286]—lead to aggregation of the lipides into larger particles which increase the turbidity of the solution markedly. In other words, when the native structure is disrupted, the particles coalesce, like the particles of an emulsion. On the other hand, it will be brought out later that the native lipoprotein particle shows the characteristic of a thermodynamically stable micelle in its ability to interact with other lipide-bearing structures, without losing its original identity and degree of dispersion.

General Structure of High Density Lipoproteins

The high density plasma lipoproteins are antigenically distinct from the low density lipoproteins.[76] Shore has made detailed studies [243] of the amino acid compositions of preparations described as having hydrated densities 1.093 and 1.149. The peptide moieties made up 46% and 53% of these preparations, respectively. The amino acid composition appeared to be identical in the two preparations, as were the N- and C-terminal residues, aspartic acid and threonine, respectively. The less dense component, besides containing a somewhat higher proportion of lipide, appears to have at least twice the particle weight of the other; Shore has suggested that it may contain two of the peptide chains of the same kind as the single chain found in the 1.14 component. Immunochemical evidence favors the idea of a single antigen associated with both of these high density classes and distinct from serum albumin.[235] The amino acid composition given by Shore is remarkable mainly for the nearly complete absence of methionine, a characteristic of certain Bence-Jones proteins observed in cases of multiple myeloma.[66] Otherwise, the composition seems to have no remarkable features setting it off from that of other proteins. Studies of amino acid sequences show distinct differences between this peptide moiety and serum albumin.[10]

The composition of the lipoproteins of density class 1.14 is shown in Table 9.4. The numbers of moles of the various constituents are computed as for Table 9.3, using a particle weight of 175,000. The relative quantities of phospholipide and of cholesterol are quite different from those in the low density lipoprotein class listed in Table 9.3. If Shore's analysis of similar material [243] containing 53% protein is transferred to a basis of 57% (Tables 9.1 and 9.4) for the present purpose, the numbers of the various hydrophobic side-chain residues in the polypeptide moiety may be computed. Their sum comes to about 280 residues.

The high density lipoprotein complexes contain much higher proportions of peptide side-chain groups to lipide molecules than do the

Table 9.4

Molar Composition of Plasma Lipoproteins of Density Class 1.14

Component	Per Cent by Weight	Moles/ 175,000 g.
Phospholipide	21	48
Unesterified cholesterol	3	14
Cholesterol Ester	14	37
Triglyceride	5	10
Peptide	57	830 *

* As amino acid residues of average weight 120. For other computations see text.

low density complexes. *A priori* it is easier to imagine that most, if not all, of the lipide molecules in these complexes have some form of contact with the peptide moiety. The proportion of lipide molecules in the structure is high enough, however, that it is difficult to picture the individual molecules adhering to widely separated sites in the peptide moiety, as appears to be true of the fatty acid complexes of serum albumins.[110] Perhaps a better analogy is found in the complexes of serum albumin heavily laden with sodium dodecyl sulfate in which both lipide-protein and lipide-lipide interactions have been postulated (see Chapter 8). It is noteworthy that in these latter complexes the bound lipide molecules appear to alter the structure of the protein and stabilize some form of expanded structure.

The higher proportion of peptide to lipide molecules may account for the greater stability of the high density lipoproteins. It is probable that the polar portions of the phospholipides in these complexes are exposed to the aqueous environment.[286]

Exchange of Lipides Between Lipoproteins

A striking quality of the mixtures of lipides found in biological systems is that they tend to form arrays and layered structures having, on the average, a considerable degree of order, yet with each molecule retaining a certain degree of mobility [1, 251] within and between layers. The lipide molecules in the various classes of plasma lipoprotein complexes share this property and many of them are readily exchanged between one lipoprotein complex and another or between plasma lipoproteins and cellular lipoproteins. Studies with radioactive tracers have shown that cholesterol transfers between high and low density lipoprotein classes, and between chylomicrons and high density lipoproteins.[97] Both unesterified and esterified cholesterol transfer, although the esters appear to transfer more slowly. Cholesterol also transfers readily between plasma and red cells.[127] Many of these transfers have been observed *in vivo* as well as *in vitro*.

Some, at least, of the phospholipides exchange readily between lipoproteins.[76, 77, 96, 130] James et al. have shown that phospholipides and triglycerides synthesized in the red cell can be taken up *in vitro* by plasma lipoproteins. They found that triglycerides appear to transfer preferentially to the lipoproteins of high density, whereas the phospholipides are transferred preferentially to the complexes of low density [145] (see, however, Kruger et al.[156]).

Since the phospholipides, triglycerides, cholesterol, and cholesterol esters are very insoluble in water, it is likely that exchanges and transfers are brought about by actual collision between the lipoprotein complexes themselves. The exchange or transfer occurs in the resulting collision complex. The collision complex then decomposes once more into the individual lipoprotein complexes which are themselves more stable than the collision complex. The process of transfer of a lipide molecule from one lipoprotein complex to the other in the collision complex may be looked upon as a diffusion process in which the molecule moves out of its original environment in one complex into the new environment of the other complex without passing completely into the aqueous surroundings. Presumably the rate of diffusion is determined by energy barriers within the collision complex itself, and does not give a direct indication of how deeply a given type of lipide molecule is normally buried within an individual complex. It is interesting, however, that at least some members of all the major lipide classes seem to be free to transfer to some other class of lipoprotein complex.

Of all the plasma lipides only unesterified cholesterol represents a pure molecular species. For this reason, studies of rates of interchange of cholesterol molecules between lipoprotein complexes are of greatest interest. The half-lives of such processes as exchange between plasma lipoproteins and red blood cells, or between plasma lipoproteins and liver lipoproteins, appear to be of the order of 1 or 2 hours.

For many purposes blood and liver cholesterol may be looked upon as forming a single pool.[75, 115]

Presumably the plasma lipoproteins are capable of acting as carriers for cholesterol from one part of the body to another by equilibrating in turn with lipoproteins in different tissues. Individual cholesterol molecules may be passed from one tissue to another without the overall destruction of the lipoprotein carrier. The persistence of the peptide moiety in the circulation has been found to be many times that of most of the component lipide moieties.[78, 104, 278]

The driving force for a net transfer of cholesterol from one tissue to another via the plasma lipoproteins is probably the impoverishment of the final receptor lipoprotein in the tissue that is removing the cholesterol. Formation of the collision complex between plasma lipoprotein and tissue lipoprotein then leads to an uneven exchange so that the collision complex decomposes to yield a tissue lipoprotein enriched by one or more cholesterol molecules and a plasma lipoprotein lacking the corresponding number of its previous complement of cholesterol molecules. A similar picture has been put forward by Glover and Morton to describe the successive stages in the absorption of cholesterol in the intestine,[106] and by Fillerup et al. and Goodman to describe the transport of fatty acids.[84, 111]

Interaction of Fatty Acid Anions with Lipoproteins

The very low solubility of the plasma lipides in aqueous solution hampers a direct measurement of their binding affinity to the lipoprotein complexes. Quantitative studies have been possible only in the special case of the fatty acid anions. As was described in Chapter 8, Goodman was able to measure the affinity of human serum albumin for a series of fatty acid anions by equilibration of the aqueous protein solution with an n-heptane phase.[110] The traces of fatty acid unbound to the protein in the aqueous phase were in equilibrium with much larger concentrations of fatty acid in the organic phase which could be determined accurately.

Serum albumin is much more stable to exposure to an organic solvent interface than are the lipide-rich complexes. The heptane equilibration technique is not suitable for such studies with the major lipoproteins, but fortunately a good deal of valuable information can be obtained by measuring the distribution of fatty anions between various lipoprotein classes and serum albumin. For example, Goodman and Shafrir have equilibrated the two lipoprotein fractions of lowest density (<1.019 and 1.019 to 1.063) with serum albumin in the presence of various fatty acid anions.[112] The lipoprotein complexes were then separated from the serum albumin by ultracentrifugation. Heavy water was used to raise the density of the medium, because it was found that the presence of high concentrations of anions disturbed the distribution of the fatty acid anions. Competition between different anions for binding sites on serum albumin is well known.

In keeping with earlier evidence from electrophoretic studies,[113] it was found that the anions of the higher fatty acids have a high affinity for these lipoproteins as well as for serum albumin. At low total concentrations of the fatty acid anions studied—stearate, palmitate, oleate, linoleate, and laurate—the numbers of moles bound per mole of lipoprotein were of the same order of magnitude as for serum albumin. Taking into account the molar concentrations of the lipoproteins and serum albumin in normal plasma, only about 0.3% of the fatty acids in plasma should be bound to each of the two lipoprotein fractions studied. Only about 0.01% of these fatty acids are free in solution. A small amount may also be bound to high density lipoproteins.

By coupling the measurements of competition between lipoprotein complexes and serum albumin with the separate absolute measurements of binding of fatty anions by serum albumin, Goodman and Shafrir were able to estimate values of the apparent association constants for the interaction of a lipoprotein with the five fatty acid anions. The results for the two lipoprotein preparations are shown in Tables 9.5 and 9.6. In each case a small number of binding sites showed affinities of the same order of magnitude as the strongest sites in serum albumin. A larger number of weaker sites are also available, and these sites show higher affinities than the weakest sites in serum albumin. In general, therefore, the proportion of fatty anions bound to the lipoproteins increases relative to serum albumin as the total concentration of fatty acid anions is increased beyond the normal physiological range. It is interesting that in human plasma relatively more stearate than palmitate and more palmitate than oleate will be bound to lipoproteins than to serum albumin.

Goodman and Shafrir offer a suggestion to explain the difference in affinity between the small number of strong binding sites and the larger number of weak ones observed with all the fatty acid anions and both lipoprotein preparations.[112] They suggest that the main factor in the binding may be that of solubility of the hydrocarbon chain of the fatty acid in the lipide portion of the lipoprotein, with a lining up of the fatty acid anions at the lipoprotein-water interface. The

Table 9.5

The Apparent Association Constants for the Interaction of Human Lipoprotein of Density <1.019 with Fatty Acid Anions *

pH 7.45; ionic strength 0.160; 23°
Lipoprotein unit of weight $= 2 \times 10^6$
Two classes of binding sites, with $n_1 = 4$, and $n_2 = 150$

Fatty Acid Anion	k_1'	k_2'
Stearate	7×10^7	1.2×10^5
Palmitate	7×10^6	2×10^5
Oleate	3×10^7	5×10^4
Linoleate	2×10^7	4.4×10^4
Laurate	7×10^5	2×10^3

* Taken from D. S. Goodman and E. Shafrir, *J. Am. Chem. Soc.*, **81**, 364 (1959).

Table 9.6

The Apparent Association Constants for the Interaction of Human Lipoprotein of Density 1.019 to 1.063 with Fatty Acid Anions *

pH 7.45; ionic strength 0.160; 23°
Lipoprotein unit of weight $= 10^6$
Two classes of binding sites, with $n_1 = 4$, and $n_2 = 150$

Fatty Acid Anion	k_1'	k_2'
Stearate	3.8×10^7	5×10^4
Palmitate	3×10^6	1.7×10^5
Oleate	1.3×10^7	3×10^4
Linoleate	2.5×10^6	7×10^3
Laurate	1.8×10^5	1.2×10^3

* Taken from D. S. Goodman and E. Shafrir, *J. Am. Chem. Soc.*, **81**, 364 (1959).

small number of sites of higher affinity may represent the effects of additional interaction of the fatty acid anions with one or more side-chain groups of the peptide moiety.

As may be seen by comparing Tables 9.5 and 9.6, the two lipoprotein preparations show very similar behavior towards the fatty anions. Of the two preparations, the less dense shows slightly stronger binding. Very little effect of pH was noted at low levels of palmitate. The effect of pH on binding is always difficult to study in such systems where phosphates are the buffers of choice and the variation in the competitive effects of the different phosphate anions cannot be avoided. It should be pointed out as well that the binding constants for serum albumin were determined in the presence of heptane[110] which might compete with the fatty acid anions to a slight extent; the errors due to this source are probably small, but they would be carried over to the interpretation of the lipoprotein interactions.

Binding and Displacement of Major Lipide Components

A method has not yet been found for studying quantitatively the affinity of lipoprotein complexes for their major constituents, such as cholesterol, cholesterol esters, phospholipides, and triglycerides. Direct equilibration of the lipoproteins with particles of these substances or with their solutions in organic solvents offers difficulties. The lipoprotein complexes tend to spread at interfaces and presumably undergo drastic changes in structure. Particles of purified lipides may act as solvents which remove other lipides from the lipoprotein complexes, thereby disrupting the complexes. No intermediary systems like the serum albumin-fatty acid system are known.

The behavior of the major lipide components in the lipoprotein complexes probably differs in another sense from that of the non-esterified fatty acids. The major lipide components almost certainly play a structural role in lipoprotein complexes, whereas the quantities of fatty acid anions incorporated in the lipoprotein complexes are probably very small under some physiological conditions. The evidence that the major components play a structural role is based on three principal sources: (1) the idea that such plentiful constituents of any particle must be looked upon as contributing to its structure; (2) the difficulty of retaining a native-seeming protein moiety after removal of the lipides from the low density lipoproteins; (3) the observations by Macheboeuf, Tayeau, and their collaborators that related substances sometimes may be used to displace a given type of lipide from the complexes.

Macheboeuf and Tayeau predicted that the lipides in lipoproteins might be displaced by compounds containing hydrocarbon chains, provided that the displacing compounds were sufficiently soluble in water to approach the lipoproteins as discrete molecules.[189,190] It was found that the addition of neutral aqueous sodium oleate to horse serum resulted in the release of considerable quantitites of lipides. These lipides were readily collected by shaking with ether, even though ether alone removed very little lipide under comparable conditions of shaking and time of exposure. The removal of lipides from the globulins was practically complete, whereas the lipides of the C.A.M. were quite unaffected. The concentrations of soap used, of the order of 1%, were far in excess of the quantities that were studied later by Goodman and Shafrir.[112] If the quantity of soap was increased fourfold or fivefold, the excess of soap held part of the released lipides in the aqueous phase and prevented their passage into the ether.

The addition of the oleate served to extract all the unesterified cholesterol from horse serum, 87% of the ester cholesterol, and 80% of the phospholipides.[191] A study of the optimal quantity of soap required led to the discovery that the same optimum existed for the total lipides, phospholipides, or cholesterol considered separately. It was concluded that the action of the soap depended on a property of the proteins and not of the lipides. The process was progressive with time as far as both cholesterol and phospholipide were concerned. The optimal activity occurred at the same molar concentration for each of a series of soaps, which suggests a stoichiometric binding of the soap molecules to the lipoproteins or to their peptide moieties. The order of decreasing effectiveness of the soaps tested was sodium ricinoleate, linoleate, dibromstearate, oleate, undecylenate, undecylate, and sebacate. Differences in chain length (oleate, undecylenate), although not extensively studied, were less important among the higher fatty acids than was solubility in water (ricinoleate). The presence of a hydrocarbon end group was obligatory, as evidenced by the almost complete ineffectiveness of the dicarboxylic sebacic acid. Similar tendencies were found for the sera of man, ox, sheep, pig, dog, rabbit, guinea pig, and chicken.[191]

Macheboeuf and Polonovski showed subsequently that the cationic detergent dodecyltrimethylammonium chloride also promoted the extraction of nearly all the cholesterol of horse serum by ether. In this case the phospholipides which were freed along with the cholesterol became associated with the cationic detergent in the aqueous phase and were not extracted by the ether.[186]

Macheboeuf, Tayeau, and co-workers extended the studies of the displacement of serum lipides to substances bearing some structural relationship to cholesterol.[184, 187, 261-264] The substances chosen were a saponin preparation from Sapidus, dihydroabietate, and sodium cholate. All three preparations promoted the extraction of cholesterol. It is probable that phospholipides again were displaced from their combination with the peptide moieties of the lipoproteins, but formed complexes with the added surface active agents which resisted extraction into the ether. This effect was clearly demonstrated when the agents were added in excess. The saponin preparation disrupted the C.A.M., and in this respect differed from the soaps.

Passing reference should be made to the interesting studies of Macheboeuf and Perrimond-Trouchet, who mixed dialyzed horse serum with solutions of complexes (micelles) prepared by mixing oleic or dibromstearic acid with either sodium taurocholate or sodium glycocholate. The mixtures of serum with the conjugated bile salt-fatty acid complexes were then dialyzed to remove the conjugated bile acid salts and leave the fatty acids combined with the serum proteins and lipoproteins.[185]

It is tempting to assume that the saponins and cholate simply replace lipides in the structure of the lipoproteins without disturbing the configuration of the peptide moieties. However, Anson pointed out some time ago that bile salts denature certain lipide-poor proteins.[6]

Promotion of Ether Extraction by Alcohols

As has been mentioned previously, the lipoproteins in whole plasma yield very little lipide when exposed to ether alone. The emulsification caused by shaking an aqueous solution with ether does cause aggregation of the lipoproteins and appears to cause some modification in structure (denaturation) without actually leading to the ready extraction of the lipides. The present discussion will deal with studies in which shaking with ether was neither prolonged nor vigorous and will be concerned largely with whole serum. More recent studies of the extraction of purified human plasma lipoproteins will be discussed in a later section.

The extraction of lipides from plasma lipoproteins by exposure to ether is promoted by various substances which are less obvious structural antagonists than the fatty acid anions or saponins. Macheboeuf studied the effect of ethanol in promoting the ether extraction of lipides from the C.A.M. prepared from horse serum.[181–183] This lipoprotein preparation contained 22.7% phospholipide, 17.9% cholesterol esters, and 59.1% protein material. More recent studies have shown the phospholipide to be exclusively lecithin.[63] This material has some similarity to the high density lipoproteins of human plasma except for the absence of unesterified cholesterol. Ether removed no phospholipide from its solutions and less than 1% of the cholesterol esters. The presence of salts did not improve the extraction with ether. Prolonged treatment with boiling alcohol served to remove the lipides. When the solution was mixed with an aqueous emulsion of lecithin, ether extraction gave 100% recovery of the added lecithin. Similarly, addition of the lipides which had been extracted previously from the C.A.M. by alcohol to an albumin solution gave unstable emulsions easily extracted with ether.

The material isolated by Macheboeuf contained, therefore, exclusively ether-resistant lipides. Alcohol was found to cause precipitation of the C.A.M. except in alkaline solutions. After a time, the precipitate was observed to be composed of amorphous protein and needles of cholesterol esters. With high concentrations of alcohol at pH 9.0, no amorphous precipitate formed at room temperature or below, but cholesterol esters crystallized out. If the material precipitated by alcohol was immediately treated with large volumes of water, clear solutions were obtained. Macheboeuf concluded that alcohol denaturation was stepwise and led first to a product soluble in strong alcohol which in turn was further altered so as to release cholesterol esters, lecithin which remained in the alcoholic solution, and an insoluble protein coagulum.

The effect of alcohols in promoting ether extraction of lipides from tissues was ascribed by early workers to their dehydrating power.[157, 218] The question was reopened in 1932 by Macheboeuf and Sandor,[184, 188] who sought to study the effect on serum lipides of small concentrations of alcohol, conditions which could hardly be described as grossly dehydrating. Concentrations of ethanol of the order of 10% added to horse serum led to the extraction by ether of about 50% of the total lipides. About 68% of the lipides in the globulin fraction were extracted, in contrast to only 39% in the albumin fraction. Similar results were obtained with the sera of man, sheep, and rabbit. Presumably the globulin fraction contained the lipoproteins of lower density. Concentrations of alcohol as high as 14% led to the formation of stable emulsions on even the most gentle shaking with ether and reduced the yield of extracted lipides. The lipides extracted during an initial exposure to ether for 6 hours at room temperature seemed to be a well-defined fraction, since renewal of the ether yielded mere traces of additional lipides. It was found that relatively more cholesterol than phospholipide was extracted and that the composition of the extracted lipide mixture was approximately constant within the optimal zone of about 6–12% ethanol.[188]

Ethanol concentrations of this magnitude did not cause obvious disruption of the lipoprotein complexes in the absence of ether. It is very interesting, therefore, that Macheboeuf and Sandor observed that the ether layer could be removed from the alcohol-serum mixture without stopping the process of breakdown of the lipoprotein complexes. In this case the process would continue to completion with the eventual collection of lipide droplets on the surface of the solution. This observation proved that dissolved ether and alcohol were responsible jointly for the breakdown of the complexes.

Macheboeuf and Sandor found that the process of release of serum lipides into ether in the presence of ethanol showed an induction period. The induction period was shorter the higher the concentration of ethanol, even though the final quantity of lipide extracted was always independent of the alcohol concentration when the latter lay between the limits 6–12%.[188] A possible explanation of the existence of the induction period could be that the released lipide sensitizes other lipoprotein molecules, either in the bulk phase or at the interface between the aqueous and ether phases. It would be interesting to repeat these observations using fresh serum exposed to an ether phase containing the extractives from a separate portion of serum.

Macheboeuf and Sandor suggested on the basis of their extraction experiments that the proteins and lipides are associated in complexes in such a way that the hydrophobic groups of each interact, while the hydrophilic groups point outwards and are surrounded by a protective layer of water. The alcohol was assumed to modify the affinities of the solvent for the various groups and especially to affect the ionization and hydration of the protein groups. In this way it was assumed that the protective zone could become permeable to ether which would remove the lipides. The authors considered that this process left room for an induction period.[188]

In 1935 Delage extended the observations of Macheboeuf and Sandor by finding that ethanol could be replaced by propanol, butanol, isoamyl alcohol, or cyclohexanol.[59] Methanol and acetone were effective in somewhat higher concentrations. In each case more than 50%

of the total lipides of horse serum was extractable. Delage showed that related compounds that were insoluble in ether, such as ethylene glycol, were ineffective.[60]

Effect of Low Temperatures on Stability

Freezing and particularly freeze-drying of plasma lipoproteins appear to cause aggregation and increase in turbidity.[204] Keltz and Lovelock have studied the behavior of low density lipoproteins (density class 1.035) in buffers at pH values between 4.0 and 8.6 and in unbuffered saline.[149a, 175] Qualitatively, aggregation did not seem to be very marked when the system was brought to −20° and thawed, but was extensive if the temperature was lowered to −40°. The pH did not appear to be an important variable.

On the other hand, a correlation was found between the extent of damage judged by turbidity and the relation between the temperature of freezing and the eutectic temperature of the medium. Lipoprotein preparations were made up in salt solutions having eutectic temperatures between −4° and −86°. The mixtures were frozen at −40° for 24 hours. The lipoprotein preparations in solutions of higher eutectic temperature sustained the greater apparent damage. In solutions with eutectic points below −40°, the damage was judged to be no greater than that caused by exposure to very concentrated salt solutions.[150] The conclusion drawn by Keltz and Lovelock was that damage to the lipoproteins occurred when the last traces of water were removed as ice, so that the lipoprotein complexes were brought into actual contact with one another. Glycerol, glucose, and sucrose were found to protect against damage by freezing at −37°. Low concentrations of alcohol were also somewhat protective. Sucrose also afforded considerable protection against damage during drying under vacuum from the frozen state.

The protection afforded to plasma lipoproteins by polyhydroxyl compounds against damage by freezing or drying has a parallel in the case of cells such as erythrocytes.[175] The general importance of this protective action is so great that more detailed studies of the mechanism would be most welcome. The use of ultracentrifugation, solubility measurements, and other techniques for defining the quantitative changes in the lipoproteins would be desirable.

Keltz and Lovelock's picture[175] of the mechanism of the damage caused by freezing and drying has some points of similarity to the picture of temporary collision complexes developed to explain the observed phenomena of exchange of lipides between lipoprotein complexes. The difference lies in the availability of water molecules to interact with any exposed groups in the parent lipoprotein complexes or collision complexes in solution. In the frozen system the water molecules are rigidly confined to the ice lattice and may not be free to form hydrogen bonds with groups in the lipoprotein complexes, or in so doing may disrupt the structure of the complexes. It is noteworthy that all the species of molecules that protect against damage by freezing or drying are themselves rich in hydroxyl groups. Possibly their presence offers the lipoprotein complexes some alternative molecules to associate with them, in place of water molecules that have become unavailable. In the absence of either water or some other molecule containing hydroxyl groups, the lipoprotein complex may rearrange to allow some form of internal compensation, and assume a configuration which does not lead back uniquely to the original structure when water is readmitted to the system.

The mutual reinforcement of the effect of alcohol and ether in decreasing the stability of plasma lipoprotein complexes has already been mentioned. A special effect of freezing in the presence of ether has also been observed. In 1942 McFarlane showed that considerable quantities of lipides were extracted into ether when human serum was shaken with ether and the mixture first brought to $-25°$ and then thawed.[179] The effect was not obtained when temperatures above $-20°$ were used. Conversely, temperatures down to $-70°$ did not increase the yield. Successive treatments of 1 liter of serum yielded 3.5, 0.85, and 0.2 g. of lipide; a further 2.5 g. could be obtained by treatment with alcohol-ether. The process occurred when the serum was simply saturated with ether before freezing, and a macroscopic ether/water interface evidently was not necessary. The ether probably dissolves in the lipoprotein complexes and may facilitate the postulated rearrangement of the lipoprotein structure in the absence of the liquid water environment.

Extraction of Lipides from Purified Lipoproteins

Avigan has reported [9] a comparison of the effects of extraction with ether and with alcohol-ether mixtures of a series of lipoprotein complexes prepared according to Havel, Eder, and Bragdon.[131] The fractions were obtained by sequential preparative ultracentrifugation at densities of 1.019, 1.063, and 1.21. Before treatment with the solvent all the fractions were adjusted to a concentration of 1–2% and to density 1.063. The concentration of salt was therefore many times that in plasma. The salt consisted of a mixture of sodium chloride and potassium bromide.

The extraction of the lipides was carried out at 4° by placing 2 ml. of the lipoprotein solutions in a 30-ml. vessel which was filled completely with peroxide-free ether or ether-alcohol mixture. No air space was left. The flask was revolved at a speed of 4 to 6 r.p.m. The phases were separated by centrifugation, and the lower phase washed once with ether and then dialyzed against a large quantity of 0.9% salt solution. This well-controlled procedure involves much more turbulence and exposure of the lipoproteins to the solvent/water interface than the rather static extraction employed earlier by Macheboeuf and co-workers.[184, 188]

The two lipoprotein fractions of lowest density released most of their cholesterol to ether during 16 hours of extraction.[9] Very little phospholipide was extracted at the same time. After the treatment with ether the major low density fraction, isolated between densities 1.019 and 1.063, reacted with an antiserum to the original preparation but not with an antiserum to the original high density material. The removal of lipide, however, did reduce the difference in density of the various lipoprotein species. The ether extraction of the major low density component (1.035) increased its density to about 1.137. The electrophoretic mobility, however, was unchanged by the extraction. This material also retained the ability of the native fraction to bind sodium oleate. The low density lipoproteins were irreversibly precipitated from solution with alcohol-ether mixtures.

The high density lipoprotein fraction, on the other hand, yielded very little lipide to ether extraction. The ultracentrifugal behavior was likewise unaltered. The lipides could be extracted in the cold with an alcohol-ether mixture (3:2, v/v). The fully extracted protein was easily soluble in water and remained in solution after addition of alcohol up to a final concentration of 80%. It behaved as a single component in sodium chloride solution of density 1.005, and sedimented at density 1.21. Electrophoretically it resolved into two components, one with the mobility of the untreated material and the other with a lower mobility indicating a decrease in net negative charge.

Avigan further contrasted the behavior of the major fraction of low density lipoproteins with that of the high density lipoproteins by measurements of specific optical rotation and by observations on the effect of urea. For the low density preparation a good correspondence was obtained between the observed specific rotation of the extracted lipoprotein and that calculated by subtracting the value contributed by the extracted lipide (measured in chloroform solution) from the value for the material before treatment. The high density lipoprotein, on the other hand, underwent a substantial drop in specific optical rotation below the calculated value after treatment with the alcohol-ether mixture. Such a drop in specific rotation commonly accompanies the action on native proteins of denaturing agents such as urea. Avigan found that $7M$ urea caused a marked decrease in specific rotation of the intact high density lipoprotein preparation, of about the same order as that observed with bovine serum albumin and bovine γ-globulin. The intact low density lipoprotein preparation (1.035 density class) showed no change in specific optical rotation after the addition of $7M$ urea. However, the ether-extracted low density lipoprotein preparation did show the usual drop in specific optical rotation in urea solution.

The insensitivity to urea of the intact low density lipoprotein preparation but not of the ether-extracted preparation was interpreted by Avigan as evidence that the cholesterol and cholesterol esters in the intact complexes helped stabilize the configuration of the peptide chain. An analogy was drawn between this stabilization and that afforded by ergosterol in artificial mixtures with ovalbumin.[57, 58]

The difference between the low and high density lipoprotein preparations in their sensitivity to the ether extraction is very striking.[9] At the ether/water interface the low density complexes seem to bind their cholesterol considerably less tightly, from which one might predict that they would show a tendency to lose cholesterol to the high density complexes. Yet, when mixed together in solution, the two species of complexes can exchange cholesterol molecules with each other freely without any apparent net transfer of cholesterol. Presumably the high density lipoproteins normally bear a full charge of cholesterol or, alternatively, the low density lipoproteins suffer such a marked change in structure in the ether/water interface that their affinity for cholesterol is sharply decreased. Both explanations may be correct.

Presumably a more violent extraction procedure would have yielded a less satisfactory preparation, and a less violent one would not have overcome the resistance of the cholesterol to ether extraction.

The preparation of phospholipide-rich, cholesterol-poor lipoprotein complexes by ether extraction of low density lipoproteins is a most interesting discovery. This material may be able to play the part of an "apoprotein" for cholesterol, capable of taking up cholesterol when equilibrated in solution with another lipoprotein preparation bearing a full charge of cholesterol. It would be interesting to contrast the behavior of this derived lipoprotein with that of the nearly lipide-free material obtained by Oncley, Gurd, and Melin from rather similar preparations of low density lipoproteins.[204] The nearly complete removal of lipides was effected in two steps, the first by freezing in the presence of ether with very slow warming from —50° to 0° and the second by extraction of the residue with 3:1 ethanol-ether at the same temperatures. The residue was soluble in the distilled water, unlike the original lipoprotein which requires low concentrations of salts for solubility. Some heterogeneity was observed in the ultracentrifugal analysis of the extracted material. In contrast to the method of Avigan, this extraction is probably affected adversely by high concentrations of salts. The extraction studies of Oncley et al.[204] were made on some of their earliest preparations which were not completely free of lipide-poor proteins, and should be repeated on highly purified preparations.

Avigan suggested that the protein derived by extraction of the high density lipoprotein preparation with alcohol-ether had undergone some denaturation as judged from measurements of optical rotation.[9] More recently Scanu, Lewis, and Bumpus prepared a nearly lipide-free residue by extraction of high density lipoproteins in two stages.[233] The lipoprotein solution in phosphate buffer pH 6.8, ionic strength 0.1, was first extracted at —20° for 2 hours with 25 volumes of 3:1 alcohol-ether mixture. The precipitate was then filtered and extracted with ether at —20° for 24 hours in a modified Soxhlet extractor. The residue contained only traces of phospholipide and was moderately soluble in salt solutions of physiological ionic strength. Measurements of optical rotation were not reported. Qualitative determinations of amino acid composition agreed with the results of Shore on similar preparations of high density lipoproteins.[243] The lipide-poor material showed the same characteristics in electrophoresis as the original material. The material showed hydrodynamic properties very similar to those of serum albumin, and was estimated to have a molecular weight near 75,000.[233] This value is about 20% smaller than the molecular weight of the peptide moiety computed by Shore.[243]

Present Objectives

The present objectives of research on plasma lipoproteins are primarily directed at an understanding of their structure and metabolism with the hope that such knowledge will lead to a better understanding of atherosclerosis. A number of searching reviews dealing with the metabolic aspects of the problem have appeared recently.[2, 76, 96, 108, 248] From the purely chemical point of view, the principal objectives remain to define the nature of the lipide and peptide moieties as fully as possible and to study their interaction. The recent recognition of the importance of non-esterified plasma fatty acids in fat metabolism illustrates the danger of overlooking a minor component whose rate of turnover may be very rapid.[69, 96, 114]

The availability of partially extracted plasma lipoprotein preparations opens the way to further study of the interactions between lipides and proteins. It will be of interest to compare in detail (1) the untreated lipoproteins, (2) the fully extracted high density lipoproteins, (3) the ether-extracted low density lipoproteins, and (4) the fully extracted low density lipoproteins, with respect to the binding of various substances. As has been indicated earlier, the binding of water-insoluble lipides appears to be accessible to thermodynamic study only by direct transfer between lipoprotein complexes themselves. More general studies of water-soluble substances are also of great interest. Only a few studies of the latter types have been reported. Rosenberg, Lever, and Lyons found that low density (1.035) lipoproteins bind the anion methyl orange with an affinity comparable to that of the serum albumins at pH 7.4.[230] Binding studies on the same lipoproteins with sodium estrone sulfate have shown a binding affinity greater than that of the human γ-globulins but inferior to that of serum albumins.[205] In these cases the dialysis equilibrium technique was employed. For some purposes the technique of ultrafiltration may be preferable. Ultrafiltration has the advantage that it defines the distribution of the small molecules without disturbing the equilibrium in the solution (except for the usually second order effects of changes in protein concentration), involves less turbulence, and is faster.

Detailed information about the fatty acid composition of the plasma lipoproteins is being collected at present. It has been pointed out frequently in this volume that differences in the fatty acid composition of individual molecules of phospholipides, cholesterol esters, or triglyceride contribute differences to the properties of each lipide molecule as a whole. For example, the types of fatty acids contained in these molecules determine to some extent the mode of packing that the molecule as a whole can assume.[141] It is possible that individual fatty acids will be found concentrated preferentially in lipide molecules associated with different classes of lipoproteins and with different members of the same gross class. For example, slight gradations in fatty acid composition may be found to parallel the gradations in gross composition that were detected by Oncley, Walton, and Cornwell [209] in subfractions of the 1.035 density class of lipoproteins. Similar comments might apply to the distribution of the different phospholipide structures, particularly in terms of minor components in the "cephalin" fraction. The more detailed studies of composition will probably be particularly fruitful when applied to the various distributions of lipoprotein components recognized in pathological sera.[76, 108, 232, 241]

Using less refined methods than are now available, Gillies et al. reported that the lipoproteins of density class 1.035 (S_f 0–20) contained more polyunsaturated fatty acids and less palmitoleic acid than the less dense class (S_f 20–400).[103]

It is possible that an isolated lipoprotein fraction of relatively low apparent heterogeneity with respect to size and density may contain particles of widely varying composition in which the heterogeneity is masked. For example, a particle having relatively more peptide and triglyceride could have the same density as a particle containing less peptide but enough cholesterol replacing the triglyceride to effect a balance. An objective of present research should be to develop means whereby such heterogeneity might be detected. The problem would have to be worked out against the background of the known heterogeneity of the peptide moieties, where end-group analysis and quantitative immunochemical techniques can be of great assistance.[96, 104, 229]

TISSUE LIPOPROTEINS

Introduction

As has been indicated earlier, certain of the tissue lipoproteins are associated with microscopically identifiable structures in cells and others may be present in solution in the cytoplasm. Material with the immunochemical characteristics of certain plasma lipoproteins has been recognized within cells by the fluorescent antibody technique.[105]

The importance of lipides to the structure and properties of cell membranes has been recognized for many years.[55] The role of lipoproteins in other membranous structures within the cell has been recognized only very recently, following the development of refined techniques of electron microscopy and of tissue fractionation.[46] Lipoproteins have been found in all the gross fractions derived from carefully fractionated cells. Fractionation of liver, pancreas, kidney, or heart usually takes the form of first macerating the organ and if necessary straining out connective tissue, then breaking up the cells in a homogenizer, and finally separating different subcellular fragments by differential centrifugation. Hypertonic sucrose solution is a favorite homogenizing medium and allows adjustment of the density of the medium during the centrifugal separations at high speed. Density gradients have been used in some cases to give sharper separations.[3, 217, 244]

The major fractions usually prepared consist primarily of (1) nuclei, (2) mitochondria, (3) microsomes, and (4) the supernatant fraction. The supernatant fraction usually contains some particles large enough to be detected by the electron microscope, as well as smaller proteins. The enzymes of the glycolytic sequence are often present in this fraction. Large lipide droplets of low density are harvested in this fraction and sometimes may be separated by a preliminary centrifugation introduced before fractionating the homogenate.

The nuclei and mitochondria are harvested in their respective fractions as pellets at the bottom of the centrifuge tubes. With proper precautions they retain their original morphology. The mitochondria contain, among others, the enzymes catalyzing the sequences of reactions involved in the citric acid cycle and often the related system for oxidative degradation of fatty acids, as well as the terminal electron transport system that is coupled with these processes and with oxidative phosphorylation.[116, 165] The mitochondria may assume a considerable variety of shapes but are always bounded by an external membrane and an inner membranous structure that is highly convoluted.[64, 283] The inner folds are often called cristae. When mitochondria are swollen in hypotonic solutions the outer membrane usually stretches and pulls away from the inner membranous structure. The extraction from mitochondria of functional fragments rich in lipides will be discussed below.

The microsome fraction is now recognized to be composed of debris derived from the endoplasmic reticulum.[126, 212] This membranous structure is very varied in form and is found in all cells except the mature anucleate red blood cell. It often extends throughout most of the cytoplasm in the form of tubular or interconnected vesicular structures, often with broad flat vesicles called cisternae. These cisternae sometimes align together to give a lamellar appearance. The endoplasmic reticulum is not easily studied because its three-dimensional extent is much greater than the useful thickness of sections taken for electron microscopy. Evidence has been obtained, however, that it can be continuous with the nuclear membrane and with the outer cell membrane. Varying numbers of small particles are seen to be attached to parts of the system either in the cell or in the microsome fraction. These particles are of the order of 150 A in diameter and consist largely of ribonucleoprotein.[212]

The debris of the endoplasmic reticulum isolated in the microsome fraction is remarkable in that the membranes all appear to be closed in the form of various sizes and shapes of vesicles. Apparently the parts of the structure separate from each other by pinching off under the shearing stress of homogenization. The torn edges fuse together sufficiently rapidly that only closed forms are observed.[213] Various dispersing conditions may have an effect on the quantity of microsome fraction isolated, since the smallest fragments tend to escape into the supernatant fraction. An effect of salts has been observed and it has been concluded that under certain conditions either the endoplasmic reticulum is split into smaller fragments at low concentrations of inorganic ions or the fragmented reticulum aggregates in the presence of ions.[133]

Distribution of Lipides Among Subcellular Fractions

The distribution of lipides among rat liver cell fractions has been studied by Spiro and McKibbin[254] and by Clement, Clement, and LeBreton.[44] Table 9.7 shows the per cent of lipide in the dry weight of the fractions representing nuclei, mitochondria, microsomes, and supernatant material. All fractions contain appreciable quantities of lipide. The fractions richest in lipide are the microsomes (32%) and the mitochondria (21%). The distribution of lipide between phospholipide, cholesterol, and neutral fat is remarkably similar for all fractions except the supernatant. The supernatant fraction contains a high proportion of neutral fat.

An alternative procedure for fractionation was used by Clement et al.,[44] some of whose results are shown in Table 9.8. In this procedure the homogenate was first centrifuged lightly to cause the larger lipoprotein particles of lowest density to rise to the surface where they were harvested as the "free fat" fraction. This fraction contained a small amount of protein nitrogen, and apparently represents a lipoprotein fraction. Clement makes the point that the proportion and nature of the lipides present set it apart from the lipides that are without question bound to proteins in the recognized structures of the cell.

Table 9.7

Lipide Composition of Rat Liver Cell Fractions *

Fraction	Total Lipide (Per Cent Dry Weight)	Per Cent Total Lipide		
		Phospho-lipide	Cho-lesterol	Neutral Fat
Nuclei	16	93	4.5	2.5
Mitochondria	21	93	5.5	1.4
Microsomes	32	94	5.8	0
Supernatant	7	28	3.9	68

* Taken from M. J. Spiro and J. M. McKibbin, *J. Biol. Chem.*, **219**, 643 (1956).

Table 9.8

Distribution of Lipides Among Rat Liver Fractions *

mg./g. fresh liver

Fatty Acids

Fraction	Phospho-lipide	Glycerides and Cho-lesterol Esters	Un-saponi-fiable X	Unesteri-fied Cho-lesterol	Esteri-fied Cho-lesterol
Total liver	23.7	24.3	6.2	2.6	0.35
Connective tissue	0.60	1.03	—	—	—
Nuclei	0.10	0.38	0.185	0.01	0.01
Mitochondria	4.5	1.2	0.725	0.23	0.005
Microsomes	5.5	2.4	1.36	0.55	0.01
Soluble	9.2	8.7	2.18	1.13	0.035
"Free fat"	0.74	9.5	0.955	0.11	0.245

* Taken from G. Clement, J. Clement, and E. LeBreton, in *Biochemical Problems of Lipids*, edited by G. Popjak and E. LeBreton, p. 385, Interscience, New York (1956).

The distinction is somewhat akin to the small but convenient distinction drawn by many workers between chylomicrons and other lipoproteins in the circulation.

As shown in Table 9.8, the "free fat" fraction is relatively rich in triglycerides and poor in phospholipides and other components. Presumably it is contained within the "supernatant" fraction listed in Table 9.7, which also includes the "soluble" fraction listed in Table 9.8. The lipoproteins in these fractions deserve detailed study in many ways, notably (1) to determine their relation to plasma lipoproteins which appear to be able to enter cells; (2) to determine their relation to the soluble enzyme systems; (3) to determine the degree of damage sustained by these lipoproteins during the homogenization procedure in which the cell membranes are ruptured. According to most methods of homogenization employed thus far, the soluble lipoproteins are probably exposed to a degree of turbulence that would be extremely dangerous for lipoproteins of comparable sensitivity to those in plasma. Admixture of plasma lipoproteins with the tissue during homogenization would serve as a partial control. Table 9.8 shows, however, that the "free fat" and soluble fraction differ considerably in composition and that the "free fat" could scarcely represent solely breakdown products from the manipulative destruction of lipoproteins of the soluble fraction.

The soluble fraction, as defined by Clement et al.,[44] contains more of each gross class of lipide (except for triglyceride) than any other cellular fraction. Olson has suggested that the yield of lipide in the soluble fraction may depend on the degree of damage sustained by the particulate fractions during homogenization.[199]

Olson has reported the existence of a component in the soluble fraction of rat liver that sediments in the ultracentrifuge in a medium of density 1.063 but shows rapid flotation in a medium of density 1.21.[199, 200] The ratios of nitrogen, total lipide, phospholipide, and cholesterol are 2:20:10:1. The rapidity of the flotation at density 1.21, contrasted with sedimentation at 1.063, suggests that the material is present in much larger aggregates than are seen in the plasma or that the high concentration of salt used to achieve the high density medium causes aggregation.

Most of the vitamin A ester in chicken and beef liver cell fractions has been found to be concentrated in the supernatant fraction.[154] The vitamin A ester and alcohol components are associated to some extent with different proteins in the supernatant fraction of rat liver.[153, 154] These liver lipoproteins appear to be distinguishable from the plasma lipoproteins on the basis of solubility behavior.[74,152,154] Like the vitamin A in plasma, that in liver is resistant to ether extraction.[74,154] The maintenance of definite plasma concentrations of vitamin A in the presence of varying stores in the liver probably involves interaction between liver and plasma lipoproteins.[73,134]

The particulate fractions, microsomes, mitochondria, and nuclei all contain considerable proportions of lipides (Table 9.7). In each case phospholipides are predominant. The unsaponifiable fractions are of particular interest in view of the recent discovery of mitochondrial factors of the coenzyme Q series (Q_{275}, ubiquinone) [52,81,166,197,287] and the importance of other cofactors,[31,70,71,194,226,280] as well as the recent evidence concerning steroid-mediated transhydrogenation.[144,258,259,277] Comparison of the values for "unsaponifiable X" in Table 9.8 with those for unesterified cholesterol shows that simple cholesterol analyses such as those reported in Table 9.7 give an incomplete indication of lipide composition. Joel et al. have reported about three times as much "cholesterol" in the lipides of a mitochondrial preparation by color tests than by isolation as the digitonide.[147]

The proportions of the major types of phospholipides in each cell fraction have been determined by Spiro and McKibbin [254] and are shown in Table 9.9 as molar ratios of choline, sphingosine, ethanolamine, serine, and inositol to phosphorus. The general pattern of distribution is similar in all fractions, although the differences are probably significant and hint at more obvious differences that may appear on further subfractionation.

Table 9.9

Composition of Phospholipide Moieties of Rat Liver Cell Fractions *

Molar Ratio of Lipide Component to Phosphorus

Fraction	N	Choline	Sphingo-sine	Ethanol-amine	Serine	Inositol
Nuclei	0.91	0.44	0.07	0.20	0.09	0.06
Mitochondria	1.04	0.49	0.11	0.18	0.11	0.09
Microsomes	1.01	0.58	0.09	0.17	0.10	0.11
Supernatant	1.04	0.56	0.18	0.21	0.14	0.10

* Taken from M. J. Spiro and J. M. McKibbin, *J. Biol. Chem.*, **219**, 643 (1956).

Aqueous Extractions of Tissues and Cell Fractions

In 1934, Bensley and Hoerr reported that aqueous salt solutions would not disrupt entirely the visible structure of cells but that subsequent extraction with strong alkali would disrupt the remaining structure.[21] The treatment with strong alkali yielded a protein fraction containing about 30% "fatty substances" which was called "ellipsin". Recently, Dallam studied the composition of materials isolated by serial extraction of cell fractions prepared from dog kidney, rat kidney, rat spleen, rabbit kidney, and rabbit liver. The tissues were homogenized in an uncooled room using prechilled solutions and apparatus. Fractionation was performed at 4° using glycerol to adjust the density of the media. Whole cells were prepared by meshing. The cell fractions were designated as nuclei and large and small granules. The granular fractions presumably corresponded to the usual mitochondrial and microsomal fractions, respectively.[53]

The cell fractions were extracted serially in the cold with three solutions: 0.14M sodium chloride, 1.0M sodium chloride, and finally enough 0.1N sodium hydroxide to bring the pH to 11–12. Table 9.10 shows the approximate percentages by dry weight of each cell fraction recovered in the four fractions derived from the three extraction steps applied to dog kidney cell fractions. Dallam reported a qualitative analysis showing that lipides were present in each extract derived from the nuclei but that the neutral salt solution extracted very little lipide from large or small granules.

Table 9.10

Approximate Composition of Dog Kidney Particulate Fractions *

	Per Cent Soluble in			
Cell Fraction	0.14M NaCl	1.0M NaCl	NaOH	Residue
Nuclei	61	22	14	3
Large granules	57	20	21	2
Small granules	59	25	12	4

* Taken from R. D. Dallam, *Arch. Biochem. Biophys.*, **54**, 24 (1955).

The material extracted with alkali was studied in more detail, and found to have much the same properties regardless of the cell fraction from which it was derived. The nitrogen content was about 10.5–11.0% of the total fraction and the lipide content near 30%. The material yielded only a small part of its lipide to ether extraction and required alcohol for complete extraction. It could be brought out of solution by precipitation with dilute acetic acid and redispersed by dilute alkali. Some electrophoretic analyses failed to demonstrate marked heterogeneity in the material.[53]

Thomas and co-workers have extended the study of the residue obtained after extraction of broken or intact cells with neutral salt solutions.[34, 249] The broken cell preparation was made by macerating frozen rat liver and straining out connective tissue. Serial extractions were made at 3°–5° with 0.16M potassium chloride and 1.0M potassium chloride containing iodoacetate and citrate. The residue after the final centrifugal washing with the 1.0M potassium chloride solution was resuspended in the same solution and subjected to differential ultracentrifugation to bring down three fractions. The three fractions had sufficiently similar properties that their separation probably did not depend primarily on density but on the size of the fragments. For example, the composition of the three fractions in terms of percentage of total lipide, phosphorus, nitrogen, and hexosamine was practically identical. From this it was concluded that the fractions represented a single substance or group of closely related substances.[249]

Some very valuable observations were made on the stability of the insoluble lipoprotein material. First, it was found that if the temperature during centrifugation was allowed to rise to about 20° lipide-rich droplets would collect on the surface. With proper temperature control only the first two or three centrifugal extractions yielded floating lipide-rich material ("free fat"). Second, it was found that the material after exhaustive extraction with 1.0M potassium chloride was rendered unstable by threefold washing with distilled water. Centrifugation at high speed yielded a turbid supernatant solution from which a lipide-rich material could be precipitated with acetic acid. Instead of the usual 11% nitrogen, this material contained about 5% nitrogen and was greasy to the touch. Third, treatment in the Waring blendor was very disruptive and allowed a fraction containing only 3.8% nitrogen to be recovered. Thomas and co-workers also pointed out that the dispersion in alkali employed by Dallam is accompanied by some decomposition and suggest that the decomposition becomes noticeable at pH values above the physiological range.

Commenting on the similarity in composition of the various preparations from different organs and cell fractions, Thomas and co-workers summarized neatly as follows: [249] "Any similarity in properties, especially in gross chemical composition, exhibited by cellular lipoproteins as a class of substances, is at present a point of interest, as is usual during the period when a class of substances is little known, e.g. nucleic acids ca. 1905. It seems reasonable to expect, however, that it will later become possible to demonstrate specific differences in chemical composition, and in other properties among various cellular lipoproteins, where such differences exist."

In a companion study of the residue from exhaustive neutral salt extractions, Bruemmer and Thomas treated whole rat liver cells with $1.0M$ sodium chloride alternately at pH 7 and at pH 4 until no further material was liberated.[34] The residue retained the gross structural features of the original cells. Chemical analysis yielded almost identical results to those of the broken cell preparations. Since these "ghost cells" were prepared without freezing the tissue, it appears that the freezing step in the preparation of the broken cells probably did not affect the composition of the residue obtained. It was concluded that the lipoprotein material remaining after exhaustive neutral salt extraction represented the main membranous structures in the cell.

Lipoproteins of Microsomes and Mitochondria

As pointed out previously in the brief description of the various cell fractions, the microsomes and mitochondria are both fundamentally membranous structures. The microsomes are derived from the endoplasmic reticulum, and consist of continuous membranes that form vesicular structures and usually have associated with them small, dense ribonucleoprotein particles. The membranes have some properties in common with myelin forms made with purified phospholipides.[227] Only about one-third of the microsomal fraction consists of lipide (Table 9.7), however, and the membranes contain both lipide and protein. The general mode of association between phospholipides and protein illustrated in Fig. 8.9 may well apply to these membranes.

Considerable attention has been paid to the relation between the membranes and the small particles often found attached to them.[50, 173, 174, 211, 213] Together they appear to represent the major site of protein synthesis in cells. The lipoprotein membranes are disintegrated by the action of deoxycholate. Applied to liver microsomes, such treatment "solubilizes" 80% of the protein present and about

20% of the ribonucleic acid.[213] The "solubilized" fraction retains nearly all the phospholipide, and DPNH-cytochrome c reductase activity, as well as an alcohol-soluble hemochromogen.[213, 256] Crude phospholipase preparations have also been used to release cytochrome reductase.[257] Siekevitz and Palade have suggested that the digestive proenzymes elaborated by the pancreas are synthesized by the attached ribonucleoprotein particles and that the membranous structure plays a role in segregating the proenzymes during the formation of the mature zymogen granules.[245, 246] The part played by the lipoprotein structure is not yet well defined but suggestions have been made that it may be involved in the transition from an unfinished polypeptide structure to the completed protein molecule.[173] These questions have been reviewed by Loftfield.[174] The active involvement of phospholipides of the endoplasmic reticulum in secretory processes is strongly implied by the work of Hokin and Hokin.[139]

The internal membranous structures in mitochondria have been described on p. 299. Like the microsomal membrane, the lipide-rich mitochondrial membranes can be disrupted by agents which may be expected to modify the structure of lipoprotein complexes, e.g., t-amyl, isobutyl or n-butyl alcohol, dodecyl sulfate, cholate, deoxycholate, digitonin, or phospholipases.[14, 18, 80, 117, 165, 250, 279] These agents have made possible the preparation of a variety of particles which retain parts of the many enzyme systems in the intact mitochondria. Under some circumstances a preparation of large particles derived from the mitochondrial membranes and showing, for example, respiratory chain activity may be fragmented to much smaller size without alteration in enzymatic activity.[98, 165] Conversely, fragmentation may interrupt the chain of enzymatic processes and bring about profound changes in activity. Workers in several laboratories have developed a general picture of repeating units of enzyme systems set in a lipide-rich matrix.[13-15, 54, 68, 116, 165, 247, 283, 290] The following discussion will treat in detail a particular example of a lipoprotein preparation isolated from beef heart mitochondria.

Basford and Green have pointed out that the lipides of the mitochondria are distributed among the various submitochondrial fragments in a characteristic way, so that the lipide content of the various degraded particles is either higher or lower than the lipide content of the starting mitochondria.[18] They reason that the concept of the localization of lipide in the form of lipoproteins has to be invoked. Together with Järnefelt and Tisdale, they separated the succinic and DPNH chains of their succinic dehydrogenase complex [19] in such a

Table 9.11

Composition of Coenzyme Q Lipoprotein Prepared with Butanol *

mg./mg. Protein

Neutral lipide	1.21
Cholesterol	0.40
Coenzyme Q	0.154
Phospholipide	24.5

Phospholipide	Micro-equivalents/ mg. protein	Molar ratio to P
Fatty acid esters	36.9	1.46
Plasmalogen	9.36	0.37
Choline	13.4	0.53
Amino acids	10.9	0.43

* Taken from R. E. Basford, *Biochim. et Biophys. Acta,* **33,** 195 (1959).

way as to release a lipoprotein which they believe to have a central place in the complex both structurally and functionally.[146] They refer to it as the "coenzyme Q lipoprotein".

The soluble lipoprotein could be released from the succinic dehydrogenase complex by two different methods.[18] The first method made use of cholate in the presence of $3M$ potassium chloride and the second of deoxycholate in the presence of ammonium sulfate and *n*-butyl alcohol. The latter procedure yielded a material freer of obvious contaminants and which consisted of about 96% lipide and 4% protein. The composition is shown in Table 9.11.[17] The preponderance of phospholipides is striking. Of the phospholipide 53% was found to be lecithin, 43% phosphatidyl ethanolamine and phosphatidyl serine, and 3% inositide. Some minor constituents of the neutral lipide fraction were distinguished but not identified. Both major fractions of phospholipides contained plasmalogens. It will be interesting to determine whether any of the polyglycerolphospholipide of Marinetti et al.[195] is associated with the coenzyme Q lipoprotein.

The coenzyme Q lipoprotein is stable in a buffer containing ethylenediaminetetraacetate for at least 6 months when stored at 2°. Traces of bile salt may be responsible for the implied resistance to the growth of bacteria or molds.[275] Freezing or drying from the frozen state causes denaturation. Ether at room temperature does not extract lipide from the lipoprotein, but only after freezing and thawing or in the presence of alcohol. The material has been reported to have ultracentrifugal homogeneity comparable to that of the serum lipoproteins.[18]

The binding properties of the coenzyme Q lipoprotein are of the greatest interest. Basford and Green determined the approximate maximum amounts of various substances taken up by the lipoprotein.[18] Their results are presented in Table 9.12. The compounds whose binding is described in the first part of the table were introduced in solution in organic solvents and the excess removed by centrifugation. The capacity to take up coenzyme Q is striking. It would be most interesting if a way could be found to test whether the coenzyme Q taken up in this way is bound in a similar manner to that of the coenzyme Q isolated in the original lipoprotein complex (cf. reactivation studies [226] or the reduction of DPN in mitochondrial fragments [165]).

Table 9.12

Uptake of Various Substances by the Coenzyme Q Lipoprotein *

Substance Studied	Maximum Amount Taken up (μmole/mg. Lipoprotein Protein)
Compounds soluble in organic solvents	
Vitamin K_1	0.012
Vitamin A (acetate)	0.04
α-Tocopherol	0.10
Coenzyme Q	0.50
Compounds soluble in water	
Cytochrome c	0.0173
Silicomolybdate + Mg^{++}	2.43
Silicomolybdate − Mg^{++}	0.48
Indophenol	0.11
Phenazine methosulfate	0.08

* Taken from R. E. Basford and D. E. Green, *Biochim. et Biophys. Acta*, **33**, 185 (1959).

The binding of water-soluble compounds was measured by the technique of ultracentrifugal sedimentation of the lipoprotein complex from the solution of the substance to be tested, whereupon the remaining material in the supernatant solution could be measured and the quantity bound obtained by difference.[18] The binding of cytochrome *c* is of great interest because, like coenzyme Q, it is believed to be combined with the coenzyme Q lipoprotein in the original mitochondrial fragment. A bacterial cytochrome *c* was found not to bind to the mammalian coenzyme Q lipoprotein. When the lipoprotein-cytochrome *c* complex was made up in 50% ethanol and extracted with heptane, all the hemoprotein passed into the heptane layer. Basford and Green concluded that the coenzyme Q lipoprotein is responsible, at least in part, for the formation of lipide-soluble cytochrome *c*.[285] It is possible that the release of cytochrome *c* from mitochondrial fragments by the action of phospholipase involves an attack by this enzyme on the phospholipides associated specifically with the coenzyme Q lipoprotein.[5]

Table 9.12 also lists the uptake of several water-soluble electron receptors. The increased binding of silicomolybdate in the presence of magnesium ions may represent the formation of ternary complexes.[125] Extraction of the silicomolybdate complex with heptane in the presence of ethanol serves to bring the silicomolybdate into the heptane solution. The requirement for ethanol in the heptane extraction procedures in the presence of silicomolybdate or cytochrome *c* suggests that the lipoprotein as such may be disrupted. The normally water-soluble components carried into the heptane may be incorporated into the micelles which are presumably formed by the phospholipides in the non-polar solvent.[82]

As mentioned above, the coenzyme Q lipoprotein can also be isolated by a procedure involving the use of cholate in the presence of concentrated potassium chloride.[17,18] This material contains some flavin and heme and can be converted to the material that has been under discussion by the butanol procedure, an operation which also involves the removal of some lipide. The composition and interactions described above confirm that this lipoprotein is a highly specific complex. Any lipoprotein complex isolated from such elaborate structures as mitochondria must be thought of as a derived lipoprotein which may not be entirely similar in structure to its forerunner in the intact mitochondria. In the present case, the coenzyme Q lipoprotein not only shows affinities for appropriate components of the functional system from which it is derived but can be used as a substitute for certain components in the succinoxidase assay system. Basford and Green present an interesting tentative scheme showing the probable functional interactions of this lipoprotein.[18]

The high content of phospholipide in the coenzyme Q lipoprotein suggests that much of its structure and perhaps some of its specificity may be dependent on interactions between phospholipide molecules. If these are arranged in regular array, X-ray diffraction measurements in solution may yield useful information. The structural importance of the peptide moiety might be brought out by the action of proteolytic enzymes. Particularly fascinating will be the study of the interaction of this lipoprotein with other materials derived from the mitochondrial membranes in an effort to rebuild the insoluble membranous fragments from which it is derived.

Green, Järnefelt, and Tisdale reported recently the isolation of a cytochrome c_1-lipoprotein complex containing about 52% lipide.[117] The hemoprotein and lipoprotein can be separated by treatment with dodecyl sulfate. Since no coenzyme Q is present in this complex, the material is probably not identical with the coenzyme Q lipoprotein.

Lamellar Lipoprotein Systems

Lamellar lipoprotein systems, such as nerve myelin sheath, and the photoreceptive structures, chloroplasts and retinal rods, are more obviously organized on a macromolecular scale than the lipoproteins that have been described up to now. The structure of the nerve myelin sheath appears to have much in common with the membranous structures that have been discussed. Since it is made up of many layers of lipide and protein arranged concentrically, it is much easier to study by physical techniques than the thin membranes of the endoplasmic reticulum.

That myelin sheath has a rather high degree of order in the arrangement of its components is shown by polarized light microscopy and low-angle X-ray diffraction measurements.[236, 237] Schmitt, Bear, and Palmer attributed [237] the spacings of 185 A in fresh mammalian nerve to the sum of the following: 2 bimolecular layers of lipides, 2×67 or 134 A; protein, 25 A; water inserted between protein-lipide or lipide-lipide polar groups, 26 A. A diagram of a possible structure is shown in Fig. 9.5. The diagram shows the polar groups of the lipides in the middle of the repeating pattern interacting with each other, or more strictly with an aqueous layer probably containing salts, and the other polar groups of the lipides interacting more directly with

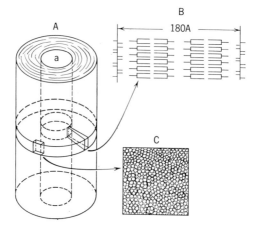

Fig. 9.5. Schematic representation of myelin sheath structure showing: (A) Concentric lipide-protein layers. (B) Structure in the radial direction (perpendicular to the planes of the layers). (C) Structure in the planes of the layers (paraffin chains of lipide molecules shown as open circles). After F. O. Schmitt; taken from H. Fernández-Morán, *Prog. in Biophysics and Biophys. Chem.*, **4**, 112 (1954).

protein. This picture implies a differentiation between the lipide molecules. Indeed, it is known that lecithin, sphingomyelin, phosphatidyl ethanolamine, phosphatidyl serine, cerebrosides, and cholesterol are present.[20] Finean has suggested more recently that part of the protein is intercalated in the central layer so that the type of structure of alternating layers of protein and bimolecular leaflets of lipide which was observed in artificial mixtures is preserved (see Fig. 8.9). Differences in the alternating protein layers are sufficient to keep the repeating pattern at the long spacing, and are attributed to some unknown "difference factor."[85, 87]

The repeating structure made by the successive layers greatly facilitates the interpretation of these measurements. Similar layering has been observed by electron microscopy and a comprehensive study has been reported correlating electron microscopy and X-ray scattering techniques on the same specimens.[83] Characteristic changes were observed on freezing and thawing, ultracentrifugation, and extraction with lipide solvents. For example, extraction of fresh nerve at 0° with acetone, which preferentially removes cholesterol rather than phospholipide, causes the expansion of some layer systems and the collapse of others, and internal rearrangement of the layer components.

A well-illustrated review of myelin structure has been published by Finean and Robertson, who offer an interesting suggestion for the way phospholipide and cholesterol molecules may be packed together in the lipide layers.[87]

The value of combining different experimental techniques cannot be overemphasized. The combined measurements showed, for example, that fixation in osmium tetroxide for electron microscopy yields an altered structure with a period of about 130 A instead of 180 A.[83] The nature of the reaction with osmium tetroxide is poorly defined as yet, but both lipides and proteins seem to be reactive.[11, 12, 86, 223, 238]

The myelin sheath is laid down by the enveloping Schwann cell and the course of the process can be followed continuously.[100, 238] In considering the process whereby the layers are formed it is interesting that Hodge and co-workers have presented evidence that lamellar structures in chloroplasts of *Zea* and in the endoplasmic reticulum of *Nitella* are formed from coalescence of small particles, 150 to 250 A in diameter, which they describe as lipide-rich vesicles.[137, 138] It is possible that certain plasma lipoproteins of similar size may play a role in the development and maintenance of membranous structures in animal cells. One should bear in mind also that the spreading of protein molecules on lipide surfaces probably depends considerably on the nature of the lipide, as shown by Fraser and Schulman [94, 95] and discussed in Chapter 8.

The photoreceptive structures, chloroplasts and retinal rods, have been discussed together in a recent symposium.[288] The gross similarity in lamellar organization is apparent from Fig. 9.6.[289] The functional importance of the lamellar organization in these structures has been summarized succinctly by Thomas [267] and by Wald.[281] The degree of order in the organization of chlorophyll and carotenoids in chloroplasts is not so striking as in the lipides in myelin sheath. A probable reason is that the ultimate structural unit may not lose its individuality completely in the chloroplast lamella and may retain some curvature so that pigment molecules on its surface show gross variation in orientation with respect to one another.[107, 267] Small fragments may be prepared from chloroplasts by treatment with digitonin or ultrasonic vibrations and are found to retain some of the properties of the intact structure.

The retinal rods contain a remarkable visual pigment, rhodopsin. This lipoprotein complex is composed of a specific hindered *cis* isomer of retinene—neo-b(11-*cis*)—joined to a colorless protein, rod opsin, or scotopsin.[155, 210] Here the degree of specificity in the lipide-protein

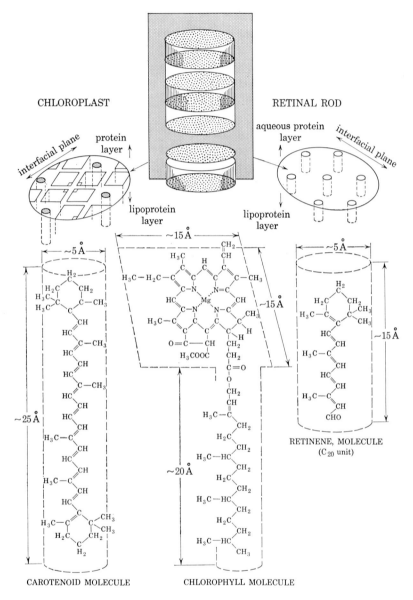

Fig. 9.6. Schematic model of chloroplast and retinal rod indicating the packing of chlorophyll and carotenoids at the interfaces in the chloroplast and the retinene in retinal rod. This model does not indicate whether the carotenoids are in a *cis* or a *trans* configuration. Taken from J. J. Wolken, *Ann. N. Y. Acad. Sci.*, **74,** 164 (1958).

interaction is particularly striking, as are the changes in mode of attachment that appear to result from the isomerization of the retinene induced by light.[67,143,155,210] In severe vitamin A deficiency the pigment is lost by both rods and cones and the structural elements break down with loss of opsin. From comparison of the time course of the structural and functional breakdown of the visual elements with other changes in the organism, Dowling and Wald have suggested recently that vitamin A or its derivatives may be necessary for the stabilization of numerous structural proteins in the body.[72,73]

Judging from the experience with observations in growing or regenerating lamellar structures, it seems possible that such material may offer a particularly convenient approach to the study of the synthesis of lipoproteins. These studies should supplement observations on such systems as liver slices,[224] developing eggs,[148,192,269,272] or the formation of the macromolecular complex reported in gall bladder bile.[273–275]

Proteolipides

In 1951, Folch and Lees described a hitherto unknown type of lipoprotein which could be extracted from many different tissues by homogenizing in a 2:1 mixture of chloroform and methanol.[90] The chloroform-methanol solution contained polypeptide material in addition to lipides. Lipoprotein fractions containing both peptide and lipides could be isolated from the chloroform-methanol and were called "proteolipides" because they were found to be insoluble in water. The largest quantities of proteolipides were found in white matter of brain from which 2.0–2.5% of the wet weight can be recovered. Gray matter of brain, heart muscle, kidney, liver, lung, skeletal muscle, and smooth muscle (uterus) contained less, and none was found in blood plasma. Proteolipides have since been extracted from beef heart mitochondria,[147] but are absent from peripheral nerve myelin.[161]

Three different proteolipide fractions can be isolated from white matter. In the original procedure the chloroform-methanol extract was washed by layering under a large volume of water.[89,90] The passage of methanol into the aqueous phase renders the chloroform layer a suitable solvent for only one proteolipide fraction (Fraction C). The remainder of the material collects as a precipitate in the aqueous layer just above the chloroform layer. It can be fractionated into two fractions of proteolipide, one of which (Fraction B) is crystalline and contains 50% peptide, 20% cerebrosides, and 30% phospholipides. Its composition is constant after resolution in chloroform-methanol mixture and reprecipitation with acetone. The composition may be varied somewhat according to small changes in procedure, however.

The three proteolipide fractions are all birefringent, indicating that the relative arrangement of lipide and peptide moieties is regular. The compositions of the three fractions are distinct with respect both to percentage and type of lipides. All three proteolipide fractions can be denatured by evaporating their solutions in chloroform-methanol mixtures containing water. Apparently, the formation of two phases during the evaporation is responsible for splitting the combination between lipide and peptide moieties. The denaturation is avoided by controlling the proportions of water and methanol in the chloroform solvent.[91]

In view of the solubility of the proteolipides in polar non-aqueous solvents, Folch and Lees suggested that the peptide and lipide moieties are combined in such a way that the lipide occupies the external surface.[90] Presumably the charged groups in the lipide molecules come into close contact with the charged groups in the peptide moiety in response to the strong interionic forces that will be active in a medium of low dielectric constant. Conceivably the galactose moiety of the cerebrosides contributes the hydroxyl groups which appear to be essential for the maintenance of the structure of some other lipoproteins in the absence of water. In this respect, it is noteworthy that only one fraction of the proteolipides is soluble in pure chloroform whereas the others require the presence of methanol.[90] The bircfringence of these preparations and their disruption at the liquid-liquid interface during evaporation of solvent both point to a highly specific orientation of lipide molecules with respect to the peptide moiety.

A few other types of lipide-protein association have been described recently by Folch and his co-workers and their stability characteristics discussed.[88,161,162] Some interesting observations have been reported also on the role of metal ions in preventing the loss of lipides from the chloroform-methanol phase into the aqueous phase. The metal ions are generally freely interchangeable with each other and their competition for the lipide anions can be studied.[92,161] It has been suggested, however, that the lipides or proteolipides of blood platelets do not exchange calcium at physiological pH.[282]

The importance of metal ions in the chemistry and physiology of lipide-protein complexes probably will be found to be very great.

Phospholipides, with their secondary phosphate groups and serine and ethanolamine residues, offer metal ions binding sites that do not correspond to structures normally recognized in proteins.[125] Chelate structures bridging one large molecule with another are recognized and are most strikingly illustrated in systems in which phosphate groups have been shown to play a prominent part.[284] It is attractive to speculate that lipide-protein interactions play a large role in cell permeability and ion transport.

REFERENCES

1. Adlersberg, D., E. T. Bossak, I. H. Sher, and H. Sobotka, *Clin. Chem.,* **1,** 18 (1955).
2. Ahrens, E. H., *Am. J. Med.,* **23,** 928 (1957).
3. Albright, J. F., and N. G. Anderson, *Exptl. Cell Research,* **15,** 271 (1958).
4. Alkalay, E., and P. Favarger, *Arch. int. Pharmacodyn.,* **68,** 332 (1942).
5. Ambe, K. S., and F. L. Crane, *Science,* **129,** 98 (1959).
6. Anson, M. L., *J. Gen. Physiol.,* **23,** 239 (1939–1940).
7. Antoniades, H. N., J. L. Tullis, L. H. Sargeant, R. B. Pennell, and J. L. Oncley, *J. Lab. Clin. Med.,* **51,** 630 (1958).
8. Armstrong, S. H., Jr., M. J. E. Budka, and K. C. Morrison, *J. Am. Chem. Soc.,* **69,** 422 (1947).
9. Avigan, J., *J. Biol. Chem.,* **226,** 957 (1957).
10. Avigan, J., and C. B. Anfinsen, *Biochim. et Biophys. Acta,* **31,** 249 (1959).
11. Bahr, G. F., *Exptl. Cell Res.,* **7,** 457 (1954).
12. Bahr, G. F., *Exptl. Cell Res.,* **9,** 277 (1955).
13. Ball, E. G., and R. J. Barrnett, *J. Biophys. Biochem. Cytol.,* **3,** 1023 (1957).
14. Ball, E. G., and O. Cooper, *J. Biol. Chem.,* **180,** 113 (1949).
15. Ball, E. G., and O. Cooper, *Proc. Natl. Acad. Sci.,* **43,** 357 (1957).
16. Bang, I., *Biochem. Z.,* **90,** 383 (1918).
17. Basford, R. E., *Biochim. et Biophys. Acta,* **33,** 195 (1959).
18. Basford, R. E., and D. E. Green, *Biochim. et Biophys. Acta,* **33,** 185 (1959).
19. Basford, R. E., H. D. Tisdale, J. L. Glenn, and D. E. Green, *Biochim. et Biophys. Acta,* **24,** 107 (1957).
20. Bear, R. S., K. J. Palmer, and F. O. Schmitt, *J. Cellular Comp. Physiol.,* **17,** 355 (1941).
21. Bensley, R. R., and N. L. Hoerr, *Anat. Record,* **60,** 251 (1934).
22. Bergström, S., *Arkiv Kemi, Mineral. Geol.,* **21A,** nos. 14, 15 (1945).
23. Bergström, S., and R. T. Holman, *Advances in Enzymol.,* **8,** 425 (1948).
24. Bergström, S., and O. Wintersteiner, *J. Biol. Chem.,* **141,** 597 (1941).
25. Bergström, S., and O. Wintersteiner, *J. Biol. Chem.,* **145,** 309 (1942).
26. Bernfeld, P., in *The Lipoproteins: Methods and Clinical Significance,* edited by Homburger and Bernfeld, p. 24, Karger (1958).
27. Bernfeld, P., M. E. Berkowitz, and V. M. Donahue, *J. Clin. Invest.,* **36,** 1363 (1957).

28. Bernfeld, P., V. M. Donahue, and M. E. Berkowitz, *J. Biol. Chem.*, **226**, 51 (1957).
29. Bjorklund, R., and S. Katz, *J. Am. Chem. Soc.*, **78**, 2122 (1956).
30. Bolland, J. L., and H. P. Koch, *J. Chem. Soc.*, **1945**, 445.
31. Bouman, J., and E. C. Slater, *Biochim. et Biophys. Acta*, **26**, 624 (1957).
32. Boyle, E., and R. V. Moore, *Circulation*, **18**, 697 (1958).
33. Bragdon, J. H., R. J. Havel, and E. Boyle, *J. Lab. Clin. Med.*, **48**, 36 (1956).
34. Bruemmer, N. C., and L. E. Thomas, *Exptl. Cell Research*, **13**, 103 (1957).
35. Burstein, M., *Compt. rend.*, **244**, 3189 (1957).
36. Burstein, M., *Compt. rend.*, **245**, 586 (1957).
37. Burstein, M., and J. Oudin, *Compt. rend.*, **246**, 2187 (1958).
38. Burstein, M., and A. Prawerman, *Rev. hématol.*, **13**, 329 (1958).
39. Burstein, M., and J. Samaille, *Compt. rend.*, **243**, 2185 (1956).
40. Burstein, M., and J. Samaille, *Clin. Chim. Acta*, **3**, 320 (1958).
41. Burstein, M., and J. Samaille, *La Presse Medicale*, **43**, 974 (1958).
42. Chargaff, E., *Advances in Protein Chem.*, **1**, 1 (1945).
43. Chick, H., *Biochem. J.*, **8**, 404 (1914).
44. Clement, G., J. Clement, and E. LeBreton, in *Biochemical Problems of Lipids*, edited by Popjak and LeBreton, p. 385, Interscience (1956).
45. Cohen, M., W. Ginoza, R. W. Donner, W. R. Hudson, and S. G. Wildman, *Science*, **124**, 1081 (1956).
46. Cohen, P. P., in *Chemistry of Lipides as Related to Atherosclerosis*, edited by Page, p. 95, Thomas (1958).
47. Cohn, E. J., F. R. N. Gurd, D. M. Surgenor, B. A. Barnes, R. K. Brown, G. Derouaux, J. M. Gillespie, F. W. Kahnt, W. F. Lever, C. H. Liu, C. H. Mittelman, R. F. Mouton, K. Schmid, and E. Uroma, *J. Am. Chem. Soc.*, **72**, 465 (1950).
48. Cohn, E. J., W. L. Hughes, and J. H. Weare, *J. Am. Chem. Soc.*, **69**, 1753 (1947).
49. Cohn, E. J., L. E. Strong, W. L. Hughes, Jr., D. J. Mulford, J. N. Ashworth, M. Melin, and H. L. Taylor, *J. Am. Chem. Soc.*, **68**, 459 (1946).
50. Cohn, P., and J. A. V. Butler, *Biochim. et Biophys. Acta*, **25**, 222 (1957).
51. Cornwell, D. G., F. A. Kruger, G. J. Hamwi, and J. B. Brown, *J. Lab. Clin. Med.*, **52**, 806 (1958).
52. Crane, F. L., Y. Hatefi, R. L. Lester, and C. Widmer, *Biochim. et Biophys. Acta*, **25**, 220 (1957).
53. Dallam, R. D., *Arch. Biochem. Biophys.*, **54**, 24 (1955).
54. Dallam, R. D., *Arch. Biochem. Biophys.*, **77**, 395 (1958).
55. Davson, H., and J. F. Danielli, *The Permeability of Natural Membranes*, Cambridge University Press (1943).
56. Deborin, G. A., M. I. Bystrova, and G. F. Ivashchenko, *Izvest. Akad. Nauk S.S.S.R., Ser. Biol.*, **1956**, no. 4, 116–120.
57. Deborin, G. A., and L. B. Gorbacheva, *Doklady Akad. Nauk S.S.S.R.*, **95**, 317 (1954).
58. Deborin, G. A., and O. M. Shibanova, *Doklady Akad. Nauk S.S.S.R.*, **105**, 526 (1955).
59. Delage, B., *Bull. soc. chim. biol.*, **17**, 927 (1935).
60. Delage, B., *Bull. soc. chim. biol.*, **18**, 1603 (1936).

61. deLalla, O. F., H. A. Elliott, and J. W. Gofman, *Am. J. Physiol.*, **179**, 333 (1954).

62. deLalla, O. F., and J. W. Gofman, in *Methods of Biochemical Analysis*, Vol. 1, edited by Glick, p. 459, Interscience (1954).

63. Delsal, J. L., *Bull. soc. chim. biol.*, **25**, 358 (1943).

64. Dempsey, E. W., *J. Biophys. Biochem. Cytol.*, *Suppl.*, **2**, 305 (1956).

65. Denstedt, O. F., and F. R. N. Gurd, unpublished observations.

66. Dent, C. E., and G. A. Rose, *Biochem. J.*, **44**, 610 (1949).

67. DeRobertis, E., *J. Biophys. Biochem. Cytol.*, *Suppl.*, **2**, 209 (1956).

68. Devlin, T. M., and A. L. Lehninger, *J. Biol. Chem.*, **233**, 1586 (1958).

69. Dole, V. P., *J. Clin. Invest.*, **35**, 150 (1956).

70. Donaldson, K. O., A. Nason, and R. H. Garrett, *J. Biol. Chem.*, **233**, 572 (1958).

71. Donaldson, K. O., A. Nason, I. R. Lehman, and A. Nickon, *J. Biol. Chem.*, **233**, 566 (1958).

72. Dowling, J. E., and G. Wald, *Ann. N. Y. Acad. Sci.*, **74**, 256 (1958).

73. Dowling, J. E., and G. Wald, *Proc. Natl. Acad. Sci.*, **44**, 648 (1958).

74. Dzialoszynski, L. M., E. M. Mystkowski, and C. P. Stewart, *Biochem. J.*, **39**, 63 (1945).

75. Eckles, N. E., C. B. Taylor, D. J. Campbell, and R. G. Gould, *J. Lab. Clin. Med.*, **46**, 359 (1955).

76. Eder, H. A., *Am. J. Med.*, **23**, 269 (1957).

77. Eder, H. A., J. H. Bragdon, and E. Boyle, *Circulation*, **10**, 603 (1954).

78. Eder, H. A., and D. Steinberg, *J. Clin. Invest.*, **34**, 932 (1955).

79. Edsall, J. T., in *The Proteins*, Vol. IB, edited by Newrath and Bailey, Chap. 7, p. 549, Academic Press (1953).

80. Edwards, S. W., and E. G. Ball, *J. Biol. Chem.*, **209**, 619 (1954).

81. Fahmy, N. I., F. W. Hemming, R. A. Morton, J. Y. F. Paterson, and J. F. Pennock, *Biochem. J.*, **70**, 1P (1958).

82. Faure, M., and J. Legault-Demare, *Bull. soc. chim. biol.*, **32**, 509 (1950).

83. Fernández-Morán, H., and J. B. Finean, *J. Biophys. Biochem. Cytol.*, **3**, 725 (1957).

84. Fillerup, D. L., J. C. Migliore, and J. F. Mead, *J. Biol. Chem.*, **233**, 98 (1958).

85. Finean, J. B., *Exptl. Cell Research*, **5**, 202 (1953).

86. Finean, J. B., in *Biochemical Problems of Lipids*, edited by Popjak and LeBreton, p. 127, Interscience (1956).

87. Finean, J. B., and J. D. Robertson, *Brit. Med. Bull.*, **14**, 267 (1958)

88. Folch, J., in *Blood Cells and Plasma Proteins*, edited by Tullis, p. 378, Academic Press (1953).

89. Folch, J., I. Ascoli, M. Lees, J. A. Meath, and F. N. LeBaron, *J. Biol. Chem.*, **191**, 833 (1951).

90. Folch, J., and M. Lees, *J. Biol. Chem.*, **191**, 807 (1951).

91. Folch, J., M. Lees, and G. H. Sloane Stanley, *J. Biol. Chem.*, **226**, 497 (1957).

92. Folch, J., M. Lees, and G. H. Sloane Stanley, in *Metabolism of the Nervous System*, edited by Richter, p. 174, Pergamon (1957).

93. Francis, G. E. C., G. A. Harrison, and L. E. R. Picken, *Lancet*, **246**, 51 (1944).

94. Frazer, M. J., J. G. Kaplan, and J. H. Schulman, *Disc. Faraday Soc.*, **20**, 44 (1955).

95. Frazer, M. J., and J. H. Schulman, *J. Colloid Sci.*, **11**, 451 (1956).

96. Fredrickson, D. S., and R. S. Gordon, *Physiol. Rev.,* **38,** 585 (1958).
97. Fredrickson, D. S., D. L. McCollester, R. J. Havel, and K. Ono, in *Chemistry of Lipides as Related to Atherosclerosis,* edited by Page, p. 205, Thomas (1958).
98. Gamble, J. L., and A. L. Lehninger, *J. Biol. Chem.,* **223,** 921 (1956).
99. Gardner, J. A., and H. Gainsborough, *Biochem. J.,* **21,** 141 (1927).
100. Geren, B. B., *Exptl. Cell. Research,* **7,** 558 (1954).
101. Geyer, R. P., F. R. Olsen, S. B. Andrus, W. R. Waddell, and F. J. Stare, *J. Am. Oil Chem. Soc.,* **32,** 365 (1955).
102. Geyer, R. P., I. Saslaw, and F. J. Stare, *J. Am. Oil Chem. Soc.,* **32,** 528 (1955).
103. Gillies, G. A., F. T. Lindgren, and J. Cason, *J. Am. Chem. Soc.,* **78,** 4104 (1956).
104. Gitlin, D., D. G. Cornwell, D. Nakasato, J. L. Oncley, W. L. Hughes, and C. A. Janeway, *J. Clin. Invest.,* **37,** 172 (1958).
105. Gitlin, D., B. H. Landing, and A. Whipple, *J. Exper. Med.,* **97,** 163 (1953)
106. Glover, J., and R. A. Morton, *Brit. Med. Bull.,* **14,** 226 (1958).
107. Goedheer, J. C., *Optical properties and in vivo orientation of photosynthetic pigments,* Thesis, University of Utrecht, Gebr. Janssen, Nijmegen (1957).
108. Gofman, J. W., *Am. J. Cardiol.,* **1,** 271 (1958).
109. Gofman, J. W., F. T. Lindgen, and H. A. Elliott, *J. Biol. Chem.,* **179,** 973 (1949).
110. Goodman, D. S., *J. Am. Chem. Soc.,* **80,** 3892 (1958).
111. Goodman, D. S., *J. Clin. Invest.,* **37,** 1729 (1958).
112. Goodman, D. S., and E. Shafrir, *J. Am. Chem. Soc.,* **81,** 364 (1959).
113. Gordon, R. S., *J. Clin. Invest.,* **34,** 477 (1955).
114. Gordon, R. S., and A. Cherkes, *J. Clin. Invest.,* **35,** 206 (1956).
115. Gould, R. G., G. V. LeRoy, G. T. Okita, J. J. Kabara, P. Keegan, and D. M. Bergenstal, *J. Lab. Clin. Med.,* **46,** 372 (1955).
116. Green, D. E., in *Chemical Pathways of Metabolism,* Vol. I, edited by Greenburg, Chap. 2, p. 27, Academic Press (1954).
117. Green, D. E., J. Järnefelt, and H. D. Tisdale, *Biochim. et Biophys. Acta,* **31,** 34 (1959).
118. Grundy, S., H. L. Dobson, and A. C. Griffin, *Proc. Soc. Exptl. Biol. Med.,* **98,** 313 (1958).
119. Gurd, F. R. N., unpublished observations.
120. Gurd, F. R. N., *Changes in the Lipoproteins of Human Blood Serum during Processing,* M.Sc. Thesis, McGill University (1946).
121. Gurd, F. R. N., *Studies on Human Serum β-Lipoprotein,* Ph.D. Thesis, Harvard University (1948).
122. Gurd, F. R. N., in *Ion Transport Across Membranes,* edited by Clarke, p. 246, Academic Press (1954).
123. Gurd, F. R. N., and S. Light, unpublished results.
124. Gurd, F. R. N., J. L. Oncley, J. T. Edsall, and E. J. Cohn, *Disc. Faraday Soc.,* **6,** 70 (1949).
125. Gurd, F. R. N., and P. E. Wilcox, *Advances in Protein Chem.,* **11,** 311 (1956).
126. Hagenau, F., *Int. Rev. Cytol.,* **7,** 425 (1958).
127. Hagerman, J. S., and R. G. Gould, *Proc. Soc. Exper. Biol. Med.,* **78,** 329 (1951).
128. Hardy, W. B., *J. Physiol.,* **33,** 251 (1905).
129. Haslam, H. C., *Biochem. J.,* **7,** 492 (1913).

130. Havel, R. J., and J. C. Clarke, *Clin. Res.*, **6**, 264 (1958).
131. Havel, R. J., H. A. Eder, and J. H. Bragdon, *J. Clin. Invest.*, **34**, 1345 (1955)
132. Hayes, T. L., and J. E. Hewitt, *J. Appl. Physiol.*, **3**, 425 (1957).
133. Hess, E. L., and S. E. Lagg, *J. Biophys. Biochem. Cytol.*, **4**, 717 (1958).
134. High, E. G., and S. S. Wilson, *Arch. Biochem. Biophys.*, **62**, 163 (1956).
135. Hillyard, L. A., C. Entenman, and I. L. Chaikoff, *J. Biol. Chem.*, **223**, 359 (1956).
136. Hillyard, L. A., C. Entenman, H. Feinberg, and I. L. Chaikoff, *J. Biol. Chem.*, **214**, 79 (1955).
137. Hodge, A. J., M. Branster, E. M. Martin, R. K. Morton, J. D. McLean, and F. V. Mercer, *J. Biophys. Biochem. Cytol.*, *Suppl.*, **2**, 221 (1956).
138. Hodge, A. J., J. D. McLean, and F. V. Mercer, *J. Biophys. Biochem. Cytol.*, **2**, 597 (1956).
139. Hokin, L. E., and M. R. Hokin, *J. Biol. Chem.*, **233**, 822 (1958).
140. Holman, R. T., *Trans 1st Conf. Biol. Antioxidants*, 37 (1946).
141. Holman, R. T., in *Biochemical Problems of Lipids*, edited by Popjak and LeBreton, p. 463, Interscience (1956).
142. Holman, R. T., W. O. Lundberg, W. M. Lauer, and G. O. Burr, *J. Am. Chem. Soc.*, **67**, 1285 (1945).
143. Hubbard, R., and G. Wald, *J. Gen. Physiol.*, **36**, 269 (1952–53).
144. Hurlock, B., and P. Talalay, *J. Biol. Chem.*, **233**, 886 (1958).
145. James, A. T., J. E. Lovelock, and J. P. W. Webb, *Biochem. J.*, in press.
146. Järnefelt, J., R. E. Basford, H. D. Tisdale, and D. E. Green, *Biochim. et Biophys. Acta*, **29**, 123 (1958).
147. Joel, C. D., M. L. Karnovsky, E. G. Ball, and O. Cooper, *J. Biol. Chem.*, **233**, 1565 (1958).
148. Joubert, F. J., and W. H. Cook, *Can. J. Biochem. and Physiol.*, **36**, 389 (1958).
149. Karrer, P., and W. Straus, *Helv. Chim. Acta*, **21**, 1624 (1938).
149a. Keltz, A., personal communication.
150. Keltz, A., and J. E. Lovelock, *Federation Proc.*, **14**, 84 (1955).
151. Kendall, F. E., *J. Biol. Chem.*, **138**, 97 (1941).
152. Krinsky, N. I., D. G. Cornwell, and J. L. Oncley, *Arch. Biochem. Biophys.*, **73**, 233 (1958).
153. Krinsky, N. I., and J. Ganguly, *J. Biol. Chem.*, **202**, 227 (1953).
154. Krishnamurthy, S., S. Mahadevan, and J. Ganguly, *J. Biol. Chem.*, **233**, 32 (1958).
155. Kropf, A., and R. Hubbard, *Ann. N. Y. Acad. Sci.*, **74**, 266 (1958).
156. Kruger, F. A., D. G. Cornwell, G. J. Hamwi, and J. B. Brown, *Federation Proc.*, **17**, 258 (1958).
157. Kumagawa, M., and K. Suto, *Biochem. Z.*, **8**, 212 (1908).
158. Kunkel, H. G., *Federation Proc.*, **9**, 193 (1950).
159. Kunkel, H. G., and R. Trautman, *J. Clin. Invest.*, **35**, 641 (1956).
160. Kutt, H., F. McDowell, and J. H. Pert, *Proc. Soc. Exptl. Biol. Med.*, in press.
161. Le Baron, F. N., and J. Folch, *Physiol. Rev.*, **37**, 539 (1957).
162. LeBaron, F. N., and J. Folch, *Federation Proc.*, **17**, 261 (1958).
163. LeBreton, E., and J. Pantaléon, *Compt. rend. soc. biol.*, **138**, 36 (1944).
164. LeBreton, E., and J. Pantaléon, *Compt. rend. soc. biol.*, **138**, 38 (1944).
165. Lehninger, A. L., C. L. Wadkins, C. Cooper, T. M. Devlin, and J. L. Gamble, *Science*, **128**, 450 (1958).

166. Lester, R. L., F. L. Crane, and Y. Hatefi, *J. Am. Chem. Soc.,* **80,** 4751 (1958).
167. Lever, W. F., F. R. N. Gurd, E. Uroma, R. K. Brown, B. A. Barnes, K. Schmid, and E. L. Schultz, *J. Clin. Invest.,* **30,** 99 (1951).
168. Levine, L., D. Kauffman, and R. K. Brown, *J. Exp. Med.,* **102,** 105 (1955).
169. Lewis, L. A., A. A. Green, and I. H. Page, *Am. J. Physiol.,* **171,** 391 (1952).
170. Lindgren, F. T., H. A. Elliott, and J. W. Gofman, *J. Phys. and Colloid Chem.,* **55,** 80 (1951
171. Lindgren, F. T., and J. W. Gofman, *Bull. schweiz. Akad. med. Wiss.,* **13,** 152 (1957).
172. Lindgren, F. T., A. V. Nichols, and N. K. Freeman, *J. Phys. Chem.,* **59,** 930 (1955).
173. Littlefield, J. W., E. B. Keller, J. Gross, and P. C. Zamecnik, *J. Biol. Chem.,* **217,** 111 (1955).
174. Loftfield, R. B., *Prog. in Biophys. and Biophys. Chem.,* **8,** 347 (1957).
175. Lovelock, J. E., *Proc. Roy. Soc. (London),* **B147,** 427 (1957).
176. Lovern, J. A., *The Mode of Occurrence of Fatty Acid Derivatives in Living Tissues,* H. M. Stationery Office (1942).
177. Lovern, J. A., *The Chemistry of Lipids of Biochemical Significance,* Wiley (1955).
178. Lundberg, W. O., *Trans. 1st Conf. Biol. Antioxidants,* 26 (1946).
179. McFarlane, A. S., *Nature,* **149,** 439 (1942).
180. McFarlane, A. S., *Disc. Faraday Soc.,* **6,** 74 (1949).
181. Macheboeuf, M. A., *Bull. soc. chim. biol.,* **11,** 268 (1929).
182. Macheboeuf, M. A., *Bull. soc. chim. biol.,* **11,** 485 (1929).
183. Macheboeuf, M. A., *Etat des Lipides dans la Matière Vivante, Actualités sci. et ind.,* no. 448 (1937).
184. Macheboeuf, M. A., in *Blood Cells and Plasma Proteins,* edited by Tullis, p. 358, Academic Press (1953).
185. Macheboeuf, M. A., and R. Perrimond-Trouchet, *Compt. rend. soc. biol.,* **132,** 274, 585 (1939).
186. Macheboeuf, M. A., and J. Polonovski, *Bull. soc. chim. biol.,* **31,** 125 (1949).
187. Macheboeuf, M. A., and P. Rebeyrotte, *Bull. soc. chim. biol.,* **26,** 475 (1944).
188. Macheboeuf, M. A., and G. Sandor, *Bull. soc. chim. biol.,* **14,** 1168 (1932).
189. Macheboeuf, M. A., and F. Tayeau, *Compt. rend. soc. biol.,* **129,** 1181 (1938).
190. Macheboeuf, M. A., and F. Tayeau, *Compt. rend.,* **206,** 860 (1938).
191. Macheboeuf, M. A., and F. Tayeau, *Bull. soc. chim. biol.,* **23,** 31, 49 (1941).
192. McIndoe, W. M., *Biochem. J.,* **67,** 19P (1957).
193. Mannick, V. G., *Heterogeneity of Human β-Lipoprotein,* Ph.D. Thesis, Radcliffe College (1955).
194. Marinetti, G. V., J. Erbland, J. Kochen, and E. Stotz, *J. Biol. Chem.,* **233,** 740 (1958).
195. Marinetti, G. V., J. Erbland, and E. Stotz, *J. Biol. Chem.,* **233,** 562 (1958).
196. Meselson, M., F. W. Stahl, and J. Vinograd, *Proc. Natl. Acad. Sci. U. S.,* **43,** 581 (1957).
197. Morton, R. A., G. M. Wilson, J. S. Lowe, and W. M. F. Leat, *Biochem. J.,* **68,** 16P (1958).
198. Nerking, J., *Arch. ges. Physiol.,* **85,** 330 (1901).
199. Olson, R. E., in *Chemistry of Lipides as Related to Atherosclerosis,* edited by Page, p. 108, Thomas (1958).

200. Olson, R. E., and J. R. Jablonski, *Federation Proc.*, **13**, 270 (1954).
201. Oncley, J. L., personal communication.
202. Oncley, J. L., in *The Lipoproteins: Methods and Clinical Significance*, edited by Homburger and Bernfeld, p. 14, Karger (1958).
203. Oncley, J. L., E. Ellenbogen, D. Gitlin, and F. R. N. Gurd, *J. Phys. and Colloid Chem.*, **56**, 85 (1952).
204. Oncley, J. L., F. R. N. Gurd, and M. Melin, *J. Am. Chem. Soc.*, **72**, 458 (1950).
205. Oncley, J. L., and F. R. N. Gurd, unpublished observations.
206. Oncley, J. L., and F. R. N. Gurd, in *Blood Cells and Plasma Proteins*, edited by Tullis, p. 377, Academic Press (1953).
207. Oncley, J. L., M. Melin, D. A. Richert, J. W. Cameron, and P. M. Gross, Jr., *J. Am. Chem. Soc.*, **71**, 541 (1949).
208. Oncley, J. L., G. Scatchard, and A. Brown, *J. Phys. and Colloid Chem.*, **51**, 184 (1947).
209. Oncley, J. L., K. W. Walton, and D. G. Cornwell, *J. Am. Chem. Soc.*, **79**, 4666 (1957).
210. Oroshnik, W., P. K. Brown, R. Hubbard, and G. Wald, *Proc. Natl. Acad. Sci.*, **42**, 578 (1956).
211. Palade, G. E., *J. Biophys. Biochem. Cytol.*, **2**, 417 (1956).
212. Palade, G. E., *J. Biophys. Biochem. Cytol.*, *Suppl.*, **2**, 85 (1956).
213. Palade, G. E., and P. Siekevitz, *J. Biophys. Biochem. Cytol.*, **2**, 171 (1956).
214. Pedersen, K. O., *Ultracentrifugal Studies on Serum and Serum Fractions*, Almquist and Wiksells (1945).
215. Pedersen, K. O., *J. Phys. and Colloid Chem.*, **51**, 156 (1947).
216. Petermann, M. L., *J. Biol. Chem.*, **162**, 37 (1946).
217. Petermann, M. L., *Texas Rep. Biol. Med.*, **12**, 921 (1954).
218. Pflüger, E., *Arch. ges. Physiol.*, **51**, 229 (1892).
219. Phillips, G. B., *Biochem. et Biophys. Acta*, **29**, 594 (1958).
220. Phillips, G. B., *Proc. Soc. Exptl. Biol. Med.*, **100**, 19 (1959).
221. Phillips, G. B., *J. Clin. Invest.*, **38**, 489 (1959).
222. Polonovski, J., M. Faure, and M. Macheboeuf, *Compt. rend.*, **227**, 1420 (1948)
223. Porter, K. R., and F. Kallman, *Exptl. Cell Research*, **4**, 127 (1953).
224. Radding, C. M., J. H. Bragdon, and D. Steinberg, *Biochem. et Biophys. Acta*, **30**, 443 (1958).
225. Ray, B. R., E. O. Davisson, and H. L. Crespi, *J. Phys. Chem.*, **58**, 841 (1954).
226. Redfearn, E. R., and A. M. Pumphrey, *Biochem. et Biophys. Acta*, **30**, 437 (1958).
227. Revel, J. P., S. Ito, and D. W. Fawcett, *J. Biophys. Biochem. Cytol.*, **4**, 495 (1958).
228. Roche, A., and F. Marquet, *Compt. rend. soc. biol.*, **119**, 1147 (1935).
229. Rodbell, M., and D. S. Fredrickson, *J. Biol. Chem.*, **234**, 562 (1959).
230. Rosenberg, M., W. F. Lever, and M. E. Lyons, *J. Am. Chem. Soc.*, **77**, 6502 (1955).
231. Russ, E. M., H. A. Eder, and D. P. Barr, *Am. J. Med.*, **11**, 468 (1951).
232. Russ, E. M., J. Raymunt, and D. P. Barr, *J. Clin. Invest.*, **35**, 133 (1956).
233. Scanu, A., L. A. Lewis, and F. M. Bumpus, *Arch. Biochem. Biophys.*, **74**, 390 (1958).
234. Scanu, A., L. A. Lewis, and I. H. Page, *J. Lab. Clin. Med.*, **51**, 325 (1958).
235. Scanu, A., L. A. Lewis, and I. H. Page, *J. Exp. Med.*, **108**, 185 (1958).

236. Schmidt, W. J., *Z. Zellforsch.,* **23,** 657 (1936).
237. Schmitt, F. O., R. S. Bear, and K. J. Palmer, *J. Cellular Comp. Physiol.,* **18,** 31 (1941).
238. Schmitt, F. O., and N. Geschwind, *Prog. in Biophys. and Biophys. Chem.,* **8,** 166 (1957).
239. Schuler, W., and R. Meier, *Z. physiol. Chem.,* **302,** 236 (1955).
240. Schulz, F. N., *Arch. ges. Physiol.,* **65,** 299 (1897).
241. Shafrir, E., *J. Clin. Invest.,* **37,** 1755 (1958).
242. Shimidzu, Y., *Biochem. Z.,* **28,** 237 (1910).
243. Shore, B., *Arch. Biochem. Biophys.,* **71,** 1 (1957).
244. Siekevitz, P., and G. E. Palade, *J. Biophys. Biochem. Cytol.,* **4,** 203 (1958).
245. Siekevitz, P., and G. E. Palade, *J. Biophys. Biochem. Cytol.,* **4,** 309 (1958).
246. Siekevitz, P., and G. E. Palade, *J. Biophys. Biochem. Cytol.,* **4,** 557 (1958).
247. Siekevitz, P., and M. L. Watson, *J. Biophys. Biochem. Cytol.,* **2,** 653 (1956).
248. Siperstein, M. D., *Diabetes,* **7,** 181 (1958).
249. Smith, J. T., A. J. Funckes, A. J. Barak, and L. E. Thomas, *Exptl. Cell Research,* **13,** 96 (1957).
250. Smith, L., and E. Stotz, *J. Biol. Chem.,* **209,** 819 (1954).
251. Sobotka, H., in *Biochemical Problems of Lipids,* edited by Popjak and LeBreton, p. 108, Interscience (1956).
252. Sørensen, S. P. L., *Comp. rend. trav. lab. Carlsberg,* **18,** no. 5 (1930).
253. Sperry, W. M., *J. Biol. Chem.,* **111,** 467 (1935).
254. Spiro, M. J., and J. M. McKibbin, *J. Biol. Chem.,* **219,** 643 (1956).
255. Steele, J. M., and H. J. Kayden, *Trans. Assoc. Am. Physicians,* **68,** 249 (1955).
256. Strittmatter, C. F., and E. G. Ball, *J. Cellular Comp. Physiol.,* **43,** 57 (1954).
257. Strittmatter, P., and S. F. Velick, *J. Biol. Chem.,* **228,** 785 (1957).
258. Talalay, P., B. Hurlock, and H. G. Williams-Ashman, *Proc. Natl. Acad. Sci.,* **44,** 862 (1958).
259. Talalay, P., and H. G. Williams-Ashman, *Proc. Natl. Acad. Sci.,* **44,** 15 (1958).
260. Tappel, A. L., *J. Am. Oil Chem. Soc.,* **32,** 252 (1955).
261. Tayeau, F., *Compt. rend.,* **212,** 575 (1941).
262. Tayeau, F., *Compt. rend. soc. biol.,* **137,** 239 (1943).
263. Tayeau, F., *Bull. soc. chim. biol.,* **26,** 287, 295 (1944).
264. Tayeau, F., *Protéides et Lipides dans le Sérum Sanguin,* Drouillard (1944).
265. Tayeau, F., and R. Nivet, in *Biochemical Problems of Lipids,* edited by Popjak and LeBreton, p. 365, Interscience (1956).
266. Theorell, A. H. T., *Biochem. Z.,* **175,** 297 (1926).
267. Thomas, J. B., *Endeavour,* **17,** 156 (1958).
268. Toro-Goyco, E., *Physical-Chemical Studies of the β-Lipoproteins of Human Plasma,* Ph.D. Thesis, Harvard University (1958).
269. Turner, K. J., and W. H. Cook, *Can. J. Biochem. Physiol.,* **36,** 937 (1958).
270. Turner, R. H., J. R. Snavely, W. H. Goldwater, and M. L. Randolph, *Yale J. Biol. Med.,* **24,** 450 (1951–1952).
271. Turner, R. H., J. R. Snavely, W. H. Goldwater, M. L. Randolph, C. C. Sprague, and W. G. Umglaub, *J. Clin. Invest.,* **30,** 1071 (1951).
272. Vandegaer, J. E., M. E. Reichmann, and W. H. Cook, *Arch. Biochem. Biophys.,* **62,** 328 (1956).
273. Verschure, J. C. M., J. de Wael, P. F. Mijnlieff, and A. Zweers, *Clin. Chim. Acta,* **1,** 511 (1956).

274. Verschure, J. C. M., and F. M. C. Hoefsmit, *Clin. Chim. Acta*, **1**, 38 (1956).
275. Verschure, J. C. M., P. F. Mijnlieff, F. M. C. Hoefsmit, and A. E. Nooter van der Hoeven, *Clin. Chim. Acta*, **1**, 154 (1956).
276. Verstraete, A., and R. Cloetens, *Arch. int. Pharmacodyn.*, **62**, 129 (1939).
277. Villee, C. A., and D. D. Hagermand, *J. Biol. Chem.*, **233**, 42 (1958).
278. Volwiler, W., P. D. Goldsworthy, M. P. MacMartin, P. A. Wood, I. R. Mackay, and K. Fremont-Smith, *J. Clin. Invest.*, **34**, 1126 (1955).
279. Wainio, W. W., in *A Symposium on Some Conjugated Proteins,* edited by Cole, p. 19, Rutgers University Press (1952).
280. Wainio, W. W., and J. Greenlees, *Science,* **128**, 87 (1958).
281. Wald, G., *Science,* **119**, 887 (1954).
282. Wallach, D. F. H., D. M. Surgenor, and B. B. Steele, *Blood,* **13**, 589 (1958).
283. Watson, M. L., and P. Siekevitz, *J. Biophys. Biochem. Cytol.,* **2**, 639 (1956).
284. Waugh, D. F., *Abstr. 135th Natl. Meeting,* Amer. Chem. Soc., Boston (Apr. 5–10, 1959).
285. Widmer, C., and F. L. Crane, *Biochim. et Biophys. Acta,* **27**, 203 (1958).
286. Williams, G. R., *Biochim. et Biophys. Acta,* **13**, 72 (1954).
287. Wolf, D. E., C. H. Hoffman, N. R. Trenner, B. H. Arison, C. H. Shunks, B. O. Linn, J. F. McPherson, and K. Folkers, *J. Am. Chem. Soc.,* **80**, 4752 (1958).
288. Wolken, J. J., editor, *Photoreception,* Ann. N. Y. Acad. Sci., **74**, 161 (1958).
289. Wolken, J. J., *Ann. N. Y. Acad. Sci.,* **74**, 164 (1958).
290. Ziegler, D. M., A. W. Linnane, D. E. Green, C. M. S. Dass, and H. Ris, *Biochim. et Biophys. Acta,* **28**, 524 (1958).

Index